Interfaces between Alcoholism
and Mental Health

NIAAA-RUCAS
ALCOHOLISM TREATMENT SERIES

Sponsored by
The National Institute on Alcohol Abuse and Alcoholism
and
The Rutgers University Center of Alcohol Studies

This series, jointly sponsored by the National Institute on Alcohol Abuse and Alcoholism and the Rutgers University Center of Alcohol Studies, makes available to the therapeutic and allied professions the best and most systematic current knowledge on helping, treating and rehabilitating those affected by alcoholism, alcohol addiction, problem drinking or drinking problems. Each volume in this series represents the views of its authors, and does not necessarily reflect the stands of the sponsoring institutions.

Interfaces between Alcoholism and Mental Health

Edited by
EARL X. FREED, Ph.D.
DEPUTY ASSISTANT CHIEF MEDICAL DIRECTOR
FOR RESEARCH AND DEVELOPMENT
Veterans Administration, Washington, D.C.

PUBLICATIONS DIVISION
RUTGERS CENTER OF ALCOHOL STUDIES
NEW BRUNSWICK, NEW JERSEY

Library of Congress catalog card number: 79-620039
ISBN: 0-911290-50-8   ISSN: 0147-0515

MANUFACTURED IN THE UNITED STATES OF AMERICA

CONTENTS

Acknowledgments

I owe the idea for this book to my wife, Chelly, to whom it is dedicated with deep affection (and gratitude for support and editorial expertise, not to mention typing). She suggested that I try to synthesize my thoughts about my research and my clinical experiences so as to give each greater meaning. When I described the proposed work to him, Timothy G. Coffey, Editor of the *Journal of Studies on Alcohol*, encouraged me to undertake it and I am very grateful to him for his continued constructive criticism as an editor and for his advice as a friend.

I am pleased to acknowledge my indebtedness to the Veterans Administration Medical Research Service and to the National Institute on Alcohol Abuse and Alcoholism, which have supported my alcohol research, the former since 1964; to the Rutgers University Center of Alcohol Studies, which has accorded me an affiliation with scholarly colleagues; and to the esteemed researchers who kindly permitted their contributions to be reprinted herein.

Thanks are due to librarians, Miss Louise Geroulo and Miss Georgia McClure, Lyons V.A. Hospital, and Miss Jane Armstrong, Rutgers University Center of Alcohol Studies, for their help with references and reprints.

While almost all of my career has been identified with the Veterans Administration, I am responsible for the views that I have expressed, which do not necessarily constitute those of the Veterans Administration.

Introduction

The present volume presents readings about the interfaces between alcoholism and mental health, which it seeks to relate to each other along a number of dimensions. Still another book about alcoholism! Why? Why write *this* book? Answers to such questions exist on a number of levels and, although they may seem simplistic or facetious at first, they all are valid. Write it because, like climbing Mount Everest, it's there to be done. The issues are there to be addressed, the papers are there to be read, the data are there to be examined. It is a challenge. Write it because no one else has written it. Thus, since I obviously think that it is important, I have an opportunity to place my imprimatur on it. I can organize it to try to make a fair presentation. Write it because it fills a need in a scholarly field. It will summate and integrate thought up to a certain point in time and it can thus serve as a baseline frame of reference for future developments. Perhaps, more grandiosely, it can be a starting point or stimulus in thought or deed for some of these future developments. Write it because we need historical mileposts which, since we are moving so fast today, tell us where we have been with some degree of certainty even as present mileposts fly by in a blur. Write it because we need a moratorium on gathering data while we gather our thoughts. Write it because, in our zeal to program and therapeutize, we have to take time out to postulate and theorize. Write it because there are very practical issues which need to be faced about lives, an estimated nine million alcoholics who need help, a growing health problem and an emerging awareness of its magnitude and implications.

Most books are about answers and solutions. This volume is about questions and problems. It is not intended for the uninitiated to whom pat answers come easily or for the naive who unrealistically seek quick clarification of complexities. The prerequisites for fully appreciating the articles gathered here are (*a*) other than bookish experience with mental health work and alcoholism, (*b*) some dissatisfaction with their vexed natures and (*c*) immense tolerance for the ambiguity and irresolution engendered by (*a*) and (*b*).

As an investigator, I encounter little which is as fascinating to me

as mixed research findings, unresolved issues, ambivalent or equivocal data. We have so many answers. We assume too much and we
take too much for granted as we search for still more answers to
the puzzles surrounding alcoholism. This book contains a lot of answers, already published answers, and the sections are organized
into the often unstated questions which underlie them. These questions are: Is alcoholism a form of psychopathology? What, if any,
psychodynamic functions does drinking subserve? Are there mental
health models by which alcoholism can be conceptualized and better understood? What is this thing (or what are these things) called
alcoholism? What is meant by mental health? And the bottom line
questions always have to be: What are the relationships between alcoholism and mental health? Is the care and treatment of alcoholics
a responsibility of the mental health professions? If so, what do
they uniquely have to offer?

There are many answers to each question in the articles gathered
here. I have included selections advocating a number of different
points of view or approaches to the questions. Their presence suggests that there probably is no one "correct" response—or that
there are many—and that still more are likely to be forthcoming.

I thus have tried to assemble significant contributions to thought
about the interfaces between alcoholism and mental health. There is
a relatively meager literature that confronts the issue directly, but
the papers gathered here are both rich in content and stimulating.
They are drawn from a vast satellite literature surrounding the core
issue of interfaces. They will not provide final answers to the questions discussed. This is as it should be—closure at this juncture
would be a closed mind. So much remains to be learned about alcohol use and misuse and mental health and illness, both separately
and in their various interactions, that significant clarification of ambiguity is premature. We shall have to continue to live with the
frustration which this engenders.

This book also tries to broaden the perspectives derived from engaging in clinical practice or in research and to integrate and synthesize them. I have been impressed by the dynamic nature of research and clinical application in mental health care, how we have
moved from theory to trial, theory to theory, trial to trial, and trial
to theory—but never in any systematic fashion so that there is no
defined procedure for attempting to unify what has taken place.
After a while, a clinician or an investigator may find himself an esoteric specialist and may question how his forte dovetails with larger
areas of concern. He seeks another who is doing what he is doing

so that they may exchange ideas and understand one another. We need periodic attempts to integrate, regroup and rethink developments, and the present volume is such a review.

Though it would certainly help clarify matters if I could define what I mean by mental health and by alcoholism, the fact is that, as used in this book, mental health has many meanings. It may refer to an individual's emotional well-being or to his personal–interpersonal adjustment. In this sense, it is a sort of state. On another level, it has reference to a humanistic movement, an awareness of human needs in treatment. In still another context, it refers to a group of professions, a new multidiscipline perhaps, sharing in common a dynamic (versus a biological) orientation. Sometimes, mental health, as contrasted with illness, bespeaks normative standards or processes or the relative absence of deviance. On the other hand, deviance in drinking behavior is the hallmark of alcoholism. I like Davies' (1) definition of alcoholism: "the intermittent or continual ingestion of alcohol leading to dependency or harm." It is sufficiently global to encompass a number of problems with alcohol.

However, as a student and later as a teacher I never cared too much for definitions in psychology. They carried with them a degree of exactitude, or definiteness, which too often proved beguiling. One could mouth or repeat a "definition," but the cognition which it implied might be absent. Nevertheless, I see those in the field of mental health (and some outside of the field, too) struggling with a definition of its role and with a delineation of its limits. The process is one of simultaneous expansion and contraction. For example, two articles in the April 1976 issue of *Hospital and Community Psychiatry*, illustrated this. On the one hand, Zwerling (2), commenting on the impact which community mental health trends have had on psychiatry, wrote that "the concept of promoting health as well as treating illness means that psychiatry becomes involved with broader concepts about improving the quality of life." On the other hand, an article in the "News and Notes" section of the same issue began, "Correctional institutions must stop trying to 'treat people for crime, as if crime were some sort of disease,' Norman A. Carlson, director of the Federal Bureau of Prisons, told the American Academy of Psychiatry and the Law. . . . He said that the corrections system is trying to more precisely define the psychiatrist's role in prisons today and that psychiatry is not expected to be a panacea for criminality" (*p. 300*). In the 12 April 1976 issue of *Time Magazine* (*p. 24*) Harvard psychiatrist Robert

Coles conceded that his profession is unsure of itself and of its own definitions." He asked, "Exactly *what*, if anything, is 'mental health'? Who is 'mentally ill'? . . . Is the whole subject of 'mental health' a phantom?" The lead article (3) in the August 1976 issue of *American Psychologist* was entitled, "What *Is* Clinical Psychology?" There clearly has been much self-examination among professionals in their quest for role definition.

A key underlying issue is whether alcoholism comes within the purview of mental health treatment. In this regard, I think that mental health definitions further include a philosophical orientation and a systems approach. It will require the efforts of historians to trace the odyssey which brought alcoholism to the mental health domain. Intuitively speaking, alcoholics are maladjusted people. It is hard to have inner peace when physically ill, out of work, alienated from family and society. Speaking deductively, the behavior of alcoholics certainly resembles a compulsive pattern. The self-destructive aspects appear obvious. So, it must have been these kinds of observations and this sort of reasoning coupled with the distress of alcoholics and their families which probably eventuated in alcoholism's coming within the mental health purview. The metamorphosis was aided by the decriminalization of alcoholism, but whether its redefinition as a form of mental illness is an improvement remains to be seen. It is certainly more euphemistic and reassuring for a judge to recommend a "course of treatment" or "psychotherapy" than for him to sentence an alcoholic to a jail term. The efficacy of this alternative will require time for demonstration. If the course of treatment means that the alcoholic has to go to a psychiatric hospital, then a whole other set of questions has to be faced, and these are set forth in the following pages.

This book, then, addresses the undeniably important question, "Are there bona-fide relationships between the field of alcoholism and the field of mental health (or illness)?" The pressing need in alcoholism treatment is to (*a*) understand what it is all about in order to (*b*) do something about it. An article in the *Newark Star-Ledger* of 6 August 1976 quoted Ernest P. Noble, then director of the National Institute on Alcohol Abuse and Alcoholism: "the most fundamental questions about the nature of alcoholism—what it is, how it is caused and how it is cured—remain unanswered. . . . Without research to answer these questions, our treatment programs will be a case of the blind leading the blind. . . . Without answers, we will be torn by rigid dogmas about how to help alcoholics."

One such dogma has been that alcoholism is a form of mental illness, and this carries with it hosts of implications about the nature of the causes of alcoholism, which individuals are predisposed to it, keys to its prevention, the conditions which maintain it, at what point drinking becomes a problem, what is to be done about it, whether what is to be done about it constitutes "treatment," who should do the latter and where the doing should take place. The responses to these issues will differ if alcoholism is seen as a form of mental illness instead of, for example, a social problem.

Why is there an issue about a bona-fide relationship between alcoholism and mental health? Because, through the years, there has been overlap between the topics, alcoholism and mental illness, but the nature of their interactions has ranged from the serendipitous to the etiological. For example, there is an obvious interface between alcoholism and mental health. The fact that a person is an alcoholic or is a problem drinker perforce results in emotional stresses and adjustment problems. A person's job may be in jeopardy or his social or family life may be threatened, all of which arouse anxiety. The same could be said about the emotional sequels of a broken leg but, while the somatopsychological aspects of physical disability are recognized, emphasis does not seem to be placed on interfaces between orthopedics and mental health. Further, to many, there is implicit in the alcoholism–mental health interface the presumption that emotional factors somehow preceded the alcoholism, not just followed it, that both can be dealt with by mental health treatment, perhaps the same treatment, and that both are somehow inextricably intertwined.

The way that this book is organized is intended to highlight some of this intertwining. The first part deals with overviews of some of the ways in which alcoholism and mental health interrelate, both historically and in contemporary thought. The remaining sections look at four of these major interfaces. Thus, part II examines mental-health-related models and conceptions of alcoholism. There are a number of different perspectives here—and I have tried to cull representative papers—because there are few limits or proscriptions on model making and conceptualizing. Rationally, what seems needed is some good solid syllogistic reasoning such as: mental health is X; alcoholism is Y; and when all the components of X and Y are spelled out, one can draw some conclusions about the common boundaries or components that alcoholism and mental health share. The problem is that consensus about X and Y separately, let alone in their interactions, has not yet been achieved. There is serious disagreement on what constitutes mental health and mental illness—let alone whether the latter is disease. We thus lack a defined major premise for our syllogism. Specifications for alcoholism and problem drinking, the minor premise, are equally disputable. For example, a paper by Paredes et al. (4) spelled out the difference between drunken behavior and intoxication. How, then, can a valid conclusion be drawn? But many are—from clinical experience, by inference, for convenience, because a good fit seemingly is achieved.

Even though models are theoretical projections, mythology if you wish, they can help to clarify and target investigative efforts; part II presents mental-health-related and non-mental-health-related conceptions of alcoholism. I think that it is important to point out that the latter flourish. It is egocentric for us, in the mental health field, to take the alcoholism–mental health relationship as given. The models per se are not as pertinent as the thinking which went into them. It is not a situation in which one has to select the "right" one from multiple choices. Rather, I have presented a sampling of the processes of conceptualizing, not just the products. The means in this case supercede the end.

In most models alcoholism is regarded as deviant behavior; statistically, at the very least, it is. Therefore, part III presents papers dealing with interfaces between alcoholism and psychopathology. They explore whether there are etiological relationships between alcoholism and other psychiatric conditions (diagnoses), whether one can be an alcoholic and mentally healthy, and to what degree alcoholism and other forms of psychopathology can coexist. The fact is that we find it easier to recognize psychopathology than to characterize mental health. Gross deviance from a norm—even a vague one—stands out. The selections in part III examine where alcoholism stands in relation to such deviance because we seem to know a lot more about mental illness than about mental health. Similarly, we think that we know much more about the stereotyped, recidivistic, debilitated alcoholic than about the nonproblem social drinker. So, part III investigates possible commonalities among individuals at one extreme of the normal curve. It is a limited approach, admittedly, but it makes sense in seeking a frame of reference and in asking, What is the status of alcoholism among the seriously mentally ill and how can we characterize psychological adjustment among those who are in the advanced stages of alcoholism? Clearly, there are other populations which need to be studied and I hope they will be. For example, in the area of primary prevention, Davis (5) has written that "if alcohol abuse is going to be minimized, attention must be given to the general population and not merely to the problem drinker." Just two of the many other questions in this regard are as follows: (1) What were the differences in mental health or psychological predisposition between those who later became alcoholics and those who later became social drinkers or abstainers? (2) Did a former social drinker who became a problem drinker undergo changes in his mental health status at the time? The problems here are obvious. Longitudinal data are needed (6), and the mutual cause-and-effect relationships between alcohol use and psychological adjustment have to be controlled in such investigations.

One such obvious cause-and-effect relationship is that alcohol would appear to do something to—and perhaps for—the drinker; it has a psychodynamic impact (among others). The selections in part IV examine what this utility might be for both users and misusers of alcohol. Also included are alternative points of view which do not regard drinking as subserving a psychological function. Again, the aim is not merely to present a number of options, but to focus on the issue of the motivation to consume alcohol. Is drinking behavior learned because of positive contingencies, or is it reinforced by its attenuation of aversive consequences? Is alcohol sought as a self-prescribed mood regulator? Is the process of addiction a social phenomenon? Does the explanation of alcohol misuse lie in the sick role and its implications, or could resort to alcohol represent an attempt to preclude some more threatening psychopathology? Once more the issue is sharp—What maintains the behavior of drinking alcohol? Since evidence does not suggest that the answers lie in alcohol's anesthetic or calorigenic or soporific properties, its psychopharmacological characteristics are implicated, at least by a process of elimination.

The final section of the book deals with some mental health approaches to alcoholism treatment. A whole series of volumes should be written on this topic, on what treatment goals should be, who should do the treatment, where the treatments should take place, different treatments for different patients, philosophies of treatment, ways of evaluating therapy, etc. One book, let alone one section of a book, cannot do justice to the topic, but it would have been presumptuous not to mention in this book, even in so cursory a manner, some of the treatment concerns about alcoholism since the rest of the book deals with so many of the psychological aspects and the mental health responsibilities surrounding alcoholism. Omission of a discussion of treatment would be equally unacceptable to those reaching part V still unconvinced about significant etiological interfaces between mental health and alcoholism, for they would argue that the application of behavioral science treatment methodologies to nonpsychological disorders is truly inappropriate and highlights the need to look at treatment orientations.

The volume's plan is simple. A commentary introduces each of the five sections and discusses some of the issues addressed in the light of a few of the more recent publications in the area. No attempt is made at a critique of the articles selected; they speak well for themselves. I have sought always to include representations of the best—but also the more contemporary—papers on a topic. Where there are more recent data than those included in one of the papers, a critique would have been unfair because everyone is always a smarter quarterback on Monday morning than the quarterback who led the team on Saturday. For example, in the section on conceptions and models of alcoholism, the commentary serves to focus on thinking about models and frames of reference rather than on which model I might advocate. Still, while I have striven to be nonjudgmental and fair, I am sure that my biases show. The commentaries really serve as organizational dividers between sections which have much overlap, and the divisions between them are more convenient than real. The papers selected need little preface. I thus have tried to avoid redundancy in the commentaries because recent publications of my own, dealing with some of the topics highlighted, are reprinted.

REFERENCES

1. DAVIES, D. L. Implications for medical practice of an acceptable concept of alcoholism. Proc. 1st Int. Med. Conf. Alcoholism, London, pp. 13–22, 1974.
2. ZWERLING, I. The impact of the community mental health movement on psychiatric practice and training. Hosp. Community Psychiat. 27: 258–262, 1976.
3. SHAKOW, D. What is clinical psychology? Am. Psychol. 31: 553–560, 1976.
4. PAREDES, A., HOOD, W. R. and SEYMOUR, H. Sobriety as a symptom of alcohol intoxication; a clinical commentary on intoxication and drunkenness. Br. J. Addict. 70: 233–243, 1975.
5. DAVIS, R. E. The primary prevention of alcohol problems. Alcohol Health Res. World, pp. 10–12, Spring 1976.
6. NATIONAL INSTITUTE OF MENTAL HEALTH. Alcohol and alcoholism; problems, programs and progress. (DHEW Publ. No. HSM-72-9127.) Washington, DC; U.S. Govt Print. Off.; 1972.

Part I

SOME RELATIONSHIPS BETWEEN ALCOHOLISM AND MENTAL HEALTH

The initial section focuses on "thinking about drinking" and why it is important that we do so, especially from the mental health perspective. It examines rationales for the involvement of mental health workers in alcohol-related problems, and it encourages questions about the validity of such rationales. Mental health professionals are called upon to intervene in crises precipitated by disabling alcoholism when the victim has ceased to function or poses distinct dangers to himself or to others. So there is a relationship between, say, psychiatry and alcoholism, but what is its range or limits? What is the generality of this relationship? Does it extend to prevention, for example? Although "about one-half of all patients undergoing open heart surgery develop psychopathological reactions post-operatively" (1) and mental health professionals are undoubtedly called in as consultants in these cases, I doubt that the relationship between the specialties of open heart surgery and psychiatry will ever become as interwoven as the relationship between alcoholism and psychiatry. This is because, as Freyhan (1) reported, "this new model psychosis seems inadvertently produced by open heart surgery," but we presume that whatever psychiatric symptomatology an alcoholic manifests is other than inadvertent. The first part of this book, then, takes a broad look at our presumptions about mental health and alcoholism.

Alcohol use and misuse no longer are taboo topics, either in the public or scientific communities. Advertisements in the media warn of the danger signals of drinking; the professional literature is full of articles on alcoholism. Investigative zeal is documented in a proliferation of alcohol studies. Therapeutic efforts are no less ardent. There are halfway houses for alcoholics, therapeutic communities, behavior therapies and other innovative treatment modalities. Many apparently subscribe to Kunkel's (2) prescription for solving social problems: "when we actually want to do something, and when learning principles and the present social context have shown us what to do, then we have to go out into the world and start doing it. We no longer can hide behind ignorance about effective procedures" (*pp. 117-118*).

With so many going out and doing something about drinking, it behooves some to be no less active, but less activist, and to resume thinking about drinking. While the philosophy of "doing and deserving" (3) has much to commend it, thought should also be prized.

There is a need for a major reexamination of thought in the field of mental health, especially with regard to the interfaces between alcoholism and mental health. Interfaces of psychiatry with other systems, such as politics (4) and the judiciary (5) have been reported. Articulations between alcoholism and mental health are rarely addressed directly in the literature, perhaps because common boundaries are vague, territoriality is involved, and the whole area has come to represent a source of mild embarassment to health care professionals. In fact, close scrutiny reveals not only interdigitation between the fields of mental health and alcohol studies but actual overlap. For example, in the Veterans Administration, a health system of 172 hospitals throughout the country, the Alcohol and Drug Dependence Division is part of the Mental Health and Behavioral Sciences Service. Within the U.S. Department of Health and Human Services, there is the Alcohol, Drug Abuse, and Mental Health Administration. So, not only clinically but also administratively, alcohol and mental health are linked with each other. Further, those who regard alcoholism as a psychodynamic disorder have essentially encompassed it and other psychological disorders within a broader, overbridging theoretical framework. In a sense, those with a biological orientation have done the same. An incident in a hospital with which I was affiliated a number of years ago is probably not atypical. The hospital research committee sought a topic for investigation which was truly interdisciplinary, a subject whose impact was felt by every major clinical service, one to which representatives of all disciplines could contribute and with which they could identify, one encountered on all wards. They wanted, in sum, an almost universally research-stimulating disorder, a disease for all seasons, so to speak. It was no surprise that the choice was alcoholism. As Keller (Chapter 2) has written, "indeed, alcohol-related problems may be the ideal model for global, multi-perspective, wholistic study and action."

In an examination of diagnosis (classification) in psychiatry,

Woodruff et al. (6) wrote that "in general, we lump rather than split." The articles in the present volume examine, in the broadest sense, the nature of this lumping of alcoholism with other behavioral disorders. Woodruff and his colleagues included a problem, such as alcoholism, as a diagnostic category because it resulted in psychiatric consultation, was associated with pain, suffering and impairment, and thus it became important that the physician be familiar with it. Such a definition has important implications for the questions of who is qualified to treat alcoholics, whether alcoholism is justifiably regarded as a disease, and, if so, then which disease specialist should be the therapist, whether there are many forms of alcoholism, whether other assessment criteria are needed to render a diagnosis, etc. An interesting question is also raised as to whether an alcoholic's coming to a psychiatrist for help necessarily means that there exists a meaningful psychiatry–alcoholism interface. There may be a kind of circular reasoning or self-fulfilling prophecy involved. "A troubled person does not always know where to turn for help, nor even that help is available" (7, *p. 1*), even though some help-seeking by families of alcoholics appears to be patterned (8). Thus, those who consult mental health workers receive mental health consultation. What other services could the latter ethically render? The same has been true in the history of psychiatric hospitals. In the past, many applicants presented themselves with adjustment problems and they were offered admission and a hospital bed because those were what the hospital had to offer. The recent emphasis is on outpatient and ambulatory care services instead of hospitalization, and thus a whole range of alternative mental health services has been developed to this end. The implication, then, is that treatment interfaces may lack the degree of permanency we might like to ascribe to them.

Paris (9) has summed up "the therapeutic scene today" as follows: "It is as if some therapists are running clothing stores with only size 40 suits in stock. Everyone receives one without a fitting on the grounds that a majority is bound to get some sort of satisfaction" (*p. 305*). A variation of this notion is the "procrustean" approach described by Babow (10). (Procrustes was the robber of ancient Greece who forced his victims to fit a bed by stretching or lopping off their legs.) Babow was referring only to the question of whether former alcoholics are best qualified to treat alcoholics, but in a broader sense one can ask whether alcoholism has been perceived in ways which make it fit the mental health bed—or couch, as the case may be. If this is so, then a "new look" at alcoholism is all the more necessary because the old look has been biased. It is to the credit of the behavioral sciences that they have a tradition of self-scrutiny and a zeal for insight which derives from psychotherapeutic inquiry and practice.

While the alcoholism field can represent a common pathway for the wholistically oriented efforts of many disciplines, the fact is, as Keller (Chapter 2) has asserted, that one-sided, narrow hypotheses, single-discipline or single-profession oriented, continue to be produced. While multidisciplinary collaboration is advocated, rarely, he added, is this notion "concretely supported." The mental health professions cannot plead innocence in this regard. Williams (11), addressing a different topic—collaboration between economists and lawyers in policy research—laid down some rules for interdisciplinary contact: "it is necessary for there to be territory of common interest to explore, complementarity of disciplines, and efficient channels of communication. . . ."

Many unilateral behavioral science approaches to alcoholism continue to be offered, and, at least in the treatment sphere, a number of mental health representatives claim purview. Psychiatrists, Zealley (12) claimed, "have strayed or been lured into fields" in which they are called upon to serve as experts but in which they may lack expertise. This expanding role led Krell et al. (13) to term the psychiatrist the "vulnerable" mental health consultant. Psychologists and sociologists, too, are courting this vulnerability (14).

Despite continuing conflicts between those whose "primary allegiance" is to either alcoholism or mental health (4), the fact that alcoholism is often regarded as a character disorder is evidence of the interface between the two fields. Zealley (12) noted that the "relationship between psychiatry and patients with so-called personality disorders is an unusual one." Seixas (Chapter 1) spoke of alcoholism being "put into the same hopper as the other psychiatric problems," echoing what Woodruff et al. (6) said about "lumping" behavioral disorders.

I have no quarrel with the notion that many alcoholics exhibit character disorders. However, considering all types of alcoholism as characterological problems is as dismaying to me as learning that a number of hospital alcoholism treatment programs are incorporated in departments of hepatology, have an internal medicine orientation and deemphasize the personality, emotional and adjustment aspects of alcoholism. Out of the real imperative to treat a serious physical illness, they focus on a pathological end product—from their point of view. One goal of this book is to examine to what degree this may also represent the interface of alcoholism with psychologically oriented programs. Such relationships are important, to be sure, but they are too circumscribed.

Seixas (Chapter 1) and Keller (Chapter 2) have traced some of the historical perspectives of alcoholism care and research and have documented issues of interface, territoriality, mutual effort and shared contribution and professional isolationism. As the accounts by Seixas (Chapter 1) and Chafetz (15) make evident, many health care professionals long entertained negative, unaccepting or at least nontherapeutic attitudes toward people with alcohol problems, an unusual interface which might differentiate alcoholism from other forms of psychological suffering. Recent reports (16, 17) attest to the lack of essential change in such attitudes. The case has been stated well before. Blane and colleagues (18, *p.* 659) wrote, "In sum, it is evident that the way physicians see alcoholism exerts a tremendous influence on the way alcoholics are treated." Similarly, Wolf et al. (19) noted that the way a patient's nonphysical problems, his psychosocial difficulties, are perceived and the attitudinal frames of reference of the perceivers seem crucial.

In many ways, the whole issue of attitudes toward alcoholics and their treatment is a sort of anachronism, recapitulating the history of the mentally ill. Plaut (20), in a report prepared for the Cooperative Commission on the Study of Alcoholism, wrote about the emotionalism associated with alcohol. Questions of will, good and evil and the like characterized the emotionalism linked to mental illness a hundred years ago. The pessimism about helping problem drinkers is of the same ilk as that which pervaded the early efforts of medical psychology. Emotionalism about alcoholism is itself an interface with the mental health fields for questions about affect fall right in their domain. But a similar argument could be made for cancer care because of the fear and anxiety that that illness generates.

We now have conjoint multidisciplinary efforts with alcoholism counselors, psychologists, social workers, psychiatrists, nurses and rehabilitation personnel banded together as mental health and behavioral science "teams," even though some of these teams may still have a single orientation—mental hygiene. To a degree, such a stance derives from the defensiveness needed to justify one's own contributions to—or interfaces with—alcoholism treatment.

George and Barrett (21) called the lack of coordination among various agencies dealing with alcoholics, and the resultant fragmentation of services, the most serious deficiencies in treatment and rehabilitation programs. Page (22) addressed similar problems in bridging the gap between biology and medicine, and Babow (10) decried monopolistic approaches to treatment. Finally, Burt (23) characterized Alcoholics Anonymous and behavioral approaches to psychology—both much involved in alcoholism treatment—as "uneasy bedfellows." On the other hand, Roebuck and Kessler (24) called for "interdisciplinary constitutionalists, psychologists, and sociologists," Kissin (25) described alcoholism in terms of "bio-psycho-social dimensions," and Hoff (26) proposed a "coordinated approach to alcohol problems." Emphasized again and again is the need to explore—at the very least, to accord some formal recognition to—interdisciplinary intersection. Plaut (20) summed it up well: "Perhaps the most important problem is the failure to see the interrelatedness of diverse alcohol problems." When this interrelatedness is seen, I would hope that the next step will be that recommended by Cleghorn et al. (27): "The permeability of barriers between academic disciplines must increase so that the empirical world of clinical scholars and scientists will have changed as they mix." I would add, "as they *all* mix."

In the selections which follow, Seixas's contribution (Chapter 1) highlights the relationship of psychiatry with alcoholism and Keller's theme (Chapter 2) is the need for multidisciplinary perspectives. My own article (Chapter 3) discusses some specific areas where alcoholism and mental health interrelate.

REFERENCES

1. FREYHAN, F. A. The import of model psychoses for behavioral science. Pp. 87-102. In: COLE, J. O., FREEDMAN, A. M. and FRIEDHOFF, A. J., eds. Psychopathology and psychopharmacology. Baltimore; Johns Hopkins University Press; 1973.
2. KUNKEL, J. H. Behavior, social problems, and change; a social learning approach. Englewood Cliffs, N.J.; Prentice–Hall; 1975.
3. FEINBERG, J. Doing and deserving; essays in the theory of responsibility. Princeton, N.J.; Princeton University Press; 1970.
4. BROWN, B. S. The interface between psychiatry and politics. Pp. 2474-2478. In: FREEDMAN, A. M., KAPLAN, H. I. and SADOCK, B. J., eds. Comprehensive textbook of psychiatry. Vol. 2. 2d ed. Baltimore; Williams and Wilkins; 1975.
5. AIKEN, R. F. and WEINER, S. The interface of mental health and judicial sys-

tems; early impressions of an ASAP-related treatment effort. Proc. 3d Annu. Alcsm Conf. NIAAA, pp. 292-300, 1974.

6. WOODRUFF, R. A., JR., GOODWIN, D. W. and GUZE, S. B. Psychiatric diagnosis. New York; Oxford University Press; 1974.

7. CORRIGAN, E. M. Problem drinkers seeking treatment. (Rutgers Center of Alcohol Studies, Monogr. No. 8.) New Brunswick, N.J.; 1974.

8. JACKSON, J. K. and KOGAN, K. L. The search for solutions; help-seeking patterns of families of active and inactive alcoholics. Q. J. Stud. Alcohol 24: 449-472, 1963.

9. PARIS, J. Diagnosis before treatment. Can. Psychiat. Ass. J. 20: 305-307, 1975.

10. BABOW, I. The treatment monopoly in alcoholism and drug dependence; a sociological critique. J. Drug Issues 5: 120-128, 1975.

11. WILLIAMS, A. Collaboration between economists and lawyers in public policy. J. Soc. Publ. Teachers Law 13: 212-218, 1975.

12. ZEALLEY, A. K. Psychological medicine; psychiatry in Britain; an introduction. Br. Med. J. 1: 497-499, 1975.

13. KRELL, R., FINE, S. and STEPHENSON, P. S. The psychiatrist as the vulnerable mental health consultant. Can. Psychiat. Ass. J. 20: 379-384, 1975.

14. LINDSEY, D. Behaviorist versus sociologist in the mental health field. Corrective Soc. Psychiat. & J. Behav. Technol. Meth. Ther. 21: 8-11, 1975.

15. CHAFETZ, M. E. Alcoholism and health professionals. Psychiat. Ann. 6 (No. 3): 47-55, 1976.

16. DEMONE, H. W., JR., HOFFMAN, H. J. and HOFFMAN, L. W. Alcoholism; an evaluation of intervention strategy in family agencies. Final report. Boston; United Community Planning Corp ; 1974.

17. FISHER, J. C., MASON, R. L., KEELEY, K. A. and FISHER, J. V. Physicians and alcoholics; the effect of medical training on attitudes toward alcoholics. J. Stud. Alcohol 36: 949-955, 1975.

18. BLANE, H. T., OVERTON, W. F., JR. and CHAFETZ, M. E. Social factors in the diagnosis of alcoholism. I. Characteristics of the patient. Q. J. Stud. Alcohol 24: 640-663, 1963.

19. WOLF, I., CHAFETZ, M. E., BLANE, H. T. and HILL, M. J. Social factors in the diagnosis of alcoholism. II. Attitudes of physicians. Q. J. Stud. Alcohol 26: 72-79, 1965.

20. COOPERATIVE COMMISSION ON THE STUDY OF ALCOHOLISM. Alcohol problems; a report to the nation. (Prepared by PLAUT, T. F. A.) New York; Oxford University Press; 1967.

21. GEORGE, J. A. and BARRETT, J. P. Systems planning for treatment and rehabilitation programs. Res. Outlook 6 (No. 1): 29-33, 1974.

22. PAGE, I. H. The fragile bridge between biology and medicine. Fed. Proc. 35: 1-2, 1976.

23. BURT, D. A behaviorist looks at A.A. Addictions 22 (No. 3): 56-69, 1975.

24. ROEBUCK, J. B. and KESSLER, R. G. The etiology of alcoholism; constitutional, psychological and sociological approaches. Springfield, Ill.; Thomas; 1972.

25. KISSIN, B. Symposium on substance abuse disorders. Proc. 20th Annu. Conf., Veterans Admin. Studies Mental Health Behavioral Sciences, Washington, D.C. (Veterans Administration Publ. No. 1 B 11-51.), 1975.

26. HOFF, E. C. The alcoholisms. Proc. 28th Int. Cong. Alc. Alcsm, Vol. 2, pp. 84-90, 1969.
27. CLEGHORN, R. A., CLEGHORN, J. M. and LOWY, F. H. Contributions of behavioral sciences to health care; an historical perspective. Milbank Meml Fund Q. Bull. 49: 158-174, 1971.

1

Preface
to The Person with Alcoholism[1]

Frank A. Seixas, M.D.

THERE HAS ALWAYS BEEN criticism of the psychiatric mode among those who work primarily with alcoholics: they claim that in trying to treat the alcoholic, psychiatrists wind up either cross-addicting him to other depressant drugs or increasing his illness by ignoring the alcoholism and instead fitting him into the mold of psychoneurotic illness, searching for an early trauma while the alcoholism gallops towards its tragic end. Those who have recovered from alcoholism in Alcoholics Anonymous have frequently recounted such detrimental experiences at the hands of psychiatrists that there has been a strong movement to divorce alcoholism from the control of psychiatrists at the National Institute of Mental Health, community mental health centers and at other organizations that have traditionally been "in charge" of the efforts to combat alcoholism. This movement might be said to be an attempt to redress an imbalance caused by an overconcentration on the psychiatric aspects of the disease, to the detriment of attention on the pharmacologicophysical aspects. It has long been apparent that there is a need to "put the alcohol back in alcoholism" if one is to understand the myriad ramifications of the disease, and to clarify and simplify what is too often presented as a mysteriously complex blend of so many diverse elements as to defy efforts at its solution.

The National Council on Alcoholism has, through its medical-scientific conferences, attempted to cut a path through these impenetrable forests, and has presented the evidence that exists on the

[1] Reprinted by permission from the *Annals of the New York Academy of Sciences*, Vol. 233, pp. 5-12, 1974. Copyright by the New York Academy of Sciences, New York 10021.

etiology of alcoholism whether environmental, congenital, hereditary (1), or, as seems likely, a blend of these aspects, and the evidence on the role of the action of alcohol on the central nervous
system (2).

We are progressively beginning to recognize that there are no
specific childhood traumas and no labeled psychiatric entities that
predispose to all cases of alcoholism. The various types of human
beings who abuse alcohol may do so for many reasons, not the least
of which may be that their bodies and brains are constitutionally
"able" to handle alcohol more easily than are those of their peers.
We also see that as a consequence of the effect of alcohol on the
brain, the further along alcoholics progress into alcoholism, the
more alike they become.

But as we look for the more mechanical aspects of this process in
this disease of dependency, and even if we could clearly lay out all
the causes and mechanisms, we would still confront an entire
person—psychological as well as physical—when we come to the
point of helping him to conquer alcoholism. And thus, although it
is essential to be aware of the pharmacological and biological basis
of the dependency, one must nevertheless employ what we broadly
conceive of as psychological and psychiatric methods in various
phases of treatment. In the psychological aspects of his work, the
therapist must first assist the individual to recognize his disease and
be willing to come to treatment. Once alcohol is removed from the
system, the therapist must then work to aid the victim to repair his
reactions, his personality and his life so that he can begin anew un-
burdened by a compulsion to drink. Although this task comes under the heading of the art of medicine and although it has often
been carried out successfully by those with no or little psychiatric
training, we would be remiss if we did not look to those who have
made a particular study of the personality and its vicissitudes.

Indeed, it has been under the heading of psychiatry that the
greatest, if not the only, attention has been paid to alcoholism.
Benjamin Rush, pioneer American physician, included his statements on alcoholism in his *Medical Inquiries and Observations upon
the Diseases of the Mind* (3):

"The use of strong drink is at first the effect of a free agency. From habit
it takes place from necessity. That this is the case, I infer from persons
who are inordinately devoted to the use of ardent spirits being irreclaim-
able, by all the considerations which domestic obligations, friendship, repu-
tation, property, and sometimes even by those which religion and the love

of life can suggest to them. An instance of insensibility to the last, in an habitual drunkard, occurred some years ago in Philadelphia. When strongly urged by one of his friends, to leave off drinking, he said, "Were a keg of rum in one corner of the room, and were a cannon constantly discharging balls between me and it, I could not refrain from passing before that cannon in order to get at the rum."

"The remedies for this disease have hitherto been religious and moral, and they have sometimes cured it. They would probably have been more successful, had they been combined with such as are of physical nature. . . To these physical remedies, I shall add one more, and that is, the establishment of a hospital in every city and town in the United States for the exclusive reception of hard drinkers. They are as much objects of public humanity and charity as mad people. They are indeed more hurtful to society, than most of the deranged patients of a common hospital would be, if they were set at liberty. Who can calculate the extensive influence of a drunken husband or wife upon the property and morals of their families, and of the waste of the former, and corruption of the latter, upon the order and happiness of society? . . . . No person would be sent to the contemplated hospital or SOBER HOUSE, without being examined and committed by a court, consisting of a physician and two or three magistrates or commissioners appointed for that purpose . . . Within the house, the patient should be debarred the use of ardent spirits, and drink only, for a while, such substitutes for them, as a physician should direct. Tobacco, one of the provocatives to intemperance in drinking, should likewise be gradually abstracted from them. They should be employed in their former respective occupations, for their own or for the publick benefit, and all the religious, moral and physical remedies to which I have referred should be employed at the same time, for the complete and radical cure of their disease."

Late nineteenth and early twentieth century psychiatrists gave much attention to alcoholism. Kraepelin, and later Bleuler (4), made extensive descriptive summaries. Bleuler, in particular, gave such a modern description of alcoholism that his points are often repeated as discoveries to this day. He differentiates between those with drinking mania (those who by disposition or habituation cannot give up the enjoyment of alcohol, despite better insight, but who still do not show the symptoms of chronic alcoholism—the latter day alcohol abuser) and the alcoholic "who . . . plainly harms himself or his family through the use of alcohol and who cannot be made to realize this, or who no longer has the will or the strength to better himself, [and therefore] must be considered an alcoholic."

He also describes the dipsomaniac (today's periodic drinker) and insists on sobriety: "The experience of a thousand years proves that training to moderation is a utopia. . . . It is just these people (alcoholics) who must be thoroughly rid of the habit of taking drugs for slight discomforts." For treatment he recommends first the immediate removal of the injurious matter, then "associative dishabituation" in an inpatient setting. He considers associations for total abstainers helpful, but warns against the "disadvantages which must not be underestimated, of dragging along until they are incurable, cases which in themselves are hopeful." In a simple statement he says, "The chemical remedies recommended are humbug." He also believes with Forel that the "incurable alcoholics [should] be removed from the active treatment group, and placed in more permanent special institutions which would offer the possibility of belated cures through protracted abstinence and training, which might return to society after years and years many a man apparently lost." Finally, he criticizes physicians for encouraging the therapeutic use of alcohol, and warns against the "unfortunate mistakes in practice . . . still being made where physicians instigate the cured inebriate to again indulge in alcohol and thereby lead him with his family into misfortune." Although he did not understand the relationship of delirium tremens to withdrawal, Bleuler deserves to be read by many who have considered the current ideas about alcoholism to be relatively new.

The advent of Freudian psychology led to serious consideration of the relationship of alcohol and drug addiction to the mind and personality. Any discussion of the psychoanalytic theories of the genesis and course of alcoholism requires understanding of general psychoanalytic theory. For those familiar with it, such a discussion is redundant; but for the uninitiated, the definitions of psychoanalytic terms relating to sexual instincts and behaviors often appear bizarre and fantastic. One must see these constructs, however, as an attempt to reduce a multiplicity of clinical pictures to a unified whole in an attempt to make intervention more rational and productive and the results long-lasting.

Freud himself addressed the question of alcoholism in *Three Contributions to the Theory of Sexuality*, suggesting that the alcoholic had regressed to the oral stage of development. Abraham linked alcoholism with repressed homosexuality. In a comprehensive review Fenichel (5) stated clearly a general assumption which had significant effects on treatment measures at the time: "The premorbid personality, therefore, is the decisive factor. Those persons become drug addicts for whom the effect of the drug has a specific significance. For them it means the fulfillment, or at least the hope of fulfillment, of a deep and primitive desire, more urgently felt by them than are sexual or other instinctual longings by normal persons."

Sandor Rado (6), looking at the psychic effects of intoxicants, called attention by analogy to the erotic nature of the states of intoxication, and compared the satisfaction gained to orgasm. Indeed, as the practice of obtaining satisfaction from drugs becomes central, sexual gratification becomes of lesser importance, and often impossible. Looking at the infant's gratification from food as an "alimentary orgasm," he then generalized a special "pharmacotoxic orgasm," which could be considered oral despite the many routes of administration of the drug. Later, he developed the concept of "pharmacothymia." When a predisposed person (who has a "tense depression") drinks or takes a drug, it has a particularly beneficial effect, a period of elation:

"The transitoriness of the elation determines the return of the depression; the latter, the renewed craving for elation, and so on. We discover that there is a cyclic course, and its regularity demonstrates that the ego is now maintaining its self-regard by means of an artificial technique. This step involves an alteration in the individual's entire mode of life; it means a change from the "realistic regime" to a "pharmacothymic regime" of the ego. A pharmacothymic, therefore, may be defined as an individual who has betaken himself to this type of regime; the ensuing consequences make up the scope of the manifestations of pharmacothymia. In other words, this illness is a narcissistic disorder, a destruction through artificial means of the natural ego organization."

Other psychoanalytic links have been made to "a flight from homosexual impulses, incestuous thoughts and masturbatory guilt" (Brill), sadistic drives and oedipal conflicts (Glover), a compromise between hysterical and obsessive compulsive neurosis (Sachs), self-destructive drives (Menninger), feelings of inadequacy, internalized fears of failure, and deficiencies in social relationships (Klebanoff), and excessive demandingness and an inability to carry out sustained effort and to express feelings of hostility and rage (Knight). Reviewing the foregoing constructs as well as his own experience, Dr. Morris Chafetz, in a current analytic construct of alcoholism, views alcohol addiction as an oral perversion: "Because the addictive alcoholic gratifies his instinctual oral wishes directly and without anxiety, we view addictive alcoholism as a perversion rather than as a neurotic mechanism, which is the disguised anxiety-ridden converse of a perversion"(7).

The diversity of these dynamic constructs masks elements of similarity in all, but more importantly demonstrates that much serious attention has been given to the mental phenomena of persons with alcoholism, based on close observation of their communications and retrospective histories. The contribution of the Freudian revolution to the emotional aspects of the patient with alcoholism has not been ended, despite many changes in the methodology of use of such constructs in treatment.

It is not widely enough known that some of the impetus and rationale for the development of A.A. came from Freud's colleague, Carl Jung. An alcoholic had, in desperation, gone to consult Jung. Having heard his story, Jung said to him, "You have a difficult problem. The only people I know who have recovered have been people who have had a deep religious conversion experience." This person obtained that experience through the Oxford Movement, and passed along the news to Ebby, a drinking companion of Bill W. Ebby had achieved sobriety when he next saw Bill and introduced him to the concepts of the Oxford Movement, which encompassed a framework of religious and spiritual principles. Back in the United States, Bill W. had yet another bout with alcohol, which resulted in his hospitalization. There, in a blinding moment, the Higher Power appeared to Bill, and gave him the conversion experience that Jung claimed was required to achieve sobriety. The principles of A.A. then emerged, closely following those of the Oxford Movement.

These beginnings may sound more auspicious for a cult than a cure, but the application of these principles soon began to achieve results that could not be denied. The earliest serious student of this remarkable phenomenon was the psychiatrist Dr. Harry M. Tiebout. In January 1944 in the *American Journal of Psychiatry*, he presented some observations on the phenomena that occur when an alcoholic responds favorably to A.A. Calling this phenomenon conversion, he detailed eight elements in the negative pattern developing during the process of alcoholism; these included depression, aggression, oppression, perfectionism, isolation, egocentricity, defiance and "walling off." By using quotations from a patient who had experienced conversion, he demonstrated a major shift in personality, in which her previous negative pattern was reversed.

In assessing the relationship of conversion to therapy, Tiebout ventured the opinion "that positive attitudes provide a favorable soil for psychological growth and maturing." In a series of further articles on the relationship of A.A. to recovery for the alcoholic, Tiebout gave further theoretical support to the fact of A.A.'s success. In 1946, he defined the process of "surrender" as opposed to mere compliance with the A.A. program. In 1951 he encouraged psychiatrists to treat alcoholism as a disease rather than a symptom—just as surgeons would treat cancer by removing the primary lesion rather than just its surface manifestations. In 1954 he called attention to the need to deflate the overexpanded ego, which resulted when surrender took place. In 1961, he pointed to the need for intervention in the psychotherapeutic treatment of alcoholics as well as for what he termed the passive supportive role of the psychiatrist. In 1958, he drew attention to the controversy regarding direct treatment of a symptom; he claimed that if drinking was a symptom, it must be first controlled before attention to other problems of the psyche could be successfully solved. Tiebout's down-to-earth, simple and practical papers have stood the test of time, and his conclusions are validated by the fact that his precepts are still used.

It is not surprising, in the glow of fascination with Freud's discoveries, that alcoholism should be put into the same hopper as the other psychiatric problems and, in the dawning new age of psychoanalytic treatment, that it should be expected to yield to the intensive use of the new method of psychoanalysis. Thus in 1937, Dr. Karl Menninger (8) could persuasively write: "Thus alcohol addiction can be thought of not as a disease but as a suicidal flight from disease—a disastrous attempt at the self-cure of an unseen inner conflict." The alcoholic was seen as "an 'oral character,' who takes through the mouth and destroys with his mouth, anything which resists his demands." Drinking then becomes an "infantile revenge reaction" of a passive aggressive person whose drinking is an unconsciously aggressive act which expresses the repressed hostility that is one of the chief determinants of the alcoholic neurosis. Other components included a fear of masculinity, expressed by overly masculine activity (however, since the alcoholic seeks mothering rather than mating with a woman, she rebels, throwing him on the superficial camaraderie of his male peers). At that time, Menninger could recommend psychoanalysis as the treatment of choice, but, even at this early point, he recognized that psychotherapy could only succeed if the patient was initially kept away from alcohol, and only later given gradually increasing freedom. Thus his final recommendation was confinement of the patient with psychoanalysis in order to give the proper direction to an increasing capacity for externally directed aggression. He also wisely allowed that a religious experience can also effect a cure.

Dr. Ruth Fox was also writing of alcoholism at this time (1955) and she discussed the problem in this way: "Excessive drinking, whether habitual or not, is a danger signal, a symptom that all may not be well with a person's mental and psychic health. The best qualified doctor to determine whether such excessive drinking is neurotic, which is to say whether such drinking may become addictive, is a psychoanalyst." However, she added, "If the person's drinking is already addictive, it is still symptomatic, but the symptom is so gross that it must be treated all by itself, and stopped, before its roots can be explored and then treated" (9).

Dr. Fox later had experiences that caused her to attribute less importance to the neurosis as the background for alcoholism; so in 1973 she wrote, "The physician must make it clear to the patient that abstinence will have to come first. *Even when* [author's italics] alcoholism is accompanied by an underlying psychopathology, the pathological drinking can, like fever, kill long before its cause is found" (10).

Similarly, Menninger would be unlikely to reiterate his early view that "Alcoholism cannot possibly be an hereditary trait, but for a father to be alcoholic is an easy way for the son to learn *how* to effect the relationship."

One can see behind all these approaches, from Benjamin Rush to Ruth Fox, the inescapable necessity of putting a barrier between the patient and the alcohol, whether by using a "sober house," psychiatric hospitalization, or a sanitarium or, as Dr. Fox so ably introduced and fostered, by using Antabuse (disulfiram). But, for some or all, some other inner change was needed to keep the person on a continuing program of sobriety, abstinence, or at least away from addictive drinking.

As A.A. grew largely independently of any medical discipline, other trends in psychiatry began to develop. First there was the introduction and rapid growth of methods of group psychotherapy during the second World War. Perhaps these were stimulated in part by the group experience of A.A., and perhaps by such great changes as the information explosion, the substitution of corporate group-think for rugged individualism, and the progressive loss of just those sexual taboos whose secrets formed the basis of neurotic behavior in Freud's time.

While critics like Eysenck began to pick holes in the psychoanalytic fabric, the diagnostic categories in psychiatric illness began to change. Hysteria was vanishing; neurosis more rare; and more and more people tended to "act out" rather than feel the overwhelming anxiety they were entitled to. The sudden emergence in Western countries of drug addiction as an alarming, rapidly growing problem suddenly crystallized what we had known all along about alcoholism, but had ignored the implications of: Alcoholism was an addiction. And as laboratory data increased our conviction of this, we struggled to determine an adequate method of treatment that might be available to all and might avoid the chance that one would "hit bottom" before he would die.

B. F. Skinner captured the modern behavioral ascendency, equating our behavior with the contingencies presented. He thus lent credence to intervention in the use of psychiatry, as well as to the growing feeling that no specific emotional flaw was needed to lead people to alcohol, but that it was equally possible that physical differences in the reaction of brain and body to alcohol might predispose certain individuals to their addictions. There were those who could attempt to allow us to retain a bit of "freedom and dignity" without the total therapeutic nihilism of a Szasz. In a psychiatric world that explored heredity in schizophrenia, an hereditary factor in alcoholism seems less frightening.

Psychiatrists thus have at least considered alcoholism. But they have done much more. They have been the first to open the doors of their institutions to alcoholics. They have been among the most open-minded of the medical profession in accepting the fact that people with alcoholism need help and should be given it. Two directors of the national effort in alcoholism have been psychiatrists, and although their approaches have been signally different, they have each forwarded important phases of the work. Those people who are in the movement to combat alcoholism and who are also in A.A. will find many friends among the ranks of the psychiatrists. . . .

We would then ask the reader not only to learn from these papers about the parameters of personality in alcoholism, but also to assess what the role of the psychiatrist is and should be in such treatment. . . .

There are those who feel that the tremendous effort expended to keep an alcoholic abstinent is a really nonspecific form of treatment similar to the form of treatment, heliotherapy, given in the early part of this century for tuberculosis: If the person was made healthy in every other way, he could mobilize his defenses to contain the tuberculosis bacterium. This line of reasoning leads in several directions. One, being attempted now in several centers, is to get those recalcitrant to A.A. and abstinence to "learn how" to do controlled drinking. These bold and experimental behavioral modification approaches are touched on here, although at this point, for the vast majority of alcoholics, they cannot be recommended as accepted therapy. Another potentiality would be to find a chemical lesion in at least some who develop alcoholism, and then find the antidote. This seems far away, although now more than ever it seems possible. The third potentiality—an improvement of the quality of life sufficient to make alcoholism unnecessary and unattempted—seems more utopian. Whether there is a fourth—the direct resolution of pregenital psychiatric disturbances through psychoanalysis—we must leave unanswered. Readers will have their opinions pro and con. There is no substantial current evidence that this has been possible. . . .

REFERENCES

1. Seixas, F. A., Omenn, G. S., Burk, E. D. and Eggleston, S., eds. Nature and nurture in alcoholism. Ann. N.Y. Acad. Sci. **197:** 1-229, 1972.
2. Seixas, F. A. and Eggleston, S., eds. Alcoholism and the central nervous system. Ann. N.Y. Acad. Sci. **215:** 1-389, 1973.
3. Rush, B. Medical inquiries and observations upon the diseases of the mind. New York; Hafner; 1962. [Orig. 1812.]
4. Bleuler, E. Textbook of psychiatry. New York; Macmillan; 1930.
5. Fenichel, O. The psychoanalytic theory of neurosis. New York; Norton; 1945.
6. Rado, S. Psychoanalysis of behavior. New York; Grune & Stratton; 1956.
7. Chafetz, M. E., Blane, H. T. and Hill, M. J., eds. Frontiers of alcoholism. New York; Science House; 1970.
8. Menninger, K. Man against himself. New York; Harcourt, Brace; 1938.
9. Fox, R. and Lyon, P. Alcoholism—its scope, cause and treatment. New York; Random House; 1955.
10. Bourne, P. G. and Fox, R., eds. Alcoholism; progress in research and treatment. New York; Academic; 1973.

2

Multidisciplinary Perspectives on Alcoholism and the Need for Integration

An Historical and Prospective Note[1]

Mark Keller

IT SEEMS APPROPRIATE to sum up what I think has been learned by way of an interdisciplinary-wholistic understanding of alcoholism, and I will try to outline it. This conception, already suggested many years ago (1) but since then confirmed by additional observations and learning, rests upon the theories and researches of many scientists—and some amateurs—in the past 40 years, and it is not possible adequately to credit all of them.

Here, then, is how, at this stage of our knowledge, I think alcoholism may be conceptualized in wholistic perspective:

There is a sharply distinct difference among individuals—possibly among groups—in degree of vulnerability (2). Whether the vulnerability is to behavioral or affective disorder generally, or to alcoholism in particular, is uncertain. More likely, I think, the former; that is, a general vulnerability. To this vulnerability a genetic factor may well contribute (3); but it might be a negative factor—that is, the genetic factor may be one that immunizes or makes the development of alcoholism, or the resort to alcoholism, difficult or unlikely, rather than one that positively increases vulnerability. The

[1] Reprinted by permission from the JOURNAL OF STUDIES ON ALCOHOL, Vol. 36, pp. 133–147, 1975. Copyright by Journal of Studies on Alcohol, Inc., New Brunswick, New Jersey 08903. The initial portion of this paper, dealing largely with the history of the multidisciplinary Center of Alcohol Studies, has been omitted.

relative freedom of the Jews from alcoholism has been largely attributed to sociocultural inhibition, but actually the possibility of a genetically determined deterrent has not been excluded by any evidence.

Whether or not a genetic susceptibility or immunity obtains, an infant-rearing and childhood-developmental factor seems decidedly to be involved in laying the groundwork of the ultimate psychological vulnerability (4, 5). The form that this development takes may well be that of excessive dependency (6, 7) or dependency conflict (8, 9). The evidence for that character or personality trait in alcoholism seems rather strong, though not yet conclusive or universal, and its origin in early experience can hardly be doubted.

Next we have a combined personality and social development. It occurs in adolescence. It may be a continuation of maldevelopment in the psychosexual sphere that was initiated already in infancy or childhood. In some societies it may directly involve drinking or other deviant behaviors. Noteworthy is the fact that social and cultural phenomena begin to play a significant positive part here. Thus, where drinking by adolescents is forbidden or discouraged, the already vulnerable young may now use forbidden drinking as a way of counteracting or compensating for the feelings of inadequacy, or of insecure self-sex image. In that case, if the societal attitudes about drinking and drunkenness grant machismo-like or heroic rewards for outstanding capacity to drink, then those who are already most vulnerable are specially set up for alcoholism. For in these circumstances, not only is heavy drinking rewarded by peer-group admiration, but the heavy-drinking youth experiences the profoundest internal reward from the drinking. This occurs because of the magical pharmacological property of alcohol: the drunken person can imagine himself, feel himself, to be the manly or womanly, heroic or charming, clever or sophisticated person that he thinks he ought to be. The insecure adolescent who experiences this magical double reward from drinking is likely to resort to alcohol repeatedly in any of the circumstances that are troublous and problematic to the developing adult. And in that case another factor comes into play: learning or conditioning (5, 10). The individual learns or becomes conditioned to resort to alcohol, unfailingly and even reflexively, in amounts sufficient to overcome troublous self-doubts, whenever certain sorts of problems arise. Thus, if in the adolescent they were problems of relating to the opposite sex, then heavy drinking in sex-related situations could become the usual reaction. But the learned response can equally prevail if the original problems were in general relating to people, or in coping with any sort of practical problem situations. Moreover, by the rule of generalization, the use of heavy drinking to relieve, or as an aid in coping with, one sort of problem will be followed by its use in meeting other problems.

The process, and it may be a long process—Jellinek (11) estimated that it took from 5 to 10 or 12 years for the average development of full-blown alcoholism—by which an individual learns to become an alcoholic, is itself a complicated one. It is a reasonable guess that the more vulnerable an individual was to begin with, whether genetically or by childhood experience and adolescent reinforcement, the more likely he is to grasp at the glass crutch and finally to arrive at the state of helpless addiction—confirmed alcoholism. We must assume a range of vulnerability and reinforcive experience. Similarly, as Jellinek hypothesized (12), there is a range of societal permissiveness, and, as Bacon (13) has hypothesized, environmental encouragement, all contributing to a society's rate of alcoholism. In a society where much and heavy drinking is accepted, as in France, the less vulnerable may develop alcoholism and a high rate will result. In a society where heavy drinking and drunkenness are discouraged, as among the Jews, only the most vulnerable will "make it" and the rate of alcoholism will be low. But conflict about drinking within a society may block the chances of the vulnerable to escape. For, indeed, not all the vulnerable make it—many sorts of significant events may intervene to save them; and this is a vital consideration for the chances of planned prevention.

To sum up: This complex hypothesis of the etiology of alcoholism incorporates a genetic or constitutional factor which imposes exceptional susceptibility or immunity; errors of infant relationship or childhood rearing and resultant psychosexual maldevelopment with a possibly defective, especially hyperdependent or dependency-conflicted, personality trait; further misfortune in the form of misdirected maturation in the adolescent phase, especially if reinforced by internally well-rewarded drinking experiences; and a subsequent learning or conditioning process, of possibly years-long duration, embedded in culturally and societally determined mores and conditions and directions, with a negative balance of interpersonal relations; and, finally, the pharmacological properties of alcohol assuming a dominant indispensable role in the individual's way of life.

If the truth is anything as complicated as this, then no wonder that people in particular disciplines and professions have mostly preferred to concentrate on just their own limb of this blind-men's elephant. But if this beast is not a product of sheer fantasy—a pink elephant—then it may be an interdisciplinary-wholistic conception of the etiology of alcoholism.

And what, then, is the nature of the beast? What is alcoholism, under this conception? In the end, it is surely a disease—if helpless addiction to a drug is a disease, as I believe. At an earlier stage it may be the symptom of another disease, if personality disorder severe enough to cause functional disablement is a disease, as I believe. At some still earlier stage, the heavy drinking or symptomatic drinking (or alcohol abuse, if we should accept that pejorative term) may not be diagnosable as disease. Then it has to be a form of misbehavior, or deviant behavior, according to the perspective from which one chooses to view it. In that case, we are not talking about alcoholism. Let us at least be clear about that. Alcoholismic behavior is indicative of disease (14, *pp. xv-xxviii*). Misbehavior with alcohol is an elephant of a different color. This simple clarification can help in determining what needs to be done about different people, how diversely we may react to them and help them in different stages of their troubles.

What do we gain from a multidisciplinary-wholistic conception of alcoholism?

At a very minimum, the recognition that no one profession, no one discipline, no single-minded approach, can hope to deal with this condition. In saying this, I am recycling old truths. But perhaps if we accept the underlying wholistic perspective, we will be able wholeheartedly to resolve the need for integration. And not only the integration of therapeutic approaches. For too long we have paid lip service also to the importance of prevention, but our actions have been responsive—for unblamably humane reasons—chiefly to the needs of the catastrophe victims, those who are already alcoholics. We have sought to create more and better repair shops, but we have not tried to initiate the era of prevention. And no wonder: we have not known how.

If, however, it is true that some people start vulnerable, and then over a life-history show increasing signs of their vulnerability, finally exhibiting the prealcoholismic behaviors of heavy and implicative drinking (15), then can we not begin to identify the vulnerables—the implicative drinkers among adults, the deviant behavers among adolescents, perhaps ultimately even the uneasy and already problem-beset children? Must we not try to identify them? Isn't that the essence of the public-health approach? And once we begin to perform the task of identifying the vulnerables, shall we stop

short of trying to help them avert the danger? I think that if we try
we shall succeed in finding means of helping which will be acceptable to them as well as to the helpers.

The interdisciplinary perspective, then, not only allows wholistic
understanding but opens a gate to the Ultima Thule, the era of prevention. Too obvious to need elaboration is the fact that all the disciplines and professions must be involved, and in an integrated program, both in testing the parts and the wholeness of the etiological
hypothesis, and in applying the actions, therapeutic and preventive,
that its conclusions must invoke.

Not enough has been said about the necessary integration.
Frankly, I do not have a clear conception of how the disciplines can
be truly integrated in performing the studies required to verify the
wholistic etiological perspective, nor exactly how the professions
can be integrated for the first experimental programs of prevention.
I suggest that the wider teaching and adoption of the wholistic perspective, and the better support of researches and actions in the
truly multidisciplinary centers, will result in the discovery and development of effective means of integration.

REFERENCES

1. KELLER, M. Cultural aspects of drinking and alcoholism. Toronto; United Church of Canada, Commission on Temperance Policy and Program; 1958.
2. JELLINEK, E. M. The disease concept of alcoholism. Highland Park, N.J.; Hillhouse Press; 1960.
3. GOODWIN, D. W. Is alcoholism hereditary? A review and critique. Archs Gen. Psychiat. 25: 545-549, 1971.
4. LOLLI, G. Alcoholism as a disorder of the love disposition. Q. J. Stud. Alcohol 17: 96-107, 1956.
5. BARRY, H., 3d. Psychological factors in alcoholism. Pp. 53-107. In: KISSIN, B. and BEGLEITER, H., eds. The biology of alcoholism. Vol. 3. Clinical pathology. New York; Plenum; 1974.
6. McCORD, W., McCORD, J. and GUDEMAN, J. Some current theories of alcoholism; a longitudinal evaluation. Q. J. Stud. Alcohol 20: 727-749, 1959.
7. LEMERT, E. M. Dependency in married alcoholics. Q. J. Stud. Alcohol 23: 590-609, 1962.
8. BACON, M. K., BARRY, H., 3d and CHILD, I. L. A cross-cultural study of drinking. II. Relations to other features of culture. Q. J. Stud. Alcohol Suppl. No. 3, pp. 29-48, 1965.
9. BACON, M. K. The dependency-conflict hypothesis and the frequency of drunkenness; further evidence from a cross-cultural study. Q. J. Stud. Alcohol 35: 863-876, 1974.
10. KINGHAM, R. J. Alcoholism and the reinforcement theory of learning. Q. J. Stud. Alcohol 19: 320-330, 1958.

11. JELLINEK, E. M. Phases of alcohol addiction. Q. J. Stud. Alcohol 13: 673-684, 1952.
12. JELLINEK, E. M. The world and its bottle. Wld Hlth 10 (No. 4): 4-6, 1957.
13. BACON, S. D. The process of addiction to alcohol; social aspects. Q. J. Stud. Alcohol 34: 1-27, 1973.
14. KELLER, M. and MCCORMICK, M. A dictionary of words about alcohol. New Brunswick, N.J.; Rutgers Center of Alcohol Studies; 1968.
15. KELLER, M. Definition of alcoholism. Q. J. Stud. Alcohol 21: 125-134, 1960.

3

Some Interfaces between Alcoholism and Mental Health[1]

Earl X. Freed, Ph.D.

THIS PAPER begins with an apologia. It is not a report of research, the traditional contribution to a scientific journal. Rather than detail an experiment performed on a certain discrete problem, it is an examination of directions of thinking about a quite broad problem—the possible interfaces between alcoholism and mental health.

Although it is easy to appreciate the value, in terms of attitudes, educational efforts, treatment, etc., of alcoholism's recognition as an illness, the fact is that such recognition should be the springboard for truly regarding alcoholism in a new way, not simply euphemistically relabeling it. If alcoholism is an illness, despite its physical and social concomitants, then it is a mental illness or behavioral disorder or psychiatric problem—in any case, it falls within the purview of the mental health and behavioral sciences. Notwithstanding the resurgence of investigations into the biological aspects of alcoholism (18), there are still multitudes of investigators studying mental health aspects of alcohol use and abuse, albeit in many cases, isolated aspects of same. As Sidman (50) wrote: "The pursuit of science is an intensely personal affair. Experimenters cannot always tell us how or why they do what they do. . . ." What seems lacking is a systematic, organized gestalt, a sort of overview. For mental health professionals interested in alcohol, this should be the interface between the two disciplines. In fact, there are many interfaces and this paper attempts to collate and examine some of them, not *in extenso* nor as a review nor as an exhaustive, all-inclusive tabula-

[1] Reprinted by permission from the *Journal of Drug Issues*, Vol. 6, pp. 213-222, 1976. Copyright by Journal of Drug Issues, Inc., Tallahassee, Florida 32303.

tion but rather as a hopefully stimulating kind of socratic dialogue. The exercise is hypothesis-generating and is an attempt to organize current theorizing and investigation around meaningful wholes. Sometimes wholes can be *too* all-encompassing. In this instance, for example, the relevant three, out of the total of 18, topics around which current literature is abstracted in the JOURNAL OF STUDIES ON ALCOHOL are psychology, psychiatry and treatment of alcoholism. Their scope is too broad.

Jaynes (30) likened the route of physical sciences to climbing a mountain, seeking height. He saw psychological sciences as a "huge entangled forest . . . so easy to walk through on different levels." The task of the behavioral scientist was to seek directions, not height. If this is so, then the top of the mountain now being viewed should be some ultimate exposition of the relationship between alcohol and mental health. Examination of the interfaces of alcoholism and psychopathology should, first of all, be from a descriptive point of view: what are the common boundaries, where do the phenomena touch each other? Questions of causal relationships and primacy in etiology come later and they will have to be faced after a detailing of the areas for focus. Interfaces obviously exist at hosts of levels. The following questions seek to enumerate and explore just some of them.

(*a*) *Is abstinence related to positive mental health?* If there is some relationship between alcoholism and psychopathology, then the obverse might be a reasonable hypothesis, a relationship between nondrinking and the absence of psychopathology. On the other hand, if abstinence constitutes inflexibility and personality rigidity, then perhaps one should seek a relationship between controlled or moderate or nonproblem drinking and positive adjustment. Jessor and Jessor (31) pointed out that an adolescent's beginning to drink is related to developmental behavior since "drinking is a normatively accepted aspect of adult status." Studying adolescents longitudinally over a 4-year period, they found that abstainers were more conventional, less prone to maturational transitions and, it seems, change. Similarly, adult male abstainers studied by Cahalan and Room (6) showed a low rate of social activity, pointing to community isolation. Thus, whether abstinence can be considered a facet of psychological health is a question calling for greater in-depth study of identified abstainers.

(*b*) *Is nonproblem drinking related to positive mental health?* If, as it seems, abstinence is a too rigid, too narrow orientation, then perhaps occasional, moderate use of alcohol, other than problem drinking, bears some relationship to over-all positive personality adjustment. In contrast to the inflexibility of the abstainer, the occasional drinker perhaps employs alcohol as a social vehicle or as an adjunctive defense mechanism. Whereas a pattern of abstinence may point to over-control, a pattern of nonproblem alcohol use could be interpreted as indicative of more adaptive control. This is one thrust of the arguments of proponents calling for controlled drinking, both as a criterion for—and goal of—alcoholism treatment (16, 21).

This might lead to the suggestion that an important interface between alcoholism and mental hygiene was in the area of ego control, and in fact, quantitative aspects of ego strength have been emphasized in both alcoholism and psychopathology (3). Alcohol is a drug which serves to lower ego boundaries.

Among the institutionalized elderly, there is evidence that small amounts of alcohol consumption yield psychologically beneficial effects (52). The same report suggesting the latter went further (seemingly irrespective of age within the range of adulthood) in its "guidelines": "The proper use of alcohol can be socially, psychologically, and physically beneficial" (52).

If drinking alcohol is a defense mechanism, then there is the possibility that one view of problem drinking is that it represents a defensive exacerbation. As a matter of fact, Hayman (29) concluded that "the alcoholic chooses to fortify the defense mechanism of denial with alcohol." The line between suspicion and paranoia is a fine one as are those, for example, between cleanliness and compulsive hand washing or realistic fear and morbid phobia. One psychodynamic hypothesis in all cases has been that in psychopathology the defense has become the way of life. The same may be true with alcohol: "The line between alcohol misuse and alcoholism is mostly a matter of degree and consequence" (52) as is the line between healthy and pathological ego defenses. The latter exist on a continuum and so must alcohol use and misuse. Here, then, may be a context in which alcoholism and mental health are subsumed.

(c) *Does alcoholism mask psychopathology?* This is a well-known interface which has been extensively reviewed (15, 19, 29). Clinicians often cite cases of detoxified alcoholics whose psychiatric symptomatologies emerge following imposed abstinence. With regard to affective disorders, I (15) concluded, "A number of reports have documented the finding that manic-depressive reactions may initially masquerade as alcoholism because, when the patient is hospitalized, the alcoholismic symptomatology is blatant and predominant," demanding immediate attention. A good example of this appears in the discussion of multiple psychiatric diagnoses in the American Psychiatric Association *Diagnostic and Statistical Manual of Mental Disorders* (1). Quoting the principle that the condition most urgently needing treatment is listed first, the example given is that of a simple schizophrenic patient who is acutely pathologically intoxicated. Such alcoholism symptomatology may cloak severity and existence of underlying psychopathology (34). Not only affective disorders but schizophrenias, too, have been reported as concealed by an alcoholism syndrome (19). On the other hand, Hayman (29) has mounted considerable evidence against the notion that depression underlies alcoholism, concluding that alcoholism is not a mask for depression and reporting that not one of his chronic alcoholic patients developed a clinical depression following abstinence. Setting aside the confounding question of whether mania masks depression, I (13) found alcohol abuse in the histories of 15 of 23 hospitalized manic patients. This is a rare instance of psychiatric symptomatology masking problem drinking; clinical reports usually have been the other way around.

(*d*) *Is alcohol abuse a manifestation of psychopathology?* In the above study with manics, there was some suggestion that alcohol abuse was exacerbated during manic episodes as still another manifestation of the euphoric loss of control. Alcohol abuse has long been regarded as an acting out of other problems. For example, it is widely considered a depressive equivalent (35). In interviewing alcohol abusers, it is common practice to inquire what the alcohol was doing for the patient, whether there was precipitating stress, etc. All of the foregoing suggest the underlying hypothesis that alcohol abuse is a symptom of other psychopathology. A not infrequent psychiatric hospital diagnosis is "Schizophrenic reaction, manifested by delusions, hallucinations, blunted affect . . . and excessive indulgence in alcohol." Regarding chronic mental disorders, Noyes (43) considered that "associated alcoholism is either a symptom of the psychosis or another method of dealing with the same personality problems which contributed to the mental disorder."

As is so frequently the case in the interactions involving alcohol, there is another side of the coin: psychopathology unquestionably is often a symptom of alcoholism. This is seen in alcoholic psychoses due to alcohol poisoning in both acute and chronic brain syndromes. Resultant symptoms such as alcoholic hallucinosis often mimic psychogenic disorders. Korsakoff's psychosis is well known, and the mental deterioration and intellectual deficits resulting from chronic alcoholism have been documented in the literature and in the clinical folders of innumerable hospitalized patients.

When one looks at manifestation or symptom relationships between alcoholism and psychopathology, there appears a paradoxical third side of the coin: symptoms of one—or the disorder itself—may substitute for the other. For example, alcoholism appears more frequently in males and affective disorders in females (56). Different symptom patterns have been reported in alcoholics and nonalcoholics upon admission to a psychiatric hospital and many symptoms of the former "were directly referable to acute and chronic sequelae of overindulgence" (25). There is also the suggestion that "alcoholism in men sometimes [is] an alternative to schizophrenia in women" (42). Whether or not cultural influences transmitted via sex-role expectations may be implicated, clearly the topic of symptom choice becomes an important interface between alcoholism and psychopathology.

(e) *Does alcohol subserve psychodynamic functions?* Wallerstein (53) wrote that "The irresistible temptation to repeatedly induce in oneself states of semi-paralysis and semi-delirium by drinking dilute ethyl alcohol is an extraordinary psychological phenomenon." Psychological theorists have sought to explicate this phenomenon. The psychoanalytic school stressed the alcoholic's desire for ecstasy and elation, his regressive ego and lack of self-esteem (41). Another dynamic theory emphasized the alcoholic's frustration, unresolved conflicts and blocked needs (14, 40). In this view, alcohol was regarded as a disinhibitor. Phenomenologists interpreted alcohol's function in terms of the alteration of the drinker's perceptions of the field and of himself in such a manner that the changed perceptions enhanced the phenomenal self (51). Learning theorists have conceptualized alcohol as producing a reduction in fear which resulted in reinforcement of the response of drinking alcohol in future stress situations (9). Thus, whatever the orientation, the shared frame of reference seemed to be that alcohol subserved a psychodynamic function or met some emotional need of the drinker. This has been referred to as the "enabling" action of alcohol (45). We (36) sought it in laboratory research with animals: "The basic issue in orchestrating an animal model of alcoholism is the initiation of alcohol-seeking behavior specifically directed to alcohol's pharmacodynamic utility."

What this utility may be for humans again represents potential interfaces between alcohol and mental health. Two leading contenders are alcohol's role as a mood regulator and alcohol's use as a tension reducer.

(*f*) *How does alcohol regulate mood?* Affects could represent an important interface of alcohol use and mental health but mood "has been so slighted in psychological research" (54). Thus, West (55) has concluded that "the habitual use of alcohol by human beings will never be understood without a more basic understanding of the nature of emotions."

When the relationship between alcohol and mood was last reviewed (15), it was deemed "a fruitful area for continued study." These studies have been updated and the new review (23) reports an increased tempo of research in this area despite the barriers and methodological problems involved in the delineation of the relationship of alcohol to mood. The former include the essential subjectivity of mood states and the unclarified dose-response relationships of alcohol and mood. Many—but mixed—findings supported the notion that psychological benefit in the form of affective improvement derived from drinking alcohol and hence becomes the motivation for same. I (23) concluded, "Self-reported depression by alcoholics is found frequently and seems to be other than situational, but there is equivocal evidence that alcoholics are more depressed than normative groups. The consequences of drinking are related to expectancies concerning consequences and some studies point out that alcoholics drink to obtain affective relief. However, there is conflicting evidence concerning the hypothesis that craving for alcohol derives from a need to attenuate dysphoric states." Further, "generally, non-alcoholics anticipate elevated moods and relaxation as a result of drinking and this does tend to occur. The evidence suggests that alcoholics show increasing anxiety and depression with increasing alcohol consumption although they expect the reverse. There appears to be a social factor which plays a role in determining the affective consequences of drinking."

Clearly there appears to be an interface between mental health and alcohol use in the area of mood states although there is diversity of opinion as to its specificity. Some individuals apparently employ alcohol as a self-prescribed mood regulator, as a chemotherapeutic agent to reestablish some kind of emotional homeostasis. This may occur in attempts to lift depression (4) and even to reduce heightened affect (47).

A recent follow-up study (24) of 129 hospital-treated alcoholics who completed a self-report mood questionnaire underscored the significant relationship between alcoholism and affective disturbance. Three months after treatment, the former patients were classified as either totally abstinent, improved or unimproved, using prehospital drinking patterns as a baseline for comparison. Mood scale data revealed that a very low degree of affective disturbance characterized those men who had maintained the abstinence initiated in the hospital. The unimproved subjects showed the greatest affective disturbance; the improved subjects were intermediate to the other groups.

(g) *Is alcohol a conflict resolver and tension reducer?* This view of alcohol derived, in large part, from findings of studies of experimental neurosis with animals (11, 40). These rather quickly were supplemented with anecdotal and experiential data (12) which documented alcohol's reinforcing role in approach–avoidance conflict situations. Reviews (5, 7, 20) of new data, however, have failed to support strongly alcohol's utility as a conflict attenuator and tension reducer. Still, West (55) has contended that no emotion has greater significance in relation to alcohol than tension. Many alcoholics felt tension, he asserted, and they might seek relief from it via alcohol. However, he concluded that "we do not understand the nature of such tension, nor do we know how or why alcohol affects it in such a specific fashion in certain individuals." Thus, the whole area of problem solving, conflict resolution and tension reduction remains an important common surface between alcohol and mental hygiene.

In conflict or under tension, some individuals "act out" their disturbances. Such an overt manifestation, in counterdistinction to an ideational one, may take the form of an alcoholic bout, and the net effect of ingesting alcohol is often to reduce behavioral controls so that still more acting out takes place. It is an unusual psychotherapist who has treated alcoholic patients who has not witnessed their acting out in response to discomfort felt either as a result of the therapy or in their daily lives.

Acting out is also a bridge between alcoholism and psychopathology in that it appears to be a common manifestation characterizing both as so-called personality disorders (1). Antisocial acting out is the hallmark of the sociopathic or psychopathic personality. Barry (2) noted a close relationship between alcoholism and antisocial personality structure in "irresponsible, impulsive, and destructive actions."

Suicide and suicidal attempts, self-destructive behaviors, are quite specific cases of acting out which constitute a well-documented interface between alcoholism and psychopathology. Alcohol's role in fatal accidents, violent deaths and suicide, frequently referred to in the literature, continues to be cited in recent publications (8, 28).

(*h*) *Does alcoholism have a genetic base?* This interface raises the whole question of the contributions of nature and nurture to alcoholism and mental illness and there has been no dearth of data here either with humans (27, 49)[2] or animals (10, 46). Attitudes toward the relative roles of heredity and environment in the etiology and maintenance of deviant behaviors have fluctuated historically. Genetic components of alcoholism once again are becoming more prominent in biological considerations of alcoholism and some forms of mental illness such as the schizophrenias and affective disorders. On the other hand, behavior therapists point increasingly to environmental contingencies, quite often covert ones, which maintain certain behaviors (33). Included within the area of this broad interface are findings from twin studies, studies of genetic markers, longitudinal studies, family-history investigations, epidemiological investigations, and lifetime morbidity risk studies. Retrospective life history research has overshadowed prospective studies such as follow-up studies of treated and recovered alcoholics and psychiatric patients other than those readmitted to hospital settings.

Cultural and social factors constitute an important component of the nurture parameter for both alcoholism and mental illness. Some demographers have suggested that certain urban settings overcontribute to the frequency of both disorders while others emphasize the multivariate heterogeneity of both. The role of social factors in mood vis a vis drinking and emotional adjustment is important (23). The homeless man, his drinking behavior and his adjustment should be a focus of this interface.

(*i*) *Does alcohol alter states of consciousness?* This interface deals with alcohol as an agent for dissociative or state-dependent learning. At the extreme is delirium tremens as an altered state of consciousness. However, so-called blackout experiences with memory losses, often too covert for clinical detection, are also included and encompass deficits in both storage and retrieval (38). Overton (44) has raised a question whether "state dependency may play a causal role in the addictive process."

[2] CARPENTER, J., FILLMORE, K., FREED, E. and LESTER, D. Predictive factors in the development of addiction; a longitudinal study focused on alcohol. [Unpublished manuscript.]

(*j*) *Is there a developmental predisposition to alcoholism?* To assert that adult alcoholism is a manifestation of early childhood fixation at the oral state will itself not suffice but some studies (32, 39) have suggested that childhood personality antecedents may correlate with adult drinking patterns. However, unimpressive data supported the specificity theory of alcoholism (48), which posited that alcoholics may have different personality traits or different emotional and adaptive integration than other groups of psychiatric patients. Still, there has been some evidence for the uniqueness of alcoholic patients compared to other patients admitted to a psychiatric hospital (2). The retrospective attempts (37) to delineate characteristic alcoholic personality and behavioral variables have largely been in vain, yielding data which varied greatly in their specification and identity. Still, a recent historical review of psychological testing (22) revealed recurrent interest in the possibility of a characteristic alcoholic or prealcoholic personality type which, ostensibly, could be tapped by psychological testing. The underlying thesis has been that "alcohol-related behavior is to some extent an expression of pervasive personality tendencies which are exhibited before drinking patterns have been established" (32). The delineation of these pervasive personality tendencies has varied but they have figured prominently in most alcoholism paradigms and certainly in all models advocating an integrative approach among a constellation of characteristics. Some examples, reviewed in a proposal for life history research on alcoholism[2] included difficulty in coping with depression, frustration, and anxiety; social immaturity; exposure to maternal ambivalence; repressed homoerotic tendencies and compensatory strivings for male identity; conflict over being independent; a childhood history of antisocial acting out; social role ambivalence; etc. However, not all adults who display the above features of maladjustment during adolescence become problem drinkers in adulthood. Thus, it seems likely that this possible interface has to be modified to include interacting nonpersonality factors which may somehow affect any predisposing emotional base. This again relates closely to the issue of symptom choice. Do the adolescent adjustment problems enumerated above differentially eventuate in alcoholism, drug addiction, psychosis, antisocial behavior, etc.? Can one argue for an addictive personality type vs a nonaddictive, psychiatric disorder type based on findings of multiple drug abuse and transfer of addiction by some alcoholics (17)? A related interface might view alcohol abuse, or addictive behavior, for that matter, as but one case or example of compulsive behavior. The so-called alcoholic "craving" certainly seems to fit in this regard.

(k) Are there other interfaces? Their names probably are legion. Some psychologists might name the area of intellectual deficit including memory, motor and abstraction impairments. Another area shared by alcoholism and psychiatric disorders centers about nosology, criteria for diagnoses, secondary diagnoses, etc. A not insignificant interface is alcohol's role as a potentiator of other drugs and an exacerbator of behaviors, all of which are related to the struggle to define normative and deviant behaviors in the field of mental health and in alcohol use and abuse.

Treatment and treatment methodologies constitute a huge interface and pose many problems for further study. For example, the relative inability of alcoholics to generalize contingency management procedures outside of controlled institutional milieus seems to set them apart somewhat from other patients in similar settings. What should be the goals of treatment for alcoholism? If one insists upon total abstinence, why are there few other psychiatric disorders for which therapists strive for total disappearance of symptoms or manifestations? Who is qualified to treat the alcoholic also becomes a derivative interface.

Epilogue

All of the foregoing—and other common boundaries, too—merit exploration in efforts to clarify the relationships of alcoholism to mental health. "Elevation" of alcoholism to the status of a disease has not been clarifying. Dis - ease, literally, lack of ease or uncomfortable, characterizes both the alcoholic and the behavioral scientist confronting him. And this confrontation probably constitutes *the* most important interface—the alcoholic comes to the mental health worker seeking something. Exploration of this interface should help define the limits within which help can be accorded—unless mental health workers are prepared to announce that the alcoholic came to the wrong place.

That they are not is emphasized in a contemporary work on psychiatric diagnosis (57) where a psychiatric problem or symptom or behavior is "included as a diagnostic category because it leads to psychiatric consultation, meets the criteria for a useful category." In this view, "alcoholism is a behavioral disorder. The specific behavior that causes problems is the consumption of large quantities of alcohol on repeated occasions. The motivation underlying this behavior is often obscure" (57, *pp. 105-106*). Also, heterogeneous, multivariate and fluctuating, one might add. Accordingly, it is perplexing to read elsewhere (26) that "the only generally accepted and time-tested technique for treatment of this highly recidivistic illness entails the achievement of abstinence." Perplexing, that is, unless one follows Kunkel's (33, *pp. 117-118*) call to action, "when we actually want to do something, and when learning principles and the present social context have shown us what to do, then we have to go out into the world and start doing it. We no longer can hide behind ignorance about effective procedures." It is the suggestion of this paper that closer scrutiny of the interfaces between alcoholism and mental health will help to show us what to do.

REFERENCES

1. AMERICAN PSYCHIATRIC ASSOCIATION. COMMITTEE ON NOMENCLATURE. Diagnostic and statistical manual of mental disorders. 2d ed. Washington, D.C.; 1968.
2. BARRY, H., 3d. Psychological factors in alcoholism. Pp. 53-107. In: KISSIN, B. and BEGLEITER, H., eds. The biology of alcoholism. Vol. 3. Clinical pathology. New York; Plenum; 1974.
3. BLUM, E. M. Psychoanalytic views of alcoholism; a review. Q. J. Stud. Alcohol 27: 259-299, 1966.
4. BLUME, S. and SHEPPARD, C. The changing effects of drinking on the changing personalities of alcoholics. Q. J. Stud. Alcohol 28: 436-443, 1967.
5. BROWN, J. S. and CROWELL, C. R. Alcohol and conflict resolution; a theoretical analysis. Q. J. Stud. Alcohol 35: 66-85, 1974.
6. CAHALAN, D. and ROOM, R. Problem drinking among American men. (Rutgers Center of Alcohol Studies, Monogr. No. 7.) New Brunswick, N.J.; 1974.
7. CAPPELL, H. and HERMAN, C. P. Alcohol and tension reduction; a review. Q. J. Stud. Alcohol 33: 33-64, 1972.
8. CHOI, S. Y. Death in young alcoholics. J. Stud. Alcohol 36: 1224-1229, 1975.
9. DOLLARD, J. and MILLER, N. Personality and psychotherapy. New York; McGraw-Hill; 1950.
10. FORSANDER, O. and ERIKSSON, K. International symposium; biological aspects of alcohol consumption, 27-29 September 1971. (Finnish Foundation for Alcohol Studies, Vol. 20.) Helsinki; 1972.
11. FREED, E. X. The effect of alcohol upon approach-avoidance conflict in the white rat. Q. J. Stud. Alcohol 28: 236-254, 1967.
12. FREED, E. X. The crucial factor in alcoholism. Am. J. Nursing 68: 2614-2616, 1968.
13. FREED, E. X. Alcohol abuse by manic patients. Psycholog. Rep. 25: 280, 1969.
14. FREED, E. X. The dilemma of the alcoholic patient in a psychiatric hospital. J. Psychiat. Nursing 7: 113-116, 1969.
15. FREED, E. X. Alcoholism and manic-depressive disorders; some perspectives. Q. J. Stud. Alcohol 31: 62-89, 1970.

16. FREED, E. X. Abstinence for alcoholism reconsidered. J. Alcsm 8: 106-110, 1973.
17. FREED, E. X. Drug abuse by alcoholics; a review. Int. J. Addict. 8: 451-473, 1973.
18. FREED, E. X. Whither alcohol research? J. Drug Issues 5: 148-151, 1975.
19. FREED, E. X. Alcoholism and schizophrenia; the search for perspectives; a review. J. Stud. Alcohol 36: 853-881, 1975.
20. FREED, E. X. Conflict resolution and alcoholism revisited. J. Alcsm 10: 148-151, 1975.
21. FREED, E. X. Treatment goals for alcoholics. J. Med. Soc. N.J. 73: 611-613, 1976.
22. FREED, E. X. Alcoholism and the Rorschach Test; a review. J. Stud. Alcohol 37: 1633-1654, 1976.
23. FREED, E. X. Alcohol and mood; an updated review. Int. J. Addict. 13: 173-200, 1978.
24. FREED, E. X., RILEY, E. P. and ORNSTEIN, P. Self-reported mood and drinking patterns following hospital treatment for alcoholism. Br. J. Addict. 73: 231-233, 1977.
25. FREED, E. X., TRIPLETT, D. G. and FREEMAN, E. P. Characteristics of male alcoholics. J. Med. Soc. N.J. 68: 1011-1013, 1971.
26. GITLOW, S. E. Alcoholism; a disease. Pp. 1-9. In: BOURNE, P. G. and FOX, R., eds. Alcoholism; progress in research and treatment. New York; Academic; 1973.
27. GOODWIN, D. W. and GUZE, S. B. Heredity and alcoholism. Pp. 37-52. In: KISSIN, B. and BEGLEITER, H., eds. The biology of alcoholism. Vol. 3. Clinical pathology. New York; Plenum; 1974.
28. HABERMAN, P. W. and BADEN, M. M. Alcoholism and violent death. Q. J. Stud. Alcohol 35: 221-231, 1974.
29. HAYMAN, M. The relationship of depression to alcoholism. In: LESSE, S., ed. Masked depression. New York; Jason Aronson; 1974.
30. JAYNES, J. The routes of science. Am. Sci. 54: 94-102, 1966.
31. JESSOR, R. and JESSOR, S. Adolescent development and the onset of drinking; a longitudinal study. J. Stud. Alcohol 36: 27-51, 1975.
32. JONES, M. C. Personality correlates and antecedents of drinking patterns in adult males. J. Consult. Clin. Psychol. 32: 2-12, 1968.
33. KUNKEL, J. Behavior, social problems, and change. Englewood Cliffs, N.J.; Prentice-Hall; 1975.
34. LAWRENCE, F. E. The outpatient management of the alcoholic. Q. J. Stud. Alcohol, Suppl. No. 1, pp. 117-128, 1961.
35. LESSE, S. Depressive equivalents and the multivariant masks of depression. In: LESSE, S., ed. Masked depression. New York; Jason Aronson; 1974.
36. LESTER, D. and FREED, E. X. Criteria for an animal model of alcoholism. Pharmacol. Biochem. & Behav. 1: 103-107, 1973.
37. LISANSKY, E. S. The etiology of alcoholism; the role of psychological predisposition. Q. J. Stud. Alcohol 21: 314-343, 1960.
38. LISMAN, S. A. Alcoholic "blackout"; state dependent learning? Archs Gen. Psychiat. 30: 46-53, 1974.

39. McCord, W., McCord, J. and Gudeman, J. Origins of alcoholism. (Stanford Studies in Sociology, No. 1.) Stanford, Calif.; Stanford University Press; 1960.
40. Masserman, J. Behavior and neurosis. New York; Hafner; 1964.
41. Meerloo, J. A. M. Artificial ecstacy; a study of psychosomatic aspects of drug addiction. J. Nerv. Ment. Dis. 115: 246-266, 1952.
42. Newman, M. F. and Hilgard, J. R. Is alcoholism in men sometimes an alternative to schizophrenia in women? Psychiat. Digest 28: (No. 7): 33-37, 1967.
43. Noyes, A. Modern clinical psychiatry. 4th ed. Philadelphia; Saunders; 1953.
44. Overton, D. State-dependent learning produced by alcohol and its relevance to alcoholism. Pp. 193-217. In: Kissin, B. and Begleiter, H., eds. The biology of alcoholism. Vol. 2. Physiology and behavior. New York; Plenum; 1972.
45. Pollack, D. Experimental intoxication of alcoholics and normals; some psychological changes. Ph.D. dissertation, University of California; 1965.
46. Randall, C. L. Hereditary, maternal, and environmental influences on alcohol selection in the mouse. Ph.D. dissertation, Rutgers University; 1974.
47. Reich, L. H., Davies, R. K. and Himmelhock, J. M. Excessive alcohol use in manic-depressive illness. Am. J. Psychiat. 131: 83-86, 1974.
48. Rothstein, D., Zelterman, I. and Siegel, P. Non-specificity versus specificity in alcoholism. J. Maine Med. Ass. 57: 129-132, 1966.
49. Seixas, F. A., Omenn, G. S., Burk, E. D. and Eggleston, S., eds. Nature and nurture in alcoholism. Ann. N.Y. Acad. Sci. 197: 1-229, 1972.
50. Sidman, M. Tactics of scientific research. New York; Basic Books; 1960.
51. Snygg, D. and Combs, A. Individual behavior. New York; Harper; 1949.
52. U.S. National Institute on Alcohol Abuse and Alcoholism. Alcohol and health; new knowledge. Second special report to the Congress. (DHEW Publ. No. ADM-75-212.) Washington, D.C.; Govt Print. Off.; 1974.
53. Wallerstein, R. S. Hospital treatment of alcoholism; a comparative experimental study. (Menninger Clinic Monogr. Ser., No. 11.) New York; Basic; 1957.
54. Wessman, A. and Ricks, D. Mood and personality. New York; Holt, Rinehart and Winston; 1966.
55. West, L. Research strategies in alcoholism. Ann. N.Y. Acad. Sci. 197: 13-15, 1972.
56. Winokur, G. and Clayton, P. Family history studies. II. Sex differences and alcoholism in primary affective illness. Br. J. Psychiat. 113: 973-979, 1967.
57. Woodruff, R., Goodwin, D. and Guze, S. Psychiatric diagnosis. New York; Oxford; 1974.

Part II

MENTAL HEALTH-RELATED MODELS AND CONCEPTIONS OF ALCOHOLISM

Commenting that "the evidence seems to be that the phenomenon of addiction or the potentiality for addiction is too widespread to justify looking for esoteric explanations in aberrant physiology or psychology," Reinert (1) recommended "the old but common sense notion that alcoholism is fundamentally a bad habit." Nevertheless, there is no dearth of "esoteric explanations," with the "bad habit" concept placed near one end of a continuum that ranges upward in complexity. Besides the medical model, there are sociomedical, educational, sociopolitical, moral and ethical models (2), a game model (3), a responsibility model (4) and others. An excellent review of these and many more appears in the well-publicized Rand Corporation report on alcoholism and treatment (5).

The conceptualization of alcoholism, from bad habit to epidemiological disease, is at the heart of the matter of interfaces. It is the hypothesis that serves as the springboard for all sorts of different actions. Included in this section, then, are samples of some of the ways in which alcoholism has been perceived. Contradictions have been presented purposely, for only out of the confrontations and exchanges which ensue between their advocates will resolution of the issue occur. As new data are gathered, models should be revised as parts of them are confirmed and others refuted. The reader will thus be better able to evaluate the current status of alcoholism models than were the authors of the reprinted papers because the most recent of the latter appeared in 1976 after, undoubtedly, a publication lag. While the content of the contributions has intrinsic value, the method of theoretical construction is what I want to highlight because I feel that this is what needs to be brought to the problem of the interweaving of alcoholism with mental health. It is a variation of the old story—while we may disagree with what the authors have to say, we have to respect their efforts and the reasoning they went through in order to say it.

However, I want to add a disclaimer—the process of modeling sometimes goes too far afield. Often, we lose sight of the fact that conceptualizing is a means, an initial step. The point I want to emphasize is that there are *consequences* of such endeavors. Thus, when Bacon (6) set forth a social schema for the process of alcohol addiction, he proceeded to suggest what were the consequences of this notion of the development of alcoholism for "the treatment setting, the treatment personnel, the treatment methods, and the evaluation of the treatment methodology" as well as for the crucial area of prevention.

Moore (7) described the "implications of the conception of alcoholism as a mental illness for research, treatment, and community action." While Sargent (8) demurred to this concept, preferring to see alcoholism from the sociological point of view "as a way of living," she concurred that there were clear implications for the three areas noted by Moore. While Sargent's "way of living" perspective primarily addressed group drinking practices, Garitano and Ronall (9) described individual and cultural life-styles and their treatment consequences. Similarly, in a most insightful paper, Clark (10) extensively examined the consequences of conceptions, typologies and definitions of alcohol problems. He pointed out their impact on social policies, on the attitudes of physicians and police officers, and on the directions of research. Formulating models of addiction and conceptualizing alcoholism problems are not, therefore, intellectual exercises. They are behaviors entailing responsibility and accountability—others take them seriously as an impetus for social and individual action. Conceptualizations can become advocacy and social and clinical activism.

Nowadays, the word "model" has become the scientific term for "explanation." Originally, a model was supposed to be a kind of reduction, a vignette, a duplication of a disease process by transference, say, to another organism such as the laboratory rat, "a theoretical projection in detail of a possible system of relationships."[1] The obsession with medical models, models of psychopathology, patient–therapist models, models of health care systems, etc., makes one wonder whether more effort has been expended on the construction of the model than on repair of the original, the disorder which it represents. In no way is this intended to detract from the value of an alcoholism model (e.g., 11), but the remaining question is whether the model of alcoholism should be a mental health model. Van-Dijk (12) offered an excellent perspective: "The med-

---

[1] Webster's third new international dictionary. GROVE, P. B., ed. Springfield, Mass.; Merriam; 1964.

ical model does not exist in a state of splendid isolation. . . . [It] is just one value amongst many others that are adhered to within a given society." However, Jones and Helrich's study (13) suggested that physicians did not perceive alcoholism as a medical problem but as a psychiatric one because most doctors surveyed felt that its chief cause was personality or emotional factors. Yet, psychiatrists and psychologists also rejected the disease concept of alcoholism in favor of a definition in terms of a behavior problem, symptom complex or escape mechanism (14).

Alcoholism can be beguiling because the immediate precursor of alcohol problems is quite specific—people drink—and this fact often serves to mask the tremendous heterogeneity characterizing alcohol misusers. A similar situation does not obtain with, say, neurotic or psychotic or characterological disorders. It may well come to pass that there are a number of valid alcoholism models and that only a portion of these are mental health-related in terms of genesis. However, because of the psychological consequences of prolonged drinking, all will ultimately interface with the field of emotional adjustment.

There is much preoccupation with questions about why people drink (e.g., 1, 15). Yet, dynamic psychiatry teaches that "understanding why is never enough" (16); something has to be done about the why. It is largely around the questions "why" and "how did they get that way" that models of alcoholism are formulated. It is a retrospective, sort of historical approach, and professionals and laymen alike are oriented to digging back into the past to try to explain the present. In psychotherapy with neurotics, for example, the patient will sometimes seek for reasons in the dim past because this defensive posture is far less intimidating than facing his current anxiety-provoking adaptation. For alcoholics, particularly, the here-and-now is threatening, and they are prone to act this out with further drinking. A psychotherapist, too, may feel less comfortable with the stress and crises of a patient's here-and-now than with the events and feelings of his past.

The point is that models of alcoholism, particularly mental health-related models, have to have some translatable, exigency-coping clinical relevance for the person with alcohol problems and for the professional treating him. Researchers can indulge in some temporal luxuries which are denied the health-care practitioner facing a patient. Furthermore, all psychotherapists know that their understanding of "why" never benefits a patient as much as the patient's own understanding of "why." The understanding has to be more than a superficial, intellectual awareness by both the patient and the therapist.

Mental health-related conceptions of alcoholism are the products of mental health workers, and, as such, are more parochial than ecumenical. It is hard to build a model airplane, for example, without all of the parts. All of the assemblies for an alcoholism model do not come from the psyche.

I can attest to this from a personal odyssey in research on a possible animal model of alcoholism. Starting solely with the psychodynamic notion of approach–avoidance conflict, we found ourselves, of necessity, moving to studies of alcohol's caloric value to animals, then to genetic studies of central nervous system response to alcohol, which led to biochemical investigations involving serotonin, for example. Models of alcoholism are like jigsaw puzzles—there are a number of sides to the puzzles, pieces of different sizes and shapes, and pieces which may be similarly formed but colored in different tones. Plus, the model is more than two-dimensional. As a case in point, mental health researchers on alcoholism are confronted with the increasing emphasis on its biological aspects in the literature (17).

Whichever side one takes in the "Is alcoholism a disease?" controversy, one has to acknowledge Jellinek's (18) contribution in this regard. There is a lesson to be learned about models from it. Advocating one is a healthy stimulant for the scientific community. But models are not real; they are only conceptions of reality. A model is a means to an end, hardly an end in itself. We should adopt the automotive industry's notion that the 1980 model is a significant improvement over the 1970 model, constantly seeking to improve and refine what has gone before—but not necessarily on an annual basis.

Extending this analogy, it is time that more alcoholism problems were perceived as custom, rather than as stock, models. Psychological differentiation, the recognition of individual differences, enabled clinical psychology and clinical psychiatry to become specialties. Psychological individuality is at the heart of mental health problems and alcohol problems, and this represents a common boundary between them. Broad theoretical conceptualizations of alcoholism, be they psychoanalytic, behavioral, phenomenological—whatever—fail to accord this human individuality the importance it merits. All investigations in psychology are hampered (or blessed) by individual variation and heterogeneity because they are based on the behaviors of organisms. Alcoholism is hardly an exception. If we encourage individuality and spontaneity and nonstereotyped behaviors in normal lives, why should we hope to find uniformity in the atypical styles of life such as lived by alcoholics?

In the field of health, models have traditionally been sought for diseases (19). With regard to alcoholism, new interconnections may have to be sought because we are faced with a dual dilemma: (*a*) Is alcoholism a disease? Does it fit the medical model (2)? and (*b*) Is mental illness a myth (20)? An extensive critique by Moore (21) led him to reject the latter notion and to conclude that simply "a sufficient amount of antimyth antidote" will not cure the myth disease which he saw plaguing psychiatry. However, with such questions at issue, it is no wonder that the nexus between mental health and alcoholism remains obscure.

An alcoholism myth has also been postulated. Beauchamp (22) noted that "The myth is the false idea that these people have some inner condition—called alcoholism—which explains their drinking problems." He added that the disease concept of alcoholism "suggests an inner deficiency or a missing capability, much as does the 'disease' of mental illness," and he criticized research and treatment efforts. "Because of the myth of alcoholism, alcohol problems do not appear to be directly related to inadequate social, cultural or ethical norms supporting limits to the availability of alcohol or to inadequate public controls over the availability of alcohol such as taxation, physical accessibility or age restrictions. Instead of focusing on the availability of alcohol as a central public issue and instead of calling for responsible public controls, we spend our time and research trying to find out what causes a minority of drinkers to suffer from a disease which makes them 'unable' to control their drinking."

A good example of the controversy regarding alcoholism's status as a disease appeared in Smith's (23) review of a collection of articles on alcoholism. He commented that the first chapter, which describes alcoholism as a disease, is "so persuasive that all but the most obdurate of the nondisease fraternity should be convinced." However, he went on to say that the author of Chapter 2 "apparently did not read Chapter 1 or was unconvinced because he takes exception to the medical model of alcoholism as a disease. . . ." Perhaps "obdurate" is a value judgment for "unconvinced."

With such controversy and ambiguity, it came as no surprise that a recent symposium assembled to enumerate priorities in the alcohol-problems field included "the conceptualization of alcohol problems" among the final 7 topical areas distilled from a starting list of 165 (24). The articles included in this section address this topic from many points of view—it *does* have priority. Siegler et al. (Chapter 4) seek to examine alcoholism models exhaustively and systematically. The themes of the other reprinted selections amplify some of the models and conceptions of alcoholism. Hershon (Chapter 5), Pomerleau et al. (Chapter 6) and Robinson (Chapter 7) look at aspects of the disease concept of alcoholism, and Szasz (Chapter 8) offers the view that the bad habit of alcoholism does not constitute a disease process. From a sociological frame of reference, Finlay (Chapter 9) asks whether alcoholism is best represented by an illness model or an interactional model. Finally, Edwards (Chapter 10) presents a model of drug taking in terms of personality, sociocultural and environmental factors.

REFERENCES

 1. REINERT, R. E. The concept of alcoholism as a bad habit. Bull. Menninger Clin. 32: 35-46, 1968.
 2. HUDOLIN, V. Concepts of alcoholism; implications for treatment and rehabilitation. Proc. 1st Internat. Med. Conf. Alcsm, London, 10–14 September 1973, pp. 23-29, 1974.
 3. STEINER, C. M. The alcoholic game. Q. J. Stud. Alcohol 30: 920-938, 1969.
 4. RULE, B. G. and PHILLIPS, D. Responsibility versus illness models of alcoholism; effects on attitudes toward an alcoholic. Q. J. Stud. Alcohol 34: 489-495, 1973.
 5. ARMOR, D. J., POLICH, J. M. and STAMBUL, H. B. Alcoholism and treatment. Prepared for the U.S. National Institute on Alcohol Abuse and Alcoholism. Santa Monica, Calif.; Rand Corp.; 1976.
 6. BACON, S. D. The process of addiction to alcohol; social aspects. Q. J. Stud. Alcohol 34: 1-27, 1973.
 7. MOORE, R. A. The conception of alcoholism as a mental illness; implications for treatment and research. Q. J. Stud. Alcohol 29: 172-175, 1968.
 8. SARGENT, M. J. The conception of alcoholism as a mental illness; comment on the article by R. A. Moore, and a sociological alternative. Q. J. Stud. Alcohol 29: 974-978, 1968.
 9. GARITANO, W. W. and RONALL, R. E. Concepts of life style in the treatment of alcoholism. Int. J. Addict. 9: 585-592, 1974.
10. CLARK, W. B. Conceptions of alcoholism; consequences for research. Addict. Dis. 1: 395-430, 1975.
11. LESTER, D. and FREED, E. X. Criteria for an animal model of alcoholism. Pharmacol. Biochem. & Behav. 1: 103-107, 1973.
12. VAN-DIJK, W. K. Problems concerning the application of the medical model in alcoholism. J. Alcohol. 9: 9-14, 1974.
13. JONES, R. W. and HELRICH, A. R. Treatment of alcoholism by physicians in private practice; a national survey. Q. J. Stud. Alcohol 33: 117-131, 1972.

14. KNOX, W. J. Attitudes of psychiatrists and psychologists toward alcoholism. Am. J. Psychiat. 127: 1675-1679, 1971.
15. BROD, T. M. Alcoholism as a mental health problem of native Americans; a review of the literature. Archs. Gen. Psychiat. 32: 1385-1391, 1975.
16. FREEMAN, L. Fight against fears. New York; Crown; 1951.
17. FREED, E. X. Whither alcohol research? J. Drug Issues 5: 148-151, 1975.
18. JELLINEK, E. M. The disease concept of alcoholism. Highland Park, N.J.; Hillhouse Press; 1960.
19. PRITCHARD, R. W. Some human diseases for which animal models are needed. Pp. 157-167. In: Animal models for biomedical research. (National Academy of Sciences Publ. No. 1594.) Washington, D.C.; 1968.
20. SZASZ, T. S. The myth of mental illness; foundations of a theory of personal conduct. New York; Harper & Row; 1961.
21. MOORE, M. S. Some myths about "mental illness." Archs. Gen. Psychiat. 32: 1483-1497, 1975.
22. BEAUCHAMP, D. E. The alcohol alibi; blaming alcoholics. Society 12(6): 12, 14-17, 1975.
23. SMITH, J. W. Review of BOURNE, P. G. and FOX, R., eds. Alcoholism; progress in research and treatment. Q. J. Stud. Alcohol 35: 780-784, 1974.
24. FILSTEAD, W. J. and ROSSI, J. J. Some suggested priorities in the alcohol-problems field. Q. J. Stud. Alcohol 34: 1360-1363, 1973.

4

Models of Alcoholism[1]

Miriam Siegler, M.A., Humphry Osmond, M.R.C.S., D.P.M.,
M.R.C.P. and Stephens Newell

ALCOHOLISM, like schizophrenia and drug addiction, is a disputed ailment. That is to say, it is an undesirable condition which is said by some to be a disease, by others a moral failing, and by still others a psychological disturbance. It may also be identified as a social problem, an impairment, a faulty mode of family interaction, or an inexplicable result of that pleasant activity, social drinking.

The existence of so many definitions of such diversity creates hazards for those who discuss alcoholism. The physician speaks a different language from the minister, the psychotherapist from the policeman, the social drinker from the alcoholic. Each can offer evidence that alcoholism makes sense from his point of view, but when these points of view have been assembled, what is to be done with them? The rules by which physicians determine that something is a disease have nothing to do with the rules by which clergymen determine that the same thing is a sin, or by which psychotherapists conclude that it is a neurotic pattern. We are not simply faced here with the problem of comparing the evidence offered within one field for more than one theory, but with discussing different theories, each of which comes from a different discipline or profession.

In an attempt to deal with the same difficulty in discussions of schizophrenia and drug addiction, we have devised a method for making widely diverse points of view comparable: the construction of models (1, 2). In the present paper, we shall apply the same method to alcoholism by constructing and presenting eight models. We shall then compare some of the models with each other, in or-

[1] Reprinted by permission from the QUARTERLY JOURNAL OF STUDIES ON ALCOHOL, Vol. 29, pp. 571–591, 1968. Copyright by Journal of Studies on Alcohol, Inc., New Brunswick, New Jersey 08903.

der to demonstrate that their use greatly clarifies the dispute about alcoholism.

The method of constructing models for the disputed ailments is as follows: First, all possible theories and points of view are collected, regardless of their credibility, source or state of development. Then all the theories are arranged along the same set of dimensions. The dimensions are a set of questions aimed at defining the ailment, stating how it came about, what should be done about it, and how the people involved with it ought to behave. Within each model, the dimensions must be logically consistent with each other. The completed models then allow specific questions, comparing the advantages of one with another.

Many discussions of alcoholism and the other disputed ailments involve comparisons of theories of etiology or forms of treatment. We believe that a model must answer more than this if it is to be of any practical use. A model must be able to provide a course of action for every situation which arises in connection with the disputed ailment, whether for professional people, patients, their families or the general public. The dimensions, then, are a series of problems, situations or questions which will require answers or decisions in connection with the ailment. In the case of alcoholism, the model must define it, indicate how it arose, and show how the behavior of alcoholics is to be explained. Some sort of treatment must be proposed, a prediction must be made about the outcome, and, if there is a treatment facility, its function must be stated. There must be some basis for choosing appropriate people to work with alcoholics. If suicide occurs, it must be accounted for. The rights and duties of all the participants in situations which arise because of alcoholism must be spelled out. The history of the model must be related. Only a program based on an internally consistent and complete model has a chance of ending the divisive and exhausting conflict which surrounds alcoholism and the other disputed ailments.

In the present paper we shall present the following eight models of alcoholism: the impaired model; the "dry," or Prohibition, moral model; the "wet," or drinking society, moral model; the Alcoholics Anonymous model; the psychoanalytic model; the family interaction model; the "old" medical model; and the "new" medical model. The first four have been derived from the explanations given by lay people for the phenomenon of alcoholism, the last four from the views of professional people. Our reason for including the lay models is that any model of a condition such as alcoholism must have public support if it is to be of any use; its acceptance among professional people alone is not enough. The dialogue between professional and lay models is sometimes a critical factor in the emergence of a dominant model, as we shall see.

The models are a method for classifying theories of alcoholism; they are not theories themselves. Therefore, one cannot say of them that they are true or false. But one can make the following kinds of criticisms: that there is no evidence that a particular model is in use anywhere; that a model in use somewhere has been left out; that a model does not provide a course of action for every situation which may arise in connection with alcoholism; that a particular dimension of a particular model is not consistent with the model.

Another limitation might be indicated: the models are abstractions, or "ideal types." The reality from which they are abstracted is extremely complex, and in order to make models which can be compared, the complexity must be reduced to manageable proportions. In doing so, we are aware that we have necessarily distorted the reality which is experienced by the proponents of the various points of view. We trust that the exercise of constructing and contrasting models will prove sufficiently useful to compensate for the inevitable distortions occasioned by the method.

I. DESCRIPTION OF THE MODELS

A. *The Impaired Model*[2]

1. *Definition:* An alcoholic is a "drunk," souse, toper, tippler, soak, lush. When he gets drunk, he is plastered, bombed, stoned, tight, oiled.

2. *Etiology:* Some people just are that way, for unknown reasons.

3. *Behavior:* "Drunks" are repulsive and dirty. Nice people do not like to get too close to them. Sometimes they are comical: they fall down, talk to lampposts, try their door key in the wrong house, get their words mixed up, and so forth, but it is wrong to laugh at them and make fun of them, because they can't help it.

4. *Treatment:* There is none; once a "drunk," always a "drunk."

5. *Prognosis:* There will be no change.

6. *Function of the hospital:* "Drunks" don't belong in a general hospital, because they may interfere with the care of people who are really sick, but if they cannot take care of themselves, they may need some sort of shelter. Sometimes the Salvation Army takes care of them, and sometimes they end up at the state hospital.

7. *Personnel:* Kind people give "drunks" and other bums handouts. Reli-

---

[2] We have discussed the concept of impairment at length in a previous paper (3).

gious people often take care of them. It has been said, "God watches over children, fools and drunkards."

8. *Suicide:* When a "drunk" commits suicide, it is really for the best, because his life is hopeless.

9. *Rights and duties of alcoholics:* "Drunks" have the right to be kept alive by handouts from kind people. They have the right not to be made fun of. "Drunks" have the duty to stay out of good neighborhoods, so that people will not be disturbed by seeing them around.

10. *Rights and duties of families:* Families of "drunks" have the right to sympathy for having one in the family. They havé the duty either to keep the "drunk" at home, out of sight, or else they should send him away to live with other "drunks."

11. *Rights and duties of society:* Society has the right to be spared disgust from seeing "drunks" around. It has the duty to provide food and shelter for "drunks" who can't care for themselves, and to protect them from being made fun of.

12. *History of the model:* There have always been "drunks," and they have always been made fun of, but they have always received some care from kind people and especially from religious people. As a last resort, the state will always take care of them.

B. The "Dry" Moral Model

1. *Definition:* Alcoholism is a moral failing, not an illness. It is the natural penalty for drinking.

2. *Etiology:* Alcoholism occurs because drinking occurs. Some strong-willed people can apparently drink without becoming alcoholics, but the social risk of drinking is too great to allow any exceptions.

3. *Behavior:* The alcoholic behaves immorally because he drinks.

4. *Treatment:* There are many ways to try to get an alcoholic to stop drinking, including enforced church attendance, firing him from his job, pouring his whisky down the sink, marrying him off to someone strong enough to control him, divorce, shunning him, ridiculing him, giving him aversion treatments, and so forth; in short, behavior therapy. Fines and jail sentences may help, too.

5. *Prognosis:* The prognosis is poor. Unless a way is found to threaten alcoholics or punish them so that they stop drinking, the only hope is to make alcohol unavailable. Young drinkers should have the example of the alcoholic held before them.

6. *Function of the hospital:* The hospital is to remove the alcoholic from supplies of alcohol; impress him with the mess he has made of his life; exhort him to mend his ways; get him to promise never to drink again.

7. *Personnel:* All moral people can sanction the immoral alcoholic. Ministers, policemen and behavior therapists are especially suitable.

8. *Suicide:* The alcoholic who commits suicide is too much of a coward to face the mess he has made of his life. All those who drink share in the responsibility for an alcoholic suicide.

9. *Rights and duties of alcoholics:* The alcoholic has the right to re-enter the moral society of those who do not drink, once he has stopped drinking. He has the duty to stop drinking, and if he stops drinking, to try to get other drinkers to stop.

10. *Rights and duties of families:* The family has the right to a moral, nondrinking society in which to rear children. It has the duty to maintain a moral, nondrinking home, and to try to get the alcoholic member to stop drinking.

11. *Rights and duties of society:* Society has the right to be free of the curse of drinking. It has the duty to prohibit the sale of alcohol; failing that, at the very least it has the duty to educate school children about the dangers of alcohol, and to discourage in any way at all the acceptance of drinking as a normal moral activity.

12. *History of the model:* In the United States, this model has always been held by some people, but never by everyone. It reached the height of its popularity in 1919, when it merged with a social model aimed not just at changing the behavior of individuals but at reforming the society so that the undesired moral behavior would not occur. Now it is a moral model once again, a somewhat demoralized one.

C. The "Wet" Moral Model

1. *Definition:* Alcoholics are drinkers who do not obey the rules of the drinking society; they behave badly when drunk, and they cannot hold their liquor. Alcoholism is an unacceptable form of drinking behavior.

2. *Etiology:* It is a mystery why some people who drink become alcoholics.

3. *Behavior:* The behavior of alcoholics is antisocial. They spoil the happy, congenial occasions that social drinking can provide.

4. *Treatment:* Everybody in the drinking society, including the alcoholic himself, knows how to treat the alcoholic by juggling around rewards and punishments. His wife may refuse sex, refuse to speak to him, keep the family money away from him, reduce her housekeeping standards. His doctor may give him hell, try to win him over with a comradely equality (buddy-buddy), or tell him to be a man, not a bottle-baby. The drinking society may recommend particular drinking practices ("drink only sherry"), or tell him to stop drinking for a while so that he can come back to his previous state of social gaiety. The alcoholic himself may give up his luncheon drink, only to reward himself later with an extra drink; he may force himself to drink something he does not like, such as beer; he may overwork at his job; he may force himself to work off his drinks with physical exercise; he may punish himself by decreasing his share of the family budget while increasing that of his wife.

5. *Prognosis:* If only the right formula of rewards and punishments could be found, everything would be all right. Otherwise the prognosis is gloomy.

6. *Function of the hospital:* The hospital is to deprive the alcoholic

temporarily of the companionship of the drinking society; to impress him with what a mess he has made of his life, and to make him promise, when he gets out, that he will obey the rules of the drinking society.

7. *Personnel:* All moral members of the drinking society are suitable personnel for reforming the alcoholic.

8. *Suicide:* The alcoholic may commit suicide because he would be better off dead than on such bad terms with everybody. Or, he may drink himself to death.

9. *Rights and duties of alcoholics:* The alcoholic has the right to the helpful advice of members of the drinking society about how he might improve his drinking behavior and so rejoin the drinking society as a member in good standing. He does not have the right to join a temperance movement and lecture his former companions about the evils of drinking; when this happens, he is quite properly seen as a turncoat or traitor. He has the duty to listen to his friends' advice, so that he can drink normally again.

10. *Rights and duties of families:* The family has the right to expect better behavior from the alcoholic relative. It has the duty to try to get the alcoholic to drink like a human being.

11. *Rights and duties of society:* The drinking society has the right not to have the normal enjoyment of drinking spoiled by alcoholics, and not to be endangered by the alcoholic giving fuel to the temperance movement. It has the duty to censure the alcoholic and to tell him how to behave so that he can return to the drinking society; and the further duty to improve its public image so that everyone can see that drinking is a valuable, enjoyable social activity, in which ordinary moral people engage, and not some kind of vice, as the temperance movement would have us believe.

12. *History of the model:* In most parts of the United States we have always had a moral drinking society, although there have always been "drys" who, on occasion, succeed in making the sale of alcohol illegal.

D. *The Alcoholics Anonymous Model*[3]

1. *Definition:* Alcoholism is an incurable, progressive and often fatal disease. Alcoholism is also a spiritual problem for alcoholics. Alcohol is "poison" to an alcoholic, though not to others. An alcoholic is a person whose life has become intolerable through the use of alcohol. A.A. is a brotherhood of those afflicted with this disease.

2. *Etiology:* Alcoholics are emotionally impaired people who drink to

---

[3] We gratefully acknowledge the advice of Bill W., the co-founder of A.A., in constructing the A.A. model, and thank him for putting his unique knowledge at our disposal. While we tried to heed his advice, any errors of interpretation or explanation are our own. It is curious, we feel, that while many people have opinions as to why A.A. does or does not work, no one has thought to ask Bill W., in a systematic way, what he thinks A.A. does, or why he thinks it has succeeded. We hope that we have remedied this omission.

compensate for their inadequacies, and then, because of their body chemistry, become addicted to alcohol, creating a circular process of further inadequacy and further drinking.

3. *Behavior:* At the end of his drinking career, the behavior of the alcoholic derives largely from his need to get enough drink to control withdrawal symptoms. Earlier, vagaries of behavior are due to a complex physical, mental and spiritual malaise of an enduring nature.

4. *Treatment:* The best treatment for an alcoholic is permanent continuous involvement in A.A.

5. *Prognosis:* With the help of A.A., alcoholism can be arrested, although never cured. Without A.A., the prognosis is usually hopeless.

6. *Function of the hospital:* The hospital is to dry out alcoholics. The alcoholic ought to leave the hospital sober and without drugs.

7. *Personnel:* Members of A.A. are permanently charged with helping those other alcoholics who ask for help. It is difficult for anyone who is not an alcoholic to understand the world of the alcoholic. Medical doctors should treat alcoholics, but they often give damaging advice and unsound treatment, due to ignorance about alcoholism.[4]

8. *Suicide:* A.A. distinguishes between active and deliberate suicidal attempts due to despair, and the more usual slow unconscious suicide of unrelieved alcoholism.

9. *Rights and duties of alcoholics:* Alcoholics have the rights of medical patients with a grave illness; they also have the rights of A.A. members. Alcoholics have the duties of medical patients with a grave illness, and also the duty to help other alcoholics through A.A.

10. *Rights and duties of families:* The families of alcoholics have the right to be treated as the families of any gravely ill persons, plus the right to sympathy because of the damaging nature of this illness to family life. The families of alcoholics have the duties of any family with a gravely ill person, and the duty to seek help from A.A. and its affiliated family groups.

11. *Rights and duties of society:* Society has the right to be spared the dangers and social costs of the disease, alcoholism. It has the duty to recognize alcoholism as a disease, and to disseminate the necessary information pertaining to it to all members of the society. Society ought to recognize that A.A. is the only existing therapy that has a sustained and growing record of success.

---

[4] The critical attitude of A.A. toward physicians has sometimes been taken to mean that A.A. is "antimedical." For example, Szasz writes, "It is significant that groups like Alcoholic Anonymous and Synanon choose to do without medical, and especially without psychiatric, 'help.' I see in this an intuitive understanding of the fact that to define the addict as a 'patient' harms him more than it helps him" (4). We believe that this is a misunderstanding of the A.A. position. Since A.A. believes that alcoholism is a disease, it is naturally difficult for its members to get along with physicians who believe it to be a moral failing.

12. *History of the model:* A.A. was founded in 1935. Originally a rehabilitative moral model, partly derived from the Oxford Group, the co-founder was soon persuaded by his doctor that it would be better to emphasize the disease aspect. This revised medical–moral model then became the basis of A.A.

E. *The Psychoanalytic Model*

1. *Definition:* Alcoholism is the symptom of a deep, underlying neurosis. Alcoholics are addictive personalities.

2. *Etiology:* Since the alcoholic is an infantile person, the key to understanding his inability to achieve maturity lies in the early emotional experiences. As Rado (5, *p. 28*) put it: "We must penetrate into the deepest and oldest strata of the mind formed during the early stages of ontogenetic development."

3. *Behavior:* The behavior of the alcoholic is to be interpreted as a symbolic means of expressing unconscious conflict.

4. *Treatment:* For alcoholism, as for all neuroses, psychotherapy is required. As Fox (6) wrote, "Just as in treating any other neurotic symptom, the aim is not simply to clear away the one obvious symptom, but to lead the patient into a more mature attitude toward life."

5. *Prognosis:* The prognosis for alcoholics is not encouraging. According to Fox (6), "The primary addicts are usually so infantile and irresponsible that psychotherapy may be needed for a long time during their process of 'growing up'."

6. *Function of the hospital:* As with any emotional disorder, hospitalization can make it possible for the patient to give his full energy to psychotherapy. The hospital may also be able to provide a therapeutic milieu for the patient.

7. *Personnel:* People trained in psychotherapy are the appropriate personnel for treating alcoholics.

8. *Suicide:* Suicide may occur if the alcoholic has to face his underlying conflicts too suddenly.

9. *Rights and duties of alcoholics:* Alcoholics have the right to have alcoholism seen as a symptom of an underlying conflict, rather than as a moral failing. They have the duty to try to understand themselves, so that they can achieve maturity and use their full human potential.

10. *Rights and duties of families:* The family has the right to have their alcoholic relative seen as a person with a neurosis, not as immoral. It has the duty to allow the alcoholic relative to "grow up" and not to undermine his efforts in this direction.

11. *Rights and duties of society:* Society has no special rights in connection with alcoholic neurosis. It has the duty to encourage families to raise emotionally healthy children who will not become alcoholics. Society has the duty also to provide some kind of low-cost psychotherapy for families that need it, as the inadequacies of families of alcoholics often reflect difficult social conditions.

12. *History of the model:* The psychoanalytic model of alcoholism dates back at least to 1912, when Ferenczi wrote about it (7). However, this interest has been largely theoretical, for, as Landis noted (8), very few alcoholics have ever been analyzed.

F. *The Family-Interaction Model*[5]

1. *Definition:* Alcoholism, like drug addiction and schizophrenia, is best seen as a form of family interaction in which one person is assigned the role of the "alcoholic" while others play the complementary roles, such as the martyred wife, the neglected children, the disgraced parents, and so forth. As this deadly game is played by mutual consent, any attempt to remove the key actor, the alcoholic, is bound to create difficulties for the other family members, who will attempt to restore their former game. As the game is of far greater interest to the family than to the therapist, the family is almost bound to win. The family may succeed in including the therapist as another role in the game.

2. *Etiology:* As these family games are circular and self-reinforcing, it is useless to inquire how it all began. In general, basic personality inadequacies are transmitted from generation to generation, with the particular games played being determined by the accidental configuration of personalities. A child marked out for a future role as an alcoholic will either be a "little boy lost" (the most dependent child) or a "holy terror" (an incorrigible bad boy). A whole family may play the "bad clan" role, leaving the other roles to the community.

3. *Behavior:* The behavior of the alcoholic and the other family members is a series of moves in a continuous and long-drawn-out family game. It is not to be interpreted psychoanalytically (although the family may try to get the therapist to see it that way), nor is it to be taken at face value. The question to be asked about behavior in every case is: how has this move changed the relative positions of the players?

4. *Treatment:* Family therapy is the only treatment.

5. *Prognosis:* Prognosis depends on the availability of family therapy. With it, the prognosis is good; without it, poor. Also, stable working-class families and middle-class families, who need the wages of the alcoholic, may be motivated to find some less expensive game, thus improving the prognosis, but "proud" upper-class families or "shiftless" lower-class families may see no reason to stop.

6. *Function of the hospital:* The only function of the hospital is to restore the alcoholic to a state of physical health such that family therapy can begin, at home or in the therapist's office.

---

[5] It will be obvious that this model owes much to Eric Berne (9). It should be noted that Berne always carefully distinguishes between game analysis and any biochemical or physiological considerations. Berne himself is concerned only with game analysis; he does not mix models.

7. *Personnel:* Family therapists are the appropriate personnel. Whether or not they are physicians is irrelevant.

8. *Suicide:* Suicide is a final move in the family game made by a member who is losing. This member need not be the alcoholic, so the therapist must watch the whole family for signs that someone is consistently losing and thus may commit suicide as a parting shot.

9. *Rights and duties of alcoholics:* Alcoholics have the right to be seen as members of a disturbed family. They have the duty to cooperate in family therapy.

10. *Rights and duties of families:* Each member in a family which has an alcoholic has the right to be seen as a member of a disturbed family. Each member has the duty to cooperate in family therapy.

11. *Rights and duties of society:* Society has the right to be spared the dangerous consequences of this family game, e.g., automobile accidents. It has the duty to provide facilities for family therapy for alcoholics and their families.

12. *History of the model:* This model is about 10 years old. Thus far probably very few alcoholics have been treated according to it.

G. The "Old" Medical Model

1. *Definition:* Alcoholism is a serious, progressive and eventually fatal disease, which is incurred by the immoral behavior (i.e., excessive drinking) of the patient himself.

2. *Etiology:* The etiology of alcoholism is the excessive drinking of alcohol. The reason for the immoderate drinking is unknown; alcoholics seem to be unable to control themselves.

3. *Behavior:* Alcoholics are destroying their bodies and ruining their lives by drinking so much, and this is immoral.

4. *Treatment:* In the treatment of acute states of illness in alcoholism, the doctor's problem is the management of a patient in a toxic state. Attention must be given to systemic dehydration, general and cerebral edema, electrolyte imbalance, nutritional deficiency, cirrhosis of the liver, etc. The doctor must be wary of giving medication, because the alcoholic is frequently liable to become a pan or multiple addict. The ultimate goal of treatment is safe, social drinking, but unfortunately, this is rarely achieved, because the alcoholic cannot "grow up."

5. *Prognosis:* The prognosis is poor, because the patient will not take care of himself.

6. *Function of the hospital:* The hospital is to put the alcoholic in top shape, physically. This usually requires a complete "repair job." It is also the function of the hospital to frighten the alcoholic about the state of his health. ("You'll be dead in 6 months.")

7. *Personnel:* Early in the career of the alcoholic, the combined efforts of the doctor and the family are sometimes successful in returning him to safe social drinking or, failing that, in getting him to abstain altogether. However, the time often comes when the doctor must say to the family: "I

can't do anything more for him." Then the minister, A.A. and other helpful people may be called in to try to set the alcoholic straight. If this does not work, custodial care may be found for him in some sheltered environment.

8. *Suicide:* Excessive drinking is suicide by alcohol. Since alcoholics sometimes try to commit suicide with pills, the doctor should not trust the alcoholic with medicine. Suicide is often a relief to everyone, because it ends a hopeless life.

9. *Rights and duties of alcoholics:* The alcoholic has the right to a complete overhaul by the physician. Unfortunately most alcoholics soon lose this right by abusing it; shortly after leaving the hospital they begin drinking again and undo all the doctor's good work. Alcoholics have the duty to cooperate with the doctor and not to undo his work.

10. *Rights and duties of the family:* The alcoholic's family has the right to be treated like the family of a very sick and difficult person. The family has the duty to cooperate with the doctor by attempting to control the alcoholic's behavior with threats, bribes, lectures, and so forth.

11. *Rights and duties of society:* Society has the right to sensible drinking habits by all members. It has the duty to censure alcoholics about their bad drinking habits and the damage they inflict on their health.

12. *History of the model:* This model is probably as old as alcoholism.

H. The "New" Medical Model

1. *Definition:* Alcoholism is a progressive, often fatal, disease, possibly hereditary. Alcoholics are ill people whose body chemistry is such that they can become addicted to alcohol. Alcoholism must be distinguished from schizophrenia, depressions, head injuries, and so forth.

2. *Etiology:* It appears that alcoholics may have a defect in metabolism, possibly of one of the major amino acids. There are probably also psychological and sociocultural contributing factors.

3. *Behavior:* Much of the alcoholic's behavior stems from the need to control withdrawal symptoms.

4. *Treatment:* Any treatment which helps the alcoholic to abstain from drinking is valuable, provided that it does not impair his health.

5. *Prognosis:* The prognosis at the present time is grave. However, we must hope that medical science will provide new information, new treatments and preventive measures.

6. *Function of the hospital:* The hospital is to detoxify the alcoholic, to restore his health as much as possible, to teach him and his family about the illness, and to provide rehabilitative services, such as psychotherapy and social casework.

7. *Personnel:* The proper personnel for treating alcoholics are physicians, aided by nurses, psychotherapists, social workers, et al.

8. *Suicide:* Suicide is a risk in alcoholism, and so the doctor must avoid giving out medication which could be used for this purpose. The doctor must use psychiatric judgment to assess the likelihood of suicide.

9. *Rights and duties of alcoholics:* Alcoholics have the right to be treated

as medical patients with a grave disease. They have the duty to cooperate with medical treatment, and to inform themselves about their illness.

10. *Rights and duties of families:* The families of alcoholics have the right to be treated as the families of any very ill persons. They have the duty to obtain medical treatment for the patient, to cooperate with this treatment, and to inform themselves about the illness.

11. *Rights and duties of society:* Society has the right to be spared the dangers and social costs of the disease, alcoholism. It has the duty to recognize alcoholism as a disease, and to disseminate the necessary information to all members of the society, so that alcoholics can be identified early and encouraged to seek medical help. Society has the duty also to promote research on alcoholism.

12. *History of the model:* This is a new model, officially launched in 1956 when the American Medical Association recognized alcoholism as a disease. The model was created in part by pressure from A.A. It represents an attempt to move alcoholism into the class of true medical diseases.

II. COMPARISON OF THE MODELS

1. The "Old" and the "New" Medical Model

Of the many possible comparisons which can be made on the basis of the models described above, one of the most useful is that between the "old" and the "new" medical models. There must be something wrong with the older model, for physicians, who reluctantly agree that alcoholics are sick people, prefer not to take care of them. Perhaps it is this strange ambivalence on the part of physicians which has led to the proliferation of other models. When medicine takes an unequivocal stand about an illness, others usually do not contest it.

The first difference to be noticed is that while both models agree that alcoholism is a disease, the new one is concerned only with a possible medical etiology, while the old one is concerned with what might be called the "moral etiology" of the disease: what action the person took so that he contracted the disease. Now the concern with moral etiology, while quite proper for someone holding a moral model, lies outside the realm of medicine. In the case of syphilis, it should make no difference to the doctor whether the diseased contracted it through an immoral or even perverted sexual act, or as an innocent victim of a spouse's extramarital activities. Physicians are enjoined to treat people for no other reason than that they are ill, and they are discouraged from undertaking legal and moral investigations of their patients. The fact that physicians are expected to give good care to condemned criminals and enemy prisoners of war makes it quite clear that medicine has its own morality, which is different from and sometimes contrary to general social morality.

In the dimension of treatment, it should be noticed that while the new medical model has as the goal of treatment arrest of the disease pending the availability of a cure, the old model aims at restoring the patient to social drinking. While this might be a very desirable end, it is not, strictly speaking, a medical concern. In major illnesses, it is often not possible to restore the patient to his previous state of health, and it would be quackery to assure the patient that it would be possible, or even by implication to aim at it. The physician can make no promises about the outcome of any illness; he can only promise to behave like a physician. The introduction of a nonmedical goal, the restoration of social drinking, which then cannot be achieved, has tended to demoralize both the physicians using the model and their patients.

In the dimension of prognosis, the new medical model can hold out hope, no matter how grave the illness or how unsuccessful previous treatment has been. Hope depends on advances made in medicine, not on the good behavior of the patient. The hope is justified because the history of medicine has seen the most terrible diseases conquered; hope is medicine's stock-in-trade. But in the old medical model the burden of prognosis is put on the patient's behavior rather than on the impressive history of diseases conquered, and thus one of the greatest sources of strength in medicine is thrown away.

In the dimension of personnel, the new medical model states that physicians are responsible for the care of alcoholics. It is implicitly understood that they are responsible whether or not the treatment is successful. In the old medical model, however, the physician is willing to treat the patient at first, but as it becomes clear that no progress is being made, the physician may say, "I can't do anything for him." Now it is permissible for a physician to declare that further medical treatment will not change the outcome of the disease, as sometimes happens in the case of poliomyelitis; then the patient may be moved into the category of impaired persons. Or a physician may refuse to treat a patient for personal reasons while suggesting that he find some other physician to treat him. But it is not a permissible move in medicine for a physician to refuse to treat a patient who is getting steadily sicker on the grounds that he is immoral. The physician may, and in fact should, tell an uncooperative alcoholic patient that he is not being a good patient, thereby bringing the morality of medicine to bear upon him; but he may not tell the patient that he is a bad person.

Considering the dimension of suicide, the same problem arises again. For the physician using the new medical model, suicide is a medical risk which must be guarded against. It is not the place of the physician to evaluate the life of the patient and declare that it is not worth living. But in the old medical model, suicide may be seen as a relief. In this case, medicine, which is always hopeful, has been abandoned for the impaired model, in which one cannot hope for change.

The families of alcoholics, in the new medical model, are expected to inform themselves about the illness and cooperate with the medical treatment as far as they are able. In the old medical model, the family is expected to police the behavior of the alcoholic, using moral sanctions to bring him into line. The physician and the family are then aligned against the patient, instead of cooperating in his treatment.

In summary, the new medical model treats alcoholism as a bona fide disease, without reservations. It is a hopeful model, and one which encourages new scientific research. It enables those using it to draw strength from the successful campaigns against other major illnesses. The old medical model reflects the physician's dilemma when confronted with a disease which has moral overtones. It is an incomplete medical model which works only when the patient is improving; if the patient returns to drinking and gets sicker, this is seen as the cue to abandon medicine for morality of a simple and exhortative kind. When this in turn fails, the patient is seen as an impaired person who cannot change and whose life is essentially hopeless. In any truly medical situation, however, the medical model shows its full strength precisely when the illness grows worse. It is then that the medical model is able to call on the courage and resourcefulness of the patient and his family, sometimes raising the behavior of all concerned to the level of nobility. To abandon the medical model in a time of stress is to abandon a ship in a storm when it is not sinking.

2. The Alcoholics Anonymous Model and the Medical Models

Many observers have stated that A.A. has been extremely successful in combating alcoholism. Yet the reason for their success is not clear. As Maxwell (10) has written, "It is probable that more contemporary alcoholics have found sobriety through the fellowship of Alcoholics Anonymous than through all other agencies combined. Yet the 'A.A. recovery program' remains an unknown quantity to many and at least something of an enigma to most. It is agreed that, for many alcoholics, the A.A. program 'works,' but what makes it work? What are the therapeutic dynamics?"

Looking over the reasons given by various observers for the success of A.A., one is struck by the diversity of their explanations. Maxwell himself says that "the A.A. group is to be understood as an unusually intimate primary group which sponsors, in a potent learning situation, a new way of life—a new subculture." According to Fox (11), "The remarkable accomplishments of Alcoholics Anonymous attest to the value of this social and religious approach." Smith (12) says, "This group, loosely held together by individuals sharing a common problem, has accepted apparently hopeless people, and in many instances, restored them to lasting health." Vogel (13) regards A.A. as a form of group therapy: "Alcoholics Anonymous, although it differs widely from psychotherapeutic group therapy as conducted by psychiatrists, can be considered a form of group therapy, and a very successful form if the term is used broadly." Tiebout (14) believed that the method of A.A. is the direct treatment of a symptom. Trice (15) says of A.A.: "Out of their face-to-face associations with each other there arises a network of group controls for sobriety that is not present in the usual doctor–patient relationship." Bales (16) held that the policy of alcoholics working with other alcoholics is a feature unique to A.A. which might explain its success. As he put it, "The alcoholic integrated in such a group is enabled to behave in a morally ascendant, protective, mothering way toward another who in turn behaves as he once did."[6]

The common trait shared by these diverse explanations of the success of A.A. is that they all deal with treatment. It would seem at first that if all could agree on which treatment was the most successful, then the other treatments, and the models from which they come, would be abandoned; attempts would be made to extend the range of the most successful treatment to include all alcoholics. But there is no evidence that this is happening, for those who state that A.A. constitutes a very good treatment or the best present treatment for alcoholism draw no general conclusion. No attempt is made to relate the A.A. model to the other models. Perhaps there

---

[6] The authors quoted here have much more to say about the success of A.A. These excerpts were selected to illustrate the range of diverse explanations.

are other questions, raised by other dimensions, which, singly or together, are of more critical importance to the strength of a model than the dimension of treatment.

We suggest that the success of A.A. lies not only in the dimension of treatment but in the dimension of definition. Alcoholism is defined in its model as a special sort of incurable disease, and as a spiritual problem. We believe that both aspects of this definition of alcoholism are essential to the success of A.A. In order to show that it is so, let us consider what A.A. would be like if it defined alcoholism as a disease only. The A.A. model would then be a medical model. But it would have no advantage over any existing medical model, and it would have serious drawbacks. It would be without any medical treatment, even of a token kind. More serious, it would be a medical model without the special authority of the physician which is essential to any medical enterprise. Clearly, such a model would not work.

Now let us consider what A.A. would be like if it defined alcoholism as a spiritual problem only. Here it is not so immediately apparent why this would create an unworkable model. The spiritual aspect of A.A. is of central importance to it, as is evident from studying the Twelve Steps and the Twelve Traditions. A.A. prescribes continuous and effortful spiritual growth for its members, and the threefold development of body, mind and spirit is seen as continuing throughout the lifetime of A.A. members. The spiritual aspect of A.A. is far more obvious to the observer than any medical concern. Why, then, does A.A. believe that it is so beneficial to define alcoholism as a disease? Why could it not run purely as a spiritual self-help group?

The answer lies in the peculiar nature of that category of human misfortunes called "disease." A disease is a force which lies outside the control of the individual. It is ego alien. Disease "strikes" the innocent and the guilty alike, and people are discouraged from feeling personally guilty about it. It is not felt that patients will take better care of themselves or cooperate with the treatment more fully if they believe that they are personally responsible for having a particular disease. Even when a person is known to have incurred a disease through some act of personal carelessness, such as neglecting an inoculation, the tendency is to say to him, "Never mind how you got it, the important thing is to follow the doctor's advice and get better." It seems to be understood that the energy needed for fighting the disease ought not to be wasted on self-blame.

A.A. lifts the burden of personal responsibility from the shoulders of an alcoholic by persuading him that alcoholism, like any disease, is bigger than he is. He cannot control it, and therefore he need not feel sinful about being an alcoholic, just unfortunate. Once he recognizes that, A.A. is able to lay very heavy duties on the alcoholic, duties for which no psychological energy was available in his previous state. Although he is not to be held responsible for having been ill, he must make good the debts, both monetary and moral, which he incurred while ill. In this, he resembles someone recovering from injuries sustained in an automobile accident, who is expected to inquire, once he is well enough to do so, whether he has caused anyone injury or expense as a result of his accident. The alcoholic, like any chronically ill person, places heavy demands on those around him during acute phases of his illness, and he must try to compensate when his illness is under control. Being ill is a kind of social contract in which the patient gains care and indulgence while acutely ill with the understanding that he will try to be a "good patient" and that he will take up his normal social responsibilities as soon as he is able.

To put it another way, the alcoholic, under the A.A. model, has the rights and duties of a responsible patient. The set of rights and duties is extremely old and very well understood, which gives it great advantages over more recent formulations. It is the genius of A.A. that it taps this reservoir of social cohesion, to which every moral person has been exposed early in life.

By defining alcoholism as an illness the alcoholic is released from an otherwise insoluble conflict regarding the drinking society. Alcoholics were all, originally, members of the drinking society, and holders of the "wet" moral model. Within that model, it is traitorous to advocate abstinence from alcohol. Yet alcoholics cannot drink without killing themselves. A.A. provides a way out of the dilemma by defining the inability to drink as a medical problem for alcoholics only, which in no way reflects on the social delights of normal drinking by more fortunate members of society. An alcoholic who affiliates with A.A. may retire gracefully from the drinking society, maintaining a kind of honorary status among his former drinking companions. This is a great improvement over the "dry" moral model, which would have him denounce his friends.

This analysis provides us with a new insight into the phenomenon called "hitting bottom." In terms of the models, hitting bottom is that moment in the career of an alcoholic when he recognizes that illness prevents him from being a participating member of the drinking society. Hitting bottom, then, is a model-switch, from the "wet" moral model to the A.A. model.

Since A.A. defines alcoholism as a disease, its relationship to the two medical models must be shown. It is an improvement over the old medical model, in that it holds the alcoholic responsible for everything except having the disease, while the old medical model holds the alcoholic responsible for having the disease but believes him to be too irresponsible to be held to anything else. The morale deriving from the A.A. model is likely to be higher than that generated by the old medical model.

The relation of A.A. to the new medical model is an interesting one. To a large extent, A.A. is responsible for the existence of the newer model. Since 1935 it has been gently but inexorably insisting that alcoholics should be accepted by doctors as bona fide patients with a serious illness. The A.M.A. accepted that as its official position only in 1956. Although physicians have often been accused of overstepping the boundaries of medicine to take on patients who might have been better off with some other kind of professional help, they have been remarkably sluggish about claiming the 5 million or so alcoholic patients in dire need of their services.

DISCUSSION

The models we have explored here exist because they give a usable explanation of alcoholism to some people. All our models meet this simple but essential requirement. They all seem to be "true": "drunks," like the poor, are always with us; if there were no alcohol, there would be no alcoholics; most people can drink without becoming alcoholics; alcoholics can achieve sobriety through A.A.; alcoholics do display neurotic patterns; the families of alcoholics are engaged in gamelike behavior which they are reluctant to give up; alcoholic patients do abuse their medical privileges by undoing the doctor's work; and alcoholism, like cancer or multiple sclerosis, can be regarded as a disease although both a known etiology and a successful treatment are lacking.

Not only are all the models "true," but most people use more than one of them. Except for a few purists, people will cheerfully abandon one model for another when the model which they are using fails to provide a satisfactory answer. The plurality of viable models, and the inconsistency with which they are used, suggests that the problem of alcoholism has not yet been solved to everyone's satisfaction. What, then, are the requirements for a model which can resolve the conflict and enlist the support of most people?

First, as we stated earlier, a model must be complete. It must be able to provide an answer for every question, and a course of action for every situation which arises in connection with alcoholism. For example, moral models generally fail to provide an adequate account of etiology, or even indicate where one should look for it.

Second, a model must be moral. That is, it must not require any participant to act in a manner contrary to his morality. For example, alcoholics are loath to denounce their former drinking companions and see any demand that they should do so as immoral. Consequently, the "dry" moral model has much less appeal to most alcoholics than a model such as that of A.A. which does not require them to be renegades or traitors.

Third, to be used extensively, a model must be practical and economical. Both the psychoanalytic and the family-interaction models require skillful and highly trained personnel who are not only very expensive but often simply not available. This is a serious shortcoming, for there are several million alcoholics in the United States alone, and it reduces the value of these two models, whatever their other advantages may be.

Fourth, a successful model must be timely. Probably no religious model could rally the massive support today that undoubtedly occurred less than a hundred years ago, or that might again be possible at some time in the future. Aside from any intrinsic merits, the medical model has the special advantage that it is one of the few moralities about which consensus can often be achieved at the present time.

Fifth, a model must make sense both to professional and lay people. Medicine has succeeded in establishing a very favorable image with the lay public, but the relations of physicians to other professionals leaves much to be desired. Professional people who hold psychoanalytic, interactional, behavioristic, biochemical or other models of alcoholism seem to feel that it is required of them to put forth their views explicitly and argue for them. Many journals are devoted to their efforts. But practicing physicians who hold the medical model do not seem to feel the necessity of making their model clear to other professionals. This is understandable, because the everyday work of medicine is of such an immediate and practical nature that physicians do not usually develop much theoretical understanding of medicine as a social transaction. The medical model seems too obvious to require explanation. But unfortunately, the other professionals tend to interpret the silence of physicians on this issue to mean that the physicians have no point of view, and that a dialogue about alcoholism can be conducted in the absence of a medical model. The medical model has much to recommend it, but it has not yet been put in a form such that professionals in allied fields can examine it and compare it with the models which they hold.

REFERENCES

1. SIEGLER, M. and OSMOND, H. Models of madness. Br. J. Psychiat. 112: 1193–1203, 1966.
2. SIEGLER, M. and OSMOND, H. Models of drug addiction. Int. J. Addict. 3 (No. 1): 3–24, 1968.
3. SIEGLER, M. and OSMOND, H. The impaired model of schizophrenia. Schizophrenia 1: 192–202, 1969.
4. SZASZ, T. Review of LINDESMITH, A.R. The addict and the law. Int. J. Addict. 1: 150–155, 1966.
5. RADO, S. Narcotic bondage; a general theory of the dependence on narcotic drugs. Pp. 27–36. In: HOCH, P. H. and ZUBIN, J., eds. Problems of addiction and habituation. New York; Grune & Stratton; 1958.
6. FOX, R. Treatment of alcoholism. Pp. 163–172. In: HIMWICH, H. E., ed. Alcoholism; basic aspects and treatment. Washington, D.C.; American Association for the Advancement of Science; 1957.
7. FERENCZI, S. Alkohol und Neurosen. Jb. Psychoanalyt. Psychopath. Forsch. 3: 853–857, 1912.
8. LANDIS, C. Theories of the alcoholic personality. Pp. 129–142. In: Alcohol, science and society. New Brunswick, N.J.; Journal of Studies on Alcohol; 1945.
9. BERNE, E. Games people play. New York; Grove; 1964.
10. MAXWELL, M. A. Alcoholics Anonymous; an interpretation. Pp. 211–222. In: PITTMAN, D. J., ed. Alcoholism. New York; Harper & Row; 1967.
11. FOX, R. The alcoholic spouse. Pp. 148–168. In: EISENSTEIN, V. W., ed. Neurotic interaction in marriage. New York; Basic Books; 1956.
12. SMITH, J. A. The choice of treatment procedures in the alcoholic. Pp. 173–180. In: HIMWICH, H. E., ed. Alcoholism; basic aspects and treatment. Washington, D.C.; American Association for the Advancement of Science; 1957.
13. VOGEL, S. Psychiatric treatment of alcoholism. Ann. Am. Acad. Polit. Soc. Sci. 315: 99–107, 1958.
14. TIEBOUT, H. M. Direct treatment of a symptom. Pp. 17–26. In: HOCH, P. H. and ZUBIN, J., eds. Problems of addiction and habituation. New York; Grune & Stratton; 1958.
15. TRICE, H. M. Alcoholics Anonymous. Ann. Am. Acad. Polit. Soc. Sci. 315: 108–116, 1958.
16. BALES, R. F. Types of social structure as factors in "cures" for alcohol addiction. Appl. Anthrop. 1 (No. 3): 1–13, 1942.

5

Alcoholism and the Concept of Disease[1]

Howard Hershon, M.D.

IT MAY SEEM less than worthwhile to question the disease concept of alcoholism. It might be predicted that such an exercise would merely become a semantic disputation. It might be hoped that efforts be directed rather at uncovering those features of alcoholism that are considered more relevant and central to the known problems. However, it is contended that what is relevant or central can only be decided within the context of a conceptual framework. It is sometimes considered that the personal, psychiatric and social problems related to alcohol use could be resolved by more intense effort on the part of research workers. On the other hand, it could also be argued that more progress would be made if the present level of effort was redirected along channels suggested by a more realistic conceptual understanding of alcoholism.

If alcoholism is a disease, then it is appropriate to talk about the low cure rate and the high relapse rate, both of which phenomena urge us onto further efforts to improve the present situation. If alcoholism is not a disease then it is not appropriate to consider sobriety obtained by medical treatment a cure, any more than continuous drinking, because it has apparently resisted that medical treatment, a malignant condition. Seeley (31) would suggest that the research response to the problems be medically orientated because of this discipline's good record in the past at getting results; others might argue that the medical response has not produced the results so far as alcoholism is concerned. Of course concepts must be judged by

[1] Reprinted by permission from the *British Journal of Addictions*, Vol. 69, pp. 123–131, 1974. Copyright by British Journal of Addictions, Longman Group Ltd., Longman House, Burnt Mill, Harlow, Essex CM20 2JE.

more than just the results they produce. There may be other reasons why it is reasonable to look at, and deal with alcoholism as if it were a disease. Nevertheless dissatisfaction with the former and doubts about the latter do suggest the need to reconsider the validity of the claim that alcoholism is a disease.

The notion that alcoholism is a disease was first suggested some two hundred years ago by Thomas Trotter in Edinburgh and later by Benjamin Rush (16). Somewhat later the *Journal of Inebriety*, which was published in the United States between 1876 and 1914, contained many papers supporting the concept that inebriety was a disease (14). According to Jellinek, the increasing awareness of the medical consequences of alcoholism, the state's involvement in what it understood as a public health problem, and medical and other researchers' interest in the nutritional and biochemical aspects, worked together to reinforce the idea that alcoholism was a disease for which it was only right and proper for the medical profession to accept responsibility. By 1960, Jellinek (14, *p. 8*) was able to say that "now in America one may speak of a majority acceptance of the illness conception of 'alcoholism.'" Seeley (31), Williams (35), Kessel and Walton (18), Glatt (10) and many other authorities, also refer frequently in their writings to the appropriateness of the medical model to explain, at least in part, the condition known as alcoholism. However, this position is not held universally (6, 27). It would therefore be proper to attempt to evaluate the grounds on which such claims can be confirmed or refuted.

Alcoholism as a Disease: an Assertion

Alcoholics have been considered by some to be irresolute, inadequate, criminal and sinful (10, 33), but these explanations for behavior that often seem to hurt the individual at least as much if not more than those around him have become increasingly unacceptable. At the same time, medical research has repeatedly discovered disease causes for previously inexplicable conditions, discoveries which frequently seem to lead to treatment, relief and even cure. It might therefore seem quite natural that similar hopes and expectations would result from a medical interest in alcoholism. Moreover a precedent was established at the beginning of the last century in connection with the personality and psychopathic disorders, in that certain unacceptable and unwarranted behavior was thought to be caused by an illness (moral insanity). Pinel (25) and Prichard (26) thereby introduced an error in logic which has persisted until today—namely that irresponsible behavior must be due to a disease of the "faculty of responsibility," i.e., the behavior was due to an illness which itself could only be demonstrated by that behavior. That their motives were beyond reproach is not in doubt because as Ordronaught (22) was to state later that century, such a circular path of reason could only be sustained by their humane desire to absolve their patients from censure and disapprobation, which they would otherwise receive in response to their admittedly antisocial behavior. It is contended that a similar process has to some extent influenced the rejection of the emotive and judgmental values previously attached to the alcoholics' behavior by a society, which is on the whole both medically oriented and liberal minded (4).

The medical man has also been drawn into the picture because alcohol is undoubtedly a toxic chemical when ingested and the resultant effects on the body become a very proper concern of the clinician, biochemist and pathologist. There is now a very large literature on both the short-term and the long-term effects of alcohol (e.g., 13, 34). Furthermore, excessive consumption of alcohol has long been recognized to be of etiological significance in a variety of disease entities (2, 9, 30). Dementia, cirrhosis, peptic ulceration, neuropathy and cardiomyopathy are some examples. Equally serious are those complications of long-term alcohol consumption that are often encountered in psychiatric practice. Thus hallucinations, paranoid delusions, delirium tremens and convulsions are not infrequently encountered, often after withdrawal from alcohol (12, 15, 21). Many of these consequences of alcohol use are life-endangering and the most appropriate treatment is that provided by the medical services. After recovery from the immediate alcohol-produced medical problem, it may seem quite natural for the patient–doctor relationship to continue and for their joint attention to be then focussed on ways and means of prevention of further episodes. The transfer from treatment to prevention is often the responsibility of the medical practitioner in other conditions: that a similar position is also adopted for alcoholism is therefore not surprising.

Whatever the merit of the case it is possible to define a condition as a disease if those believed to be technically competent in the matter deal with that condition as if it were a disease. This may be called "medical legitimization" (28). Alcoholism is repeatedly said to be a disease by those individuals and insitutions which are considered to be informed and expert. That some parts of the medical profession do not support such a contention (33) is taken not as a valid alternative concept of the problem, but as an indication of "lack of appropriate training" (18).

It is an interesting paradox that a lay organization like Alcoholics Anonymous, which must function in nonmedical ways, is one of the strongest advocates of the disease concept of alcoholism. Although as Robinson (29) has pointed out, for a doctor to tell a patient with a disease (in this case alcoholism) to pull himself together is absurd and destined for failure. However, A.A. probably employs the concept of illness in a more subtle way: if alcoholism is a disease then the alcoholic is not responsible for his past actions, and this reduces regret and remorse which might otherwise continue to be burdensome and sufficient motivation in itself for continued drinking (33). The concept therefore gives the alcoholic a chance to wipe his slate clean and start afresh. Furthermore, it gives him a socially acceptable excuse for deviating from the norm of social drinking, in being abstinent. To A.A. then, the concept of disease seems to be both the cause for alcoholism and a ploy for sobriety.

One of the "institutionalized expectations of the sick role" described by Parsons (23) is that the sick person is obliged to want to get better and therefore to seek medical treatment. The corollary of this surely is that if a person is accepted as sick by those he believes to know about such things, then he consequently comes to see himself as sick. Jellinek (14) certainly believed that at least two types of alcoholism were diseases. He stated (14, *p.12*): "the medical profession has officially accepted alcoholism as an illness," and that "physicans know what belongs in their realm." The medical models proposed by Siegler et al. (33) decree that alcoholics have both the rights and duties of patients with grave medical illnesses and that the medical profession is obliged to respond in the appropriate way. However, bearing in mind no doubt the unpromising results from such a strategy, they go on to say "the physician can make no promises about outcome . . . he can only promise that he will behave like a physician." The alcoholic, but more probably his family, his friends and society at large, are presumably unaware of these inconsistencies and the rather shaky ground on which the medical model is based. Rather they accept what they hear from those they believe are professionally and technically competent.

In so far as alcohologists talk about loss of control and the alcoholic himself claims he cannot abstain from alcohol altogether or stop after having one or two, the condition of alcoholism seems to be equivalent to a disease. That a person cannot control a disease process by willpower alone is a basic social expectation (23, 28).

These authors however differentiate between the person's behavior in getting or catching the disease and the consequences of the disease itself. It may be, therefore, that a person is responsible for contracting venereal disease but not responsible for the pathological changes that occur in his body as a result of being infected. Jellinek (14) for example had this to say: "applying these principles to uncontrolled drinking it would appear that the acquisition of the disease is in a limited way voluntary, but that once the disease form is reached, it is no different from any other disease; that it is not any more in the sphere of volition to terminate it. . . ." Plaut (4), like Jellinek, does not claim that all drinkers are alcoholics in the sense that they have a disease. However, the phenomena of being unable to abstain, moderate or stop drinking, are repeatedly suggested as criteria of disease (4, 10, 35), although as Lemert (19) points out some societies do not automatically equate irresponsibility with illness!

Finally, the greater understanding of the mechanisms of physical dependence has seemed to dispel many doubts that alcoholism is a disease. Physical dependence (or addiction) is clinically recognized by increasing tolerance to alcohol and withdrawal symptoms on its discontinuation (17, 34). Furthermore, the explanations of physical dependence, as the name suggests, are at a physical level. Thus Collier (3) and Sharpless and Jaffe (32) propose a "disuse–hypersensitivity" of the neurones, Paton (24) suggests that there is a reduction in synaptic acetylcholine, and Martin (20) puts forward the idea that physical dependence is due to selective functioning of active and latent neuronal pathways. Other investigators have actually implicated changes in protein synthesis and enzyme concentrations in the region of cerebral synapses (1, 11). Although Kalant et al. (17) warn that these physical processes are largely unproven hypotheses, at least the possibility of a physical basis to alcoholism encourages the notion of disease.

Alcoholism as a Disease: a Question

The above section contains five possible explanations for accepting alcoholism as a disease. However, these explanations need to be critically assessed in the light of what is now known about both the concept itself and the phenomena subsumed under the label of alcoholism.

While it may be more humane to call an alcoholic ill than deviant, sinful or criminal, it does not necessarily mean that it is valid to do so. Certainly the practice of medicine should be based on an awareness of human needs, but it cannot be considered appropriate to apply the medical model just to provide this kind of approach, rather than some other which is more critical or demanding. The person may feel better if he is accorded the status of a patient, with the rights and privileges that go with it (23, 33). It has already been suggested that it is easier for the alcoholic to blame his illness than himself for all the trouble he has got himself into. It may even be the best way, at a pragmatic level, for the alcoholic and society to cope with drink and its problems. However, it should be appreciated that to do so uses the medical model as part of the strategy to regain control over drink, rather than using it as a basis for genuine medical intervention. On the other hand, as Robinson (29) warns, the use of the medical model may be counterproductive for if the alcoholic is exhorted to control his behavior he might quite reasonably argue that he cannot do so because he is ill (23).

In other conditions, patients and their doctors have little difficulty in differentiating between their responsibilities. Indeed for the doctor to deny the patient's responsibility would be antitherapeutic. The doctor would for instance accept bronchitis as a condition requiring medical treatment. However, if the patient was advised that smoking exacerbated that condition it would be up to him and not the doctor to decide whether he continued or stopped smoking. If such a warning was not given or if the patient did not accept the onus of his task, then he would probably relapse more quickly. In a similar way, it may not be in the patient's interest for the medical profession to accept responsibility for the drinking by invoking concepts of disease, because by so doing the patient may be denied the right and responsibility of making his own decisions. To be fair, however, few members of the medical profession in practice absolve their patients from such responsibilities. In fact the very opposite is usually the case. What may not be realized therefore is that this approach cannot be justified within the framework of the medical model. The paradox is quite clear. Either drinking is a disease in which case the patient cannot be expected to "help it," or it isn't a disease in which case the patient is obliged to try and "help it." Moreover, there must be agreement between the doctor and the patient and others in the drama about this issue. If not, and it is suggested that this is the case at the present time, all involved will have different expectations—expectations that inevitably will not be fulfilled. This can and does lead to doubt, confusion and pessimism.

The argument that the alcoholic can no more control his drinking than a person with pneumonia can control his fever is not really held with conviction. What appears to be generally thought is that such an alcoholic at times appears less able to say no to a drink than a nonalcoholic (10). But is the alcoholic's apparent loss of control just the consequence of choosing to drink rather than not to drink under the circumstances operating at the time, whatever he may feel about the choice at other times? If he prefers to drink rather than abstain that doesn't deny the existence of a choice and furthermore the fact that he does stop drinking, often spontaneously, or at other times because he is expected to do so, must suggest that the loss of control over drinking is not the same as loss of control over a disease process.

Similarly, it is not logical to ascribe to heavy drinking the status of disease just because such behavior leads to disease. The disease consequences of a behavior cannot themselves define that behavior as disease. Few would say that promiscuity, driving a fast car or eating refined carbohydrates were behaviors that could be called diseases even though they can all lead to physical illness and injury. In the field of alcoholism, such a distinction may not always be made. That a medical response is made at times both to the cause and the consequence does not prove that it is correct to do so. The medical profession may be wrong, but in any case there is ample evidence that many doctors do not see their relevance to the drinking aspects of alcoholism and do not, therefore, endorse the disease concept.

The demonstration or suggestion of the processes of physical dependence may seem to provide a physical basis for alcoholism, and to justify thereby the medical model (14). If this was the case, one would have to suggest that drinking behavior was automatically and directly caused by physical dependence, in the same way as the electrophysiological changes in the temporal lobe of the epileptic cause "automatic" behavior of walking and undressing, etc. Few would make such claims. Rather the link between physical dependence and drinking is more indirect. It has been suggested, for example, that the withdrawal symptoms, a consequence of physical dependence, are so unpleasant that they motivate further drinking. At some stage an operantly learned behavior is established in which the person drinks to avoid or relieve these withdrawal symptoms (3, 5, 8). While there is, of course, ultimately a physical basis to learning, such a process does not at the moment conform to our notions of disease, as exemplified by inflammation, degeneration, neoplasm, etc. The insertion of a learning process in between the state of physical dependence and poorly controlled drinking weakens the case that such drinking is a disease or directly caused by a disease. At the same time, however, it does suggest possible mechanisms that have immense theoretical and practical relevance and importance.

Running through this discussion of the criteria of disease and their relevance to alcoholism are two main themes. Firstly, although diseases may have many features, only two seem to be generally applicable, and universally constant. These are that the disease should be seen to be related to an etiologically relevant physical process which the person cannot choose not to have or will away. The second theme concerns the multiple nature of alcoholism itself. Subsumed under the one word are reference to many diverse phenomena—drinking behavior, loss of control, psychiatric and physical consequences, and family, economic and social problems. Alcoholism as a potential disease entity is no more any one of these than all of them lumped together. Before the question "is alcoholism a disease?" can be sensibly answered, the separate elements of the condition have to be teased out and defined. Throughout this paper it is the drinking behavior itself which has been considered to be the relevant issue: therefore the question can be rephrased "is alcohol drinking, which at times seems to be out of control, a disease?"

Alcoholism as a Disease: an Answer

If it is accepted that the criteria of disease suggested above are valid and that the essential part of alcoholism is the drinking behavior itself then it is possible to determine how closely the latter approximates the former. On the other hand, if these criteria are not acceptable or if considered incomplete, then the question about alcoholism being a disease cannot be answered (7). In fact drinking was not demonstrated to be directly due to any physical process recognizable as a disease, and as a behavior it was subject to personal control. The conclusion must be, therefore, that the drinking behavior of alcoholics does not conform to proper notions of disease, and it should not be so designated. The implications of such a conclusion can now be discussed.

Implications

Removing the status of disease from drinking behavior does not make medical practice redundant for other aspects of alcoholism. In fact the converse is true, because by defining out what isn't medical, it is possible to define in what is. There are actually many aspects of alcoholism that conform to the criteria of disease, which are distressing and dangerous and which are amenable to medical treatment. Examples are cirrhosis, peptic ulceration, neuropathy and myocarditis. The withdrawal syndrome itself with its symptoms of anxiety, tremulousness, nausea and sweating, as well as delirium tremens, organic cerebral reactions, psychotic reactions and convulsions, all require appropriate and urgent medical therapy.

Specifying what is and what isn't a disease in the medical sense determines the patient's expectations of his treatment. Likewise the doctor is not put in the position where he is exasperated by the failure of his treatment which in any case was not appropriate and could not be expected to produce a cure. The patient will know what to expect from his doctor and the doctor will know what to provide for his patient. Under conditions mutually agreed to be medical, failure to respond to treatment is accepted as an unhappy fact of life. The patient or his family know that some conditions are chronic or malignant and respect the doctor's efforts to do his best. However, in conditions like continued drinking in which there may well be a conflict of expectations, the doctor's failure to produce abstinence in his patient may not be construed so charitably. After all, the patient will argue, some alcoholics do stop drinking, so why don't I? If the doctor accepts the medical responsibility for such patients, he is obliged to treat them in an attempt to produce abstinence (the cure). If he fails to achieve this, he cannot defend himself by reference to malignancy since he knows only too well that sobriety is attainable. He is thus in a very vulnerable position. But if continued drinking is not perceived by either the patient or his doctor as a medical condition, and the doctor's efforts in helping the patient to control his drinking is not seen as medical treatment, then lack of success in this endeavor will not be interpreted as a therapeutic failure.

This is not to deny that psychiatrists, like all medical practitioners, relate to their patients also in a nonmedical way. The psychiatrist may try and provide the patient with the opportunity to develop insight or he may instruct, cajole, blackmail or frighten the patient in the attempt to change his drinking behavior. While all of this may or may not be valid or justifiable it is not medical treatment and cannot either cure or fail to cure medical ailments. Such intervention cannot be judged by medical standards.

It is only by making explicit the different roles, responsibilities and expectations of those involved with different aspects of alcoholism, that more efficient and effective responses can be made by existing social and psychiatric agencies. Moreover, future expansion of services should be based on a proper awareness of the multiple facets of alcoholism, so that the services provided logically satisfy the quite different medical, psychiatric, psychological and social needs.

REFERENCES

1. AXELROD, J. Cellular adaptation in the development of tolerance to drugs. In: WIKLER, A., ed. The addictive states. Baltimore, Md.; Williams & Wilkins; 1968.

2. BJURULF, P., STERNBY, N. H. and WISTEDT, B. Definitions of alcoholism; relevance of liver disease and temperance board registrations in Sweden. Q. J. Stud. Alcohol 32: 393–405, 1971.

3. COLLIER, H. O. J. Supersensitivity and dependence. Nature 220: 228–231, 1968.

4. COOPERATIVE COMMISSION ON THE STUDY OF ALCOHOLISM. Alcohol problems; a report to the nation. (Prepared by PLAUT, T. F. A.) New York; Oxford University Press; 1967.

5. DENEAU, G., YANGITA, T. and SEEVERS, M. H. Self-administration of psychoactive substances by the monkey. Psychopharmacologia 16: 30–48, 1969.

6. DOPSON, L. The G.P. and the alcoholic. Pulse 24: 9, 1972.

7. EDWARDS, G. The status of alcoholism as a disease. Pp. 140–163. In: PHILLIPSON, R. V., ed. Modern trends in drug dependence and alcoholism. New York; Appleton–Century–Crofts; 1970.

8. EDWARDS, G., HENSMAN, C. and PETO, J. Drinking problems among recidivist prisoners. Psychol. Med. 1: 388–399, 1971.

9. FARIS, A. A. and REYES, M. G. Reappraisal of alcoholic myopathy; clinical and biopsy study of chronic alcoholics without muscle wasting or weakness. J. Neurol. Psychiat. 34: 86–92, 1971.

10. GLATT, M. M. The alcoholic and the help he needs. Royston, England; Priory Press; 1970.

11. GOLDSTEIN, A. and GOLDSTEIN, D. B. Enzyme expansion theory of drug tolerance and physical dependence. In: WIKLER, A., ed. The addictive states. Baltimore, Md.; Williams & Wilkins; 1968.

12. ISBELL, H., FRASER, H. F., WIKLER, A., BELLEVILLE, R. E. and EISENMAN, A. J. An experimental study of the etiology of "rum-fits" and delirium tremens. Q. J. Stud. Alcohol 16: 1–33, 1955.

13. ISRAEL, Y. Cellular effects of alcohol; a review. Q. J. Stud. Alcohol 31: 293–316, 1970.

14. JELLINEK, E. M. The disease concept of alcoholism. Highland Park, N.J.; Hillhouse Press; 1960.

15. JOHNSON, R. B. The alcohol withdrawal syndromes. Q. J. Stud. Alcohol, Suppl. No. 1, pp. 66–76, 1961.

16. Action against alcoholism; a combined approach. [Editorial.] J. Alcsm 7: 1–2, 1972.

17. KALANT, H., LEBLANC, A. E. and GIBBINS, R. J. Tolerance to, and dependence on, some non-opiate psychotropic drugs. Pharmacolog. Rev. 23: 135–191, 1971.

18. KESSEL, N. and WALTON, H. Alcoholism. Baltimore, Md.; Penguin; 1969.
19. LEMERT, E. M. Dependency in married alcoholics. Q. J. Stud. Alcohol 23: 590–609, 1967.
20. MARTIN, W. R. A homeostatic and redundancy theory of tolerance to, and dependence on, narcotic analgesics. Pp. 206–222. In: WIKLER, A., ed. The addictive states. Baltimore, Md.; Williams & Wilkins; 1968.
21. MENDELSON, J. H., LA DOU, J. and SOLOMON, P. Experimentally induced chronic intoxication and withdrawal in alcoholics. III. Psychiatric findings. Q. J. Stud. Alcohol, Suppl. No. 2, pp. 40–52, 1964.
22. ORDRONAUGHT, J. Moral insanity. [Orig. 1872.] In: MAUGHS, S., ed. A concept of psychopathy and psychopathic personalities; its evolution and historical development. J. Crim. Psychopathol. 2: 329–356, 465–499, 1941.
23. PARSONS, T. The social system. England; Tavistock; 1952.
24. PATON, W. D. M. A pharmacological approach to drug dependence and drug tolerance. Pp. 31–47. In: STEINBERG, H., ed. Scientific basis of drug dependence. London; Churchill; 1969.
25. PINEL, P. Traité médico-philosophique sur l'alienation mentale ou la manie. [Orig. 1801.] (DAVIS, D. D., transl.) In: A treatise on insanity. New York; Hafner; 1962.
26. PRICHARD, J. C. A treatise on insanity, and other disorders affecting the mind. London; Sherwood, Gilbert & Piper; 1835.
27. REINERT, R. E. The concept of alcoholism as a bad habit. Bull. Menninger Clin. 32: 35–46, 1968.
28. ROBINSON, D. The process of becoming ill. London; Routledge & Kegan Paul; 1971.
29. ROBINSON, D. The alcohologist's addiction; some implications of having lost control over the disease concept of alcoholism. Q. J. Stud. Alcohol 33: 1028–1042, 1972.
30. SANDERS, M. G. Alcoholic cardiomyopathy; a critical review. Q. J. Stud. Alcohol 31: 324–368, 1970.
31. SEELEY, J. R. Alcoholism is a disease; implications for social policy. Pp. 586–593. In: PITTMAN, D. J. and SNYDER, C. R., eds. Society, culture, and drinking patterns. New York; Wiley; 1962.
32. SHARPLESS, S. and JAFFE, J. Withdrawal phenomena as manifestations of disease supersensitivity. In: STEINBERG, H., ed. Scientific basis of drug dependence. London; Churchill; 1969.
33. SIEGLER, M., OSMOND, H. and NEWELL, S. Models of alcoholism. Q. J. Stud. Alcohol 29: 571–591, 1968.
34. WALLGREN, H. and BARRY, H., 3d. Actions of alcohol. Vol. 1. Biochemical, physiological and psychological aspects. Vol. 2. Chronic and clinical aspects. Amsterdam; Elsevier; 1970.
35. WILLIAMS, L. Alcoholism explained. London; Evans; 1967.

6

A Critical Examination of Some Current Assumptions in the Treatment of Alcoholism[1]

Ovide Pomerleau, Ph.D., Michael Pertschuk, M.D.
and James Stinnett, M.D.

THE TREATMENT OF ALCOHOLISM has been a subject of much concern and disagreement over the years among both professionals and laymen. While the crucial issues that characterize the field of alcoholism are not likely to be resolved immediately, certain approaches to the problem appear more promising than others. Over the long run, solutions seem more likely to arise from the methods of science, which are flexible in their orientation toward knowledge and which emphasize the importance of systematic repeated measurement, rather than from tradition based rigidly on the dogma of commonly held assumptions. A special danger is created by untested assumptions, for practice based on such premises is of unknown value.

Much of the current treatment for alcoholism is based on the central assertions that alcoholism is a disease and that permanent abstinence from the use of alcohol is mandatory. Over the past 10 years considerable scientific scrutiny in disciplines as diverse as biochemistry, physiology, sociology, psychology and medicine has been directed toward the problem of alcoholism. While some of the research has been an attempt to understand basic processes without regard to applicability, other investigations have more immediate and direct implications for treatment. In the present paper we shall

[1] Reprinted by permission from the JOURNAL OF STUDIES ON ALCOHOL, Vol. 37, pp. 849–867, 1976. Copyright by Journal of Studies on Alcohol, Inc., New Brunswick, New Jersey 08903.

examine the evidence for some of the assumptions which underlie abstinence-oriented treatment.

THE DISEASE CONCEPTION OF ALCOHOLISM

General Assumptions

In 1960, Jellinek (1) summarized his pioneering contributions and promulgated a position which dominates the field of alcoholism. He proposed the following hypothesis:

"If any physiological or biochemical anomaly—which in itself may not seem grave—can strip the nervous tissue of its resistance to adaptation of its metabolism to a noxious substance, then that adaptation with all its concomitant behavioral changes may be designated as a disease. . . . I repeat that I regard the above merely as a working hypothesis, but one which can be tested by means of the newer techniques in pharmacology, physiopathology and biochemistry" (*p. 155*).

Little support for the existence of the "physiological or biochemical anomaly" has been accumulated so far, with the possible exception of a study by Goodwin et al. (2) showing evidence for a genetic basis for extreme forms of alcoholism (far in excess of the usual criteria). Despite the sparseness of the evidence and despite Jellinek's admonitions, the "working hypothesis" has been treated as if it were established fact (3). The transition from hypothesis to dogma is especially apparent in the pronouncements of various lay organizations and in the attitude of the public at large (4).

On the positive side, however, the disease conception has produced a number of major benefits, among them the establishment of treatment and rehabilitation as alternatives to moral condemnation and incarceration. Also, the way has been opened for greater physician involvement in providing medical services for alcoholics. In this sense, the disease conception has represented an important step forward.

While constituting an impressive attempt to systematize a highly complex phenomenon, Jellinek's conception was not the result of objective measurement or systematic experimentation, but was derived from his own clinical experience and from retrospective self-reports of recovered alcoholics, mostly longtime members of Alcoholics Anonymous. Jellinek was careful to identify the sources for his generalizations and suggested that his formulations be tested experimentally. Despite the care which he took to phrase his ideas, they have been extended far beyond the boundaries he established. As indicated by the Sobells (5) in a recent retrospective appreciation of Jellinek's work, "while he did not intend the disease concept to apply to all the *species of alcoholism*, but only to those labelled as *gamma* and *delta*, this fact has often been overlooked." Jellinek had indicated that only when gamma and delta alcoholics had consumed enough alcohol to produce acquired increased tolerance, withdrawal symptoms, inability to abstain, or loss of control could they be considered alcohol addicts and their drinking behavior regarded as a disease process. Jellinek hypothesized that in these cases, continued drinking occurs for the purpose of staving off the onset of withdrawal symptoms. Once a person progresses to this late stage of alcoholism, the mere ingestion of any amount of alcohol is sufficient to induce physical dependence on alcohol, and thus an active disease process is at work.

The implications of Jellinek's "working hypothesis" have led to some controversy. There is general agreement that after becoming pharmacologically dependent on alcohol, a "craving" for alcohol is exhibited, in that further drinking serves to diminish or prevent withdrawal symptoms. There is disagreement, however, as to whether an alcoholic, when sober, "craves" alcohol in a similar sense and that once he takes a single drink he is irresistibly compelled to continue drinking until he becomes severely intoxicated (6). There is also considerable question about the further implication that such an individual will never be able to use alcohol in a normal fashion again.

Scientific Evidence

The objective measurement of drinking behavior in alcoholics was pioneered by Mendelson and La Dou (7) and Mello (8). Prior to this research, most studies of drinking behavior in alcoholics, including Jellinek's, were based on retrospective reports of drinking episodes. This method severely limited the validity of inferences since self-reports can be deliberately or unintentionally distorted, and can be affected by the drinker's inability to recall or describe his experience. The object of the experimental analysis of drinking behavior was to examine and verify hypotheses advanced to account for alcoholism. The research employed an operant-conditioning paradigm in which a quantifiable behavior, such as bar-pressing, produced a predetermined amount of alcohol as a consequence. In specially designed research wards, the drinking behavior of volunteer alcoholics (screened to exclude those for whom further drinking was medically contraindicated) was studied objectively over an extended period of time. Predrinking, drinking and postdrinking intervals were designated, with some studies lasting up to several weeks. Observations of social behavior as well as psychiatrically relevant behavior were typically conducted using one-way mirrors and closed-circuit television (9). Blood alcohol determinations were made at regular intervals together with various metabolic tests (10).

Chief among the assumptions brought into question by these experiments is the concept of "loss of control" over drinking. It implies that "every time the subject starts drinking, he is compelled to continue until he reaches a state of severe intoxication" (11). As Mello (12) indicates, "the lack of experimental data about drinking patterns has led to an explicit reification of concepts like 'need' and 'craving' which are defined by the behavior that they are invoked to explain." Direct observations of alcoholics during periods when they could choose to drink any amount indicate that perpetuation of drinking behavior is controlled by a variety of complex social and environmental factors rather than by alcohol dosage per se (13). Although there were some consistencies in drinking patterns, such as a tendency toward episodic and nocturnal drinking, and a propensity for taking straight drinks in large gulps, the picture which emerged was far more complex than had been suggested previously. While the alcoholics were obviously drinking more alcohol than would social drinkers, they were not consistently drinking themselves into a stupor. The amount consumed was inversely related to the amount of work required to obtain the drinks. Some alcoholics were observed to taper off drinking in an attempt to avoid withdrawal symptoms. Several subjects appeared to adjust their intake to correspond with that of others, a few stopping drinking altogether when a drinking partner was no longer available. Thus, when drinking behavior was observed directly, economic, physiological and social factors were found to exert a marked influence on drinking patterns. The old, simple generalizations about alcohol consumption were clearly inadequate.

In addition to basic research on drinking behavior, a number of investigations have specifically tested the assumption that drinking some alcohol will lead to further drinking and to "loss of control." Merry (14) gave alcohol surreptitiously to gamma alcoholic volunteers (who were told they were receiving a vitamin preparation); he found no evidence of increased craving for alcohol after they had consumed an ounce of distilled spirits and concluded that "loss of control" precedes rather than follows taking the first drink. Merry's findings were not supported by Marconi et al. (15) in a similar experiment. Both experiments, however, failed to distinguish between the physiological effects of alcohol and psychological factors (being informed that the beverage did or did not contain alcohol).

A number of related investigations (12, 16–18) have supported Merry's thesis and argued against "loss of control," but these have also been methodologically inadequate. A study by Ludwig et al. (19) reported support for "loss of control" as a response to drinking a small dose of alcohol; however, there was no demonstration that the alcoholic and nonalcoholic beverages used were indistinguishable from one another. Also, the results were equivocal in that psychological factors (drinking a nonalcoholic beverage labeled alcoholic) resulted in more subsequent alcohol consumption and greater expressed desire to drink than did physiological factors (drinking an alcoholic beverage labeled nonalcoholic). Two recent studies have elaborated Merry's original design and have come to more definitive conclusions.

Engle and Williams (20) studied the effects of giving 1 oz of vodka to 40 hospitalized gamma alcoholics. They were routinely given a strongly flavored vitamin mixture to drink each morning. On the 5th day of testing, 20 subjects were randomly assigned to receive 1 oz of vodka disguised in their vitamin mixture. Randomly, half of each group (10 subjects) were told that they had received a solution containing an ounce of vodka; the remaining subjects received no information. All were given the opportunity to request an additional drink if so desired. The results of the study suggested that while there was no relation between consuming a single drink of alcohol and increased desire for alcohol, there was evidence of increased desire following receipt of information that alcohol had been consumed—a psychological rather than a physiological effect. In a well-controlled study, Marlatt et al. (21), after establishing that the alcoholic and nonalcoholic beverages administered were indistinguishable, demonstrated that expectancy or instructional sets significantly determined the amount of beverage consumed by both social drinkers and alcoholics. Actual alcohol content of the mixtures had no effect on the amount consumed and no "loss of control" drinking occurred.

In an important revision of Jellinek's "loss of control" mechanism, Glatt (22) proposed that the physiological mechanism might not be triggered by the ingestion of just one or two drinks but rather by a critical blood alcohol concentration which varied among alcoholics. A recent study by Paredes et al. (23) bears directly on this issue. A number of gamma alcoholics, abstinent for at least 2 weeks, participated in an experiment which included drinking on two consecutive days to a maintained blood alcohol concentration of 0.14%. The subjects did not experience "loss of control" and no evidence of physical dependence was reported. The suggestion from these and related studies (8, 17, 24–29) is that loss of control as Jellinek originally defined the term seems to occur only when a gamma alcoholic is well into a drinking bout and does not occur as a result of drinking a small amount of alcohol or as a result of brief intoxication (5). A more complex model, relying heavily on learning rather than physiological factors, has been proposed by Ludwig and Wikler (30) in a recent theoretical article: following consumption of alcohol, "craving" may be the result of a conditioned withdrawal phenomenon which leads to subsequent drinking in a "chain conditioned" sequence of excessive alcohol intake, "often terminating in intoxication, just as had occurred in many prior drinking bouts."

Another central tenet of the disease conception has been that alcoholism is irreversible—"once an alcoholic, always an alcoholic." The assumption is that once an individual who has been dependent on alcohol stops drinking, any further drinking by that person can only lead to increased dependence. "One implication of this belief is that abstinence can be the only feasible and ethical treatment objective for both alcoholics and anyone considered to be *en route* to becoming an alcoholic" (5). A number of studies challenge this assumption also.

Davies (31) performed a longitudinal follow-up of 93 recovered alcoholics seen in traditional abstinence-oriented therapy. Prior to treatment, no significant feature distinguished these patients from one another. Following treatment, however, 7 of the former alcoholics evinced a pattern of social drinking sustained for periods of 7 to 11 years. Subsequent studies have corroborated the early reports by Davies and others. Using stringent criteria for moderation, Pattison et al. (32) reviewed recovery statistics in various studies of alcoholics and reported that 4 to 10% of the total surveyed moderated their drinking. Gerard and Saenger (33) found that up to 30% of recovered alcoholics developed the capacity to drink normally and concluded that the percentage observed was greatly influenced by the treatment philosophy of the clinic in question. Sobell and Sobell (34) found 59 articles in which evidence of moderate drinking in former alcoholics (mostly gamma) was reported. A recent comprehensive review by Lloyd and Salzberg (35) presented even more extensive documentation for the idea that some alcoholics can learn to drink normally.

CONTROLLED DRINKING AS THE GOAL OF TREATMENT

Abstinence as the goal of treatment is closely associated with the disease conception of alcoholism. As mentioned above, several key assumptions in Jellinek's original formulation have not been supported by recent experimental evidence. Although important revisions in concepts such as "loss of control" have been suggested by Glatt (22) and Keller (36), a climate of doubt exists. Studies in which alcohol was administered to alcoholics as part of therapy now directly approach the question of the "irreversibility" of alcoholism. In many of these investigations the goal of treatment was controlled drinking, a term which differentiates normal social drinking from the pattern of moderate drinking practiced by the former alcoholic—a pattern which requires special training and which uses special precautions to avoid resumption of heavy drinking.

Background

Interest in controlled drinking as a goal of treatment is based on a number of observations. First, alcohol is freely available and there are many practical difficulties in preventing all contact with it. Moreover moderate drinking is generally accepted as the social norm and, in a sense, both the teetotaler and the uncontrolled drinker are deviant. Second, nondrinking may well necessitate drastic social and occupational readjustments, requiring the ex-drinker to form a new set of friends and to function less effectively in work situations in which alcohol traditionally plays a part. Third, treatment in which moderate drinking is a possible outcome is more likely to enlist the interest and cooperation of the problem drinker than one which demands total abstinence. Finally, requiring total abstinence may result in a bi-stable situation in which excessive drinking or no drinking are the only alternatives—if the goal is moderate drinking, a bout of excessive drinking does not provide an excuse for continuing uncontrolled drinking.

The above rationale, coupled with evidence from outcome studies of "spontaneous" moderation in recovered alcoholics and the lack of scientific support for the theoretical basis for mandatory abstinence, have provided the impetus for formal inquiry on controlled drinking.

The goals of treatment have themselves been based on objective measures of drinking patterns. For example, a study by Nathan and O'Brien (9) used operant conditioning techniques to compare the social, affective and drinking behavior of alcoholics and normal drinkers. Some interesting differences were found. In particular, these researchers reported that alcoholic and nonalcoholic subjects reached approximately the same high blood alcohol levels early in drinking, but that alcoholics maintained high levels much longer than nonalcoholics and returned to high levels more frequently. The behaviors which accounted for the observed differences were as follows: alcoholics preferred straight drinks to mixed ones, they gulped rather than sipped their drinks, and they did without the "niceties" of social drinking such as ice, napkins and clean glasses. Alcoholics also drank while dirty or undressed, placed more than a double "shot" in the glass at a time, remained silent while drinking and were sometimes unwilling to stop drinking while alcohol remained available. Research such as the above has had an immediate bearing on clinical treatment for it defined the behavioral characteristics to be inculcated in order to shift drinking patterns from uncontrolled to controlled.

An Evaluation of Controlled Drinking in Therapy

Lovibond and Caddy (37, 38) were among the first to use moderate drinking as the therapeutic goal. The procedure called for training patients (alcoholics with a history of problem drinking for an average of 10 years) to discriminate blood alcohol concentrations from 0 to 0.08% using a breath alcohol testing device. In the next phase, drinking was followed by strong electric shock if blood alcohol exceeded 0.065% but was allowed to occur with impunity if below this level. Follow-up data (ranging from 16 to 60 weeks) from the experimental group indicated that 21 of 31 patients were drinking in a controlled fashion, only rarely exceeding a 0.07% blood alcohol concentration. Members of the control group, however, were drinking significantly more than the criterion level even during treatment sessions. In a follow-up study 18 months after treatment, in which regular self-reports were corroborated by an informant, 10 of the 27 subjects contacted were reported to have achieved the goal of drinking in a controlled fashion (39).

Ewing and Rouse (40) set up a similar program as a pilot study to examine the use of controlled drinking for alcoholics who had not responded to participation in Alcoholics Anonymous and programs requiring mandatory abstinence or who were unwilling to accept a treatment approach requiring total abstinence. Treatment consisted of 12 or more outpatient visits in a simulated living room using mild aversive shock contingent upon exceeding a criterion breath alcohol level. In addition, therapists (medical students and a psychiatrist) sometimes drank in a moderate manner to serve as a model.

About a third of each session was spent in conversation about drinking behavior and about consequences of excessive drinking; wherever possible, the patient's spouse attended treatment. Initial reports indicated mixed results: of 6 patients who had completed a minimum of 12 sessions, 3 were drinking in a controlled fashion during a 9-month follow-up period. In subsequent research additional patients were followed up for from 27 to 55 months: of a total of 35 patients in the study, only 14 came to treatment 6 or more times and of these none were controlled drinkers in extended follow-ups (41). Ewing concluded that in his hands the method was not effective.

Using a more intensive approach, Mills et al. (42) also investigated the possibility of teaching alcoholics behaviors which constitute a social-drinking pattern. The focus of treatment was on avoiding excessive blood alcohol concentration by modifying those specific behaviors which lead to it. Thirteen hospitalized volunteer alcoholics were given alcohol ad libitum in a simulated bar setting. Electric shock was made contingent upon ordering a straight drink, gulping drinks or on ordering more than 3 drinks (behaviors which characterize the alcoholic drinking pattern). No shock was given for appropriate drinking—ordering mixed drinks, sipping, and not exceeding the equivalent of 3 oz of distilled spirits (43% alcohol). The 9 patients who completed the experiment exhibited drinking patterns characteristic of social drinkers. Twelve months after discharge, of the 13 who were trained in controlled drinking, 4 were drinking moderately (defined as less than 6 oz of 42% alcohol on a given day and less than 10 oz of alcohol on any 2 consecutive days) and 3 were abstinent; in the control group of 13, only 2 were drinking normally (43).

In addition to studies using negative reinforcers (aversive stimuli such as electric shock), some researchers have investigated the effects of positive reinforcement contingencies. A series of experiments begun in Baltimore City Hospital has used a variety of positive reinforcement procedures in an inpatient setting to treat alcoholics. Among the reinforcement contingencies used have been access to an enriched environment as a reward for moderation (44, 45), time out from positive reinforcement as a scheduled consequence for drinking (46, 47), and monetary reinforcement as a reward for abstinence or moderate drinking (48).[2] The experiments

---

[2] BIGELOW, G., LIEBSON, I. A. and GRIFFITHS, R. Experimental analysis of

demonstrated that controlled drinking or abstinence could be sustained as long as appropriate reinforcement contingencies were in effect. Several investigators have successfully used a similar approach to reinforce abstinence in outpatients (49–51).[3]

The work of Gottheil and his associates (17) also demonstrates the importance of reinforcement contingencies in alcoholism. In a procedure called Fixed Interval Drinking Decisions, inpatients were allowed to drink 0, 1 or 2 oz of 40% ethanol at 13 decision points spaced an hour apart throughout the day. By requiring the alcoholic to space his drinks, by restricting the alcohol to noncommercial ethanol, and by providing an atmosphere lacking in "social ambience" for drinking, many of the reinforcers maintaining alcohol consumption were lacking and 44% of the patients did not drink at any time during hospitalization; a substantial number of other patients discontinued drinking during their stay. In addition to the experimental treatment, individual psychotherapy, group therapy and Alcoholics Anonymous meetings were provided. A follow-up of the 98 patients who entered the program indicates that 64% were improved: 15% abstained completely for the 6-month period following their discharge, an additional 20% reported that they were not drinking during the last 30 days of the follow-up period, and 29% reported that they were drinking twice a week or less. Since most patients drank daily prior to hospitalization, Gottheil and his associates concluded that their method compared favorably with other treatment approaches (52).

Hedberg and Campbell (53) compared the efficacy of 4 different behavior-therapy procedures on treatment outcome in a 6-month follow-up. Forty-nine outpatient alcoholics were randomly assigned to either behavioral family counseling, systematic desensitization, covert sensitization or shock avoidance. In each group, patients could choose between controlled drinking or abstinence as a goal of treatment. Of the group treated with family counseling, 74% reached their goal, compared with 67% of the systematic desensitization group, 40% of the covert sensitization group, and none of the shock-avoidance group. The shock-avoidance procedure produced a high drop-out rate, only 4 of 12 patients assigned con-

alcoholic drinking. Presented at the American Psychological Association meeting, Montreal, Canada, 1973.

[3] BIGELOW, G., LIEBSON, I. A. and LAWRENCE, C. Prevention of alcohol abuse by reinforcement of incompatible behavior. Presented at the Association for Advancement of Behavior Therapy meeting, Miami, 1973.

tinuing beyond 3 sessions of treatment. Though controlled drinkers were somewhat more successful than abstainers, the difference was not statistically significant. Hedberg and Campbell pointed out that an abstinence rate of 53% for the behavioral treatments combined was much greater than that reported for nonbehavioral treatment in recent reviews by Rohan (54) and Hunt and General (55).

The most extensive test of controlled drinking as a goal of therapy has been performed by the Sobells (29, 56–58). In this project, 70 inpatient volunteer alcoholics were assigned to 1 of 4 treatment groups. Patients were assigned abstinence as their treatment goal if they could identify with Alcoholics Anonymous, requested abstinence as a treatment goal, or were judged to be lacking in sufficient social support to maintain controlled drinking outside the hospital. Patients were assigned to a goal of controlled drinking if they requested controlled drinking, had significant social support available to sustain such behavior, or had successfully practiced moderation at some time in the past. After the designation of a treatment goal, patients were assigned randomly to experimental or control groups: of the patients who qualified for the abstinence goal, 20 received behavioral treatment oriented toward abstinence (nondrinker experimental) and 20 received conventional hospital treatment oriented toward abstinence (nondrinker control); of the patients who qualified for controlled drinking as a goal, 15 received behavioral treatment oriented toward moderate drinking (controlled-drinker experimental) and 15 received conventional hospital treatment oriented toward abstinence (controlled-drinker control).

Control-group patients received conventional treatment including group therapy, chemotherapy, physiotherapy, and attended Alcoholics Anonymous meetings, with the common goal of abstinence for all. Therapy for the experimental patients consisted of 17 treatment sessions in a simulated bar or simulated living room, depending on the patient's previous drinking habits. All were allowed to become drunk during the first 2 sessions and their drunken behavior was videotaped for use in later self-confrontations. Alcohol was not available in the 3d session when the program was explained and techniques for resisting social pressure were practiced. In the 4th through the 16th sessions, alcohol was available and painful electric shocks were scheduled for inappropriate drinking behavior, except for sessions 8, 12 and 16 ("probe" sessions) when no shock was programmed. Controlled-drinker patients could avoid shock by ordering a mixed drink, by sipping rather than gulping, by allowing 20 minutes or more to elapse between drinks and by stopping at 3 drinks. Nondrinker patients could avoid shock by abstaining from drinking entirely.

Analysis of the drinking patterns of the experimental patients indicated that both controlled-drinker and nondrinker patients adjusted their drinking behavior to minimize the number of shocks. During "probe" days when shocks were not scheduled the amount of inappropriate behavior increased somewhat but, even then, straight drinks were never ordered. During all sessions training was provided in recognizing situations which triggered excessive drinking and in generating alternative responses which did not involve the use of alcohol. Emphasis was placed on strengthening patterns of behavior which minimize long-term destructive consequences, e.g., taking action to resolve a marital problem. In the 17th session no alcohol was available and selected videotaped replays of drunken behavior (from the first 2 sessions) were contrasted with videotapes of sober behavior (from session 16).

Evaluation of the program was based on outcome data taken 2 years after the end of treatment. The follow-up procedure called for periodic communications with each patient and collateral informants, such as family or employer, at 3- or 4-week intervals. Follow-up information included general emotional adjustment, vocational satisfaction, occupational status, driving status, and an index of residential status and stability as well as drinking disposition. Five drinking categories were determined: (a) abstinent days; (b) controlled-drinking days—single days in which 6 oz or less of 86-U.S.-proof distilled spirits or its equivalent were consumed, or isolated 1- or 2-day sequences in which 7 to 9 oz per day were consumed; (c) drunk days—days during which 10 oz or more were consumed, or a sequence longer than 2 consecutive days during which 7 oz or more per day were consumed; (d) hospital incarcerated days—days in which hospitalization resulted from excessive drinking; and (e) jail incarcerated days—days in which detention resulted from excessive drinking.

Table 1 shows the 2-year follow-up results of the study. Experimental groups using behavior modification, with controlled drinking or nondrinking as the goal of treatment, functioned significantly better with respect to over-all social adjustment and drinking disposition than did control subjects; of all groups, controlled drinkers functioned best in the several indicators. "Abstinent days" and "controlled drinking days" were grouped together under the heading "functioning well"; the percentage of patients in each group functioning well 80% or more of the time during the second year

TABLE 1.—*Mean Percentage of Total Days Spent by 70 Alcoholics in Various Drinking Dispositions During the Second Follow-Up Year*[a]

Drinking Disposition	CONTROLLED DRINKER GROUPS		NONDRINKER GROUPS	
	Experimental	*Control*	*Experimental*	*Control*
Abstinent days	65.8	37.3	61.3	43.6
Controlled drinking days	23.8	6.1	3.3	1.6
Total days functioning well	*89.6*	*43.4*	*64.6*	*45.2*
Drunk days	7.9	48.4	18.8	35.9
Hospital days	1.6	2.1	6.5	8.4
Jail days	0.9	6.0	10.0	10.5

[a] Data from Sobell and Sobell (58). Table adapted from Doherty (39).

of follow-up was as follows: controlled-drinker experimental, 79%; controlled-drinker control, 22%; nondrinker experimental, 54%; nondrinker control, 21%. The Sobells (58) concluded that the study demonstrated that patients who clearly met the requirements for classification as gamma alcoholics could acquire and maintain patterns of sustained moderate drinking, contradicting the tradition that alcoholic drinking patterns are irreversible. The findings of the 2-year follow-up added further support to their earlier contention that, lacking evidence, the concept of irreversibility was "but a tautology of little descriptive or predictive value" (57).

The Sobells' study constitutes the most ambitious clinical trial of the controlled-drinking concept to date. The inability to make direct comparisons of abstinence with controlled drinking as a goal, however, is a serious defect in the research. Only further investigation using random assignment of appropriate subjects to different treatment goals will resolve the difficulty. The follow-up procedure is in some respects also deficient. Recognizing this, the Sobells (58) indicated that an independent outcome evaluation was being conducted using follow-up personnel who were not familiar with the purpose of the investigation and who had no commitment to either abstinence or controlled drinking as treatment goals. A final problem, that of corroborating self-reported drinking behavior, remains unresolved. Perhaps the development of more easily administered objective tests of alcohol consumption, such as the MOBAT (59), and more sensitive physiological indicators of liver-enzyme function, such as the γ-glutamyl transpeptidase test (60), may provide practical methods for validating changes in drinking habits.

Despite its shortcomings, the Sobells' study constitutes a major contribution to knowledge about the treatment of alcoholism. Taking into account the Sobells' work and the other research on controlled drinking, as well as the studies showing that a certain percentage of recovered alcoholics moderate their drinking "spontaneously," it seems highly inappropriate at this time to exclude controlled drinking as a possible goal of therapy.

CONCLUSION

In the present article we have examined some of the assumptions which form the basis for Jellinek's disease conception and the abstinence requirement in alcoholism treatment. That the empirical support for these concepts is weak and, in some cases, absent has a number of implications for current treatment and research.

Beyond the inherent danger of promulgating a model of human behavior which is not objectively validated, the overinclusive application of the disease conception to all alcohol problems may have serious practical disadvantages as well. Unless there is an empirically validated conceptual framework resulting in effective medical intervention which does not require extensive cooperation from the patient, the concept may simply enhance irresponsibility (61). Thus the time-worn rationalization of the problem drinker, "I couldn't help it, I was drunk," can become transformed into, "I couldn't help it, I was sick," and may indicate the absence of a real effort to change the patterns of behavior which led to excessive drinking (62). Also, despite Jellinek's admonitions, considerable rigidity in therapeutic approaches seems to have resulted, as both LeBlanc (61) and the Sobells (5) have noted. Major improvement of current practice will be delayed or prevented entirely if therapeutic diversity in response to observed clinical differences is not tolerated and encouraged.

With respect to the issue of controlled drinking, the crucial question facing the clinical investigator involves differentiating those problem drinkers for whom controlled drinking is appropriate and helpful from those for whom it may be harmful or ineffective. Some practical guidelines have been proposed, such as restricting controlled drinking to problem drinkers who will not accept abstinence-oriented treatment, or who have had periods of moderate drinking in the past, and who have no medical contraindications to continued use of alcohol. While helpful in minimizing risk to the patient, these common-sense rules need to be backed up by careful scientific investigation. In this way, taking into account individual strengths and weaknesses, patients can be assigned treatment goals which are most likely to be reached and which can be sustained.

There is an increased awareness of the magnitude and social harmfulness of excessive alcohol consumption. Of the many millions of people in the United States designated as problem drinkers, however, only a small fraction (perhaps less than 10%) are currently receiving help for their problem. Most of these people are still functioning in society and may not yet have experienced the full negative impact of sustained excessive drinking, such as loss of health or of social and economic support. Moreover, the traditional approach to treatment has been designed for the problem drinker who has "hit bottom" and is now willing to "surrender to therapy" (63). Thus a possible explanation for the difficulty of getting alcoholics into therapy—especially in the early stages of the disorder—may come from their unwillingness to enter a treatment modality which demands total abstinence. In a recent address to the North American Congress on Alcohol and Drug Problems, Chafetz, then director of the National Institute on Alcohol Abuse and Alcoholism, alluded to the problem and stressed the necessity of reexamining some basic operational principles. He noted that "abstinence in every instance is not going to be a realistic objective." "While it is certainly a desirable goal," he said, "and a necessary treatment tool—especially for chronic alcoholic people, we should not allow ourselves to fall into the trap of setting up treatment systems based on exclusive objectives, especially as we learn to identify earlier stages in alcohol problems."[4]

Major spokesmen for divergent views on the nature of alcoholism have been unanimous recently in urging a temperate, reasoned approach to resolving the problems in alcoholism treatment today. The Sobells (34) stressed the importance of courtesy and scientific objectivity while the National Council on Alcoholism cautioned against hasty conclusions and sensationalism.[5] These appeals are most timely and appropriate, for the most harmful myth that needs to be debunked is the one that implies that we know all that needs to be known to treat alcoholism effectively.

[4] CHAFETZ, M. Opening remarks. Presented at the North American Congress on Alcohol and Drug Problems, San Francisco, Calif., 12–18 December 1974.

[5] NATIONAL COUNCIL ON ALCOHOLISM. News release. New York, 14 October 1974.

REFERENCES

1. JELLINEK, E. M. The disease concept of alcoholism. Highland Park, N.J.; Hillhouse Press; 1960.
2. GOODWIN, D. W., SCHULSINGER, F., HERMANSEN, L., GUZE, S. B. and WINOKUR, G. Alcohol problems in adoptees raised apart from alcoholic biological parents. Archs Gen. Psychiat. **28**: 238–243, 1973.
3. GITLOW, S. E. Alcoholism; a disease. Pp. 1–9. In: BOURNE, P. and FOX, R., eds. Alcoholism; progress in research and treatment. New York; Academic; 1973.
4. VERDEN, P. and SHATTERLY, D. Alcoholism research and resistance to understanding the compulsive drinker. Ment. Hyg. **55**: 331–336, 1971.
5. SOBELL, M. B. and SOBELL, L. C. Alternatives to abstinence; time to acknowledge reality. Addictions **21** (No. 4): 2–29, 1974.
6. JELLINEK, E. M. Phases of alcohol addiction. Q. J. Stud. Alcohol **13**: 673–684, 1952.
7. MENDELSON, J. H. and LA DOU, J. Experimentally induced chronic intoxication and withdrawal in alcoholics. Pt. 1. Background and experimental design. Q. J. Stud. Alcohol, Suppl. No. 2, pp. 1–13, 1964.
8. MELLO, N. K. Behavioral studies of alcoholism. Pp. 219–291. In: KISSIN, B. and BEGLEITER, H., eds. Biology of alcoholism. Vol. II. New York; Plenum; 1972.
9. NATHAN, P. and O'BRIEN, J. S. An experimental analysis of the behavior of alcoholics and nonalcoholics during prolonged experimental drinking; a necessary precursor of behavior therapy? Behav. Ther. **2**: 455–476, 1971.
10. MENDELSON, J. H. and MELLO, N. K. Experimental analysis of drinking behavior of chronic alcoholics. Ann. N.Y. Acad. Sci. **133**: 828–845, 1966.
11. MARDONES [-R.], J. The alcohols. Pp. 99–182. In: ROOT, W. S. and HOFMANN, F. G., eds. Physiological pharmacology. Vol. 1. New York; Academic; 1963.
12. MELLO, N. K. Some aspects of the behavioral pharmacology of alcohol. Proc. 6th Annu. Mtg. Am. Coll. Neuropsychopharmacol., pp. 787–809, 1968.
13. MELLO, N. K. and MENDELSON, J. H. A quantitative analysis of drinking patterns in alcoholics. Archs Gen. Psychiat. **25**: 527–539, 1971.
14. MERRY, I. The "loss of control" myth. Lancet **1**: 1257–1258, 1966.
15. MARCONI, J., FINK, K. and MOYA, L. Experimental study on alcoholics with an "inability to stop." Br. J. Psychiat. **113**: 543–545, 1967.
16. CUTTER, H., SCHWAAB, E. and NATHAN, P. E. Effects of alcohol on its utility for alcoholics and nonalcoholics. Q. J. Stud. Alcohol **31**: 369–378, 1970.
17. GOTTHEIL, E. ALTERMAN, A. I., SKOLODA, T. E. and MURPHY, B. F. Alcoholics' patterns of controlled drinking. Am. J. Psychiat. **130**: 418–422, 1973.
18. LUDWIG, A. M. On and off the wagon; reasons for drinking and abstaining by alcoholics. Q. J. Stud. Alcohol **23**: 91–96, 1972.
19. LUDWIG, A. M., WIKLER, A. and STARK, L. H. The first drink. Archs Gen. Psychiat. **30**: 539–547, 1974.
20. ENGLE, K. B. and WILLIAMS, T. K. Effect of an ounce of vodka on alcoholics' desire for alcohol. Q. J. Stud. Alcohol **33**: 1099–1105, 1972.

94   INTERFACES BETWEEN ALCOHOLISM AND MENTAL HEALTH

21. MARLATT, G. A., DEMMING, B. and REID, J. B. Loss of control drinking in alcoholics; an experimental analogue. J. Abnorm. Psychol. 81: 233–241, 1973.
22. GLATT, M. M. The question of moderate drinking despite "loss of control." Br. J. Addict. 62: 267–274, 1967.
23. PAREDES, A., HOOD, W. R., SEYMOUR, H. and GOLLUB, M. Loss of control in alcoholism. Q. J. Stud. Alcohol 34: 1146–1161, 1973.
24. COHEN, M., LIEBSON, I. A. and FAILLACE, L. A. A technique for establishing controlled drinking in chronic alcoholics. Dis. Nerv. Syst. 33: 46–49, 1972.
25. MACANDREW, C. and EDGERTON, R. B. Drunken comportment; a social explanation. Chicago; Aldine; 1969.
26. MCNAMEE, H. B., MELLO, N. K. and MENDELSON, J. H. Experimental analysis of drinking patterns of alcoholics; concurrent psychiatric observations. Am. J. Psychiat. 124: 1063–1069, 1968.
27. MUKOSA, H. and ARIKAWA, K. A new double medication method for the treatment of alcoholism using the drug cyanamide. Kurume Med. J. 15: 137–143, 1968.
28. NATHAN, P. E., TITLER, N. A., LOWENSTEIN, L. M., SOLOMON, P. and ROSSI, A. M. Behavioral analysis of chronic alcoholism. Archs Gen. Psychiat. 22: 419–430, 1970.
29. SOBELL, M. B. and SOBELL, L. C. Alcoholics treated by individualized behavior therapy; one year treatment outcome. Behav. Res. Ther. 11: 599–618, 1973.
30. LUDWIG, A. M. and WIKLER, A. "Craving" and relapse to drink. Q. J. Stud. Alcohol 35: 108–130, 1974.
31. DAVIES, D. L. Normal drinking in recovered alcohol addicts. Q. J. Stud. Alcohol 23: 94–104, 1962.
32. PATTISON, E. M., HEADLEY, E. B., GLESER, G. C. and GOTTSCHALK, L. A. Abstinence and normal drinking; an assessment of changes in drinking patterns in alcoholics after treatment. Q. J. Stud. Alcohol 29: 610–633, 1968.
33. GERARD, D. L. and SAENGER, G. Out-patient treatment of alcoholism; a study of outcome and its determinants. (Brookside Monogr. No. 4.) Toronto; University of Toronto Press; 1966.
34. SOBELL, M. B. and SOBELL, L. C. The need for realism, relevance and operational assumptions in the study of substance dependence. Pp. 133–167. In: CAPPELL, H. D. and LeBLANC, A. E. Biological and behavioural approaches to drug dependence. Toronto; Addiction Research Foundation; 1975.
35. LLOYD, R. W. and SALZBERG, H. C. Controlled social drinking; an alternative to abstinence as a treatment goal for some alcoholics. Psychol. Bull. 82: 815–842, 1975.
36. KELLER, M. On the loss-of-control phenomenon in alcoholism. Br. J. Addict. 67: 153–166, 1972.
37. LOVIBOND, S. H. Aversive control of behavior. Behav. Ther. 1: 80–91, 1970.
38. LOVIBOND, S. H. and CADDY, G. Discriminated aversive control in the moderation of alcoholics' drinking behavior. Behav. Ther. 1: 437–444, 1970.
39. DOHERTY, J. Controlled drinking; valid approach or deadly snare? Alc. Hlth Res. World, pp. 2–8, Fall 1974.
40. EWING, J. A. and ROUSE, B. A. Out-patient group treatment to inculcate controlled drinking behavior in alcoholics. Alcoholism 9: 64–75, 1973.

41. Controlled drinking project fails. Psychiat. News, 17 September 1975.
42. MILLS, K. C., SOBELL, M. B. and SCHAEFER, H. H. Training social drinking as an alternative to abstinence for alcoholics. Behav. Ther. 2: 18–27, 1971.
43. SCHAEFER, H. H. Twelve-month follow-up of behaviorally trained ex-alcoholic social drinkers. Behav. Ther. 3: 286–289, 1972.
44. BIGELOW, G., COHEN, M., LIEBSON, I. A. and FAILLACE, L. A. Abstinence or moderation; choice by alcoholics. Behav. Res. Ther. 10: 209–214, 1972.
45. COHEN, M., LIEBSON, I. A., FAILLACE, L. A. and ALLEN, R. P. Moderate drinking by chronic alcoholics. J. Nerv. Ment. Dis. 153: 434–444, 1971.
46. BIGELOW, G., LIEBSON, I. A. and GRIFFITHS, R. Alcoholic drinking; suppression by a brief time-out procedure. Behav. Res. Ther. 12: 107–115, 1974.
47. PICKENS, R., BIGELOW, G. and GRIFFITHS, R. An experimental approach to treating chronic alcoholism; a case study and one-year follow-up. Behav. Res. Ther. 11: 321–325, 1973.
48. COHEN, M., LIEBSON, I. A., FAILLACE, L. A. and SPEERS, W. Alcoholism; controlled drinking and incentives for abstinence. Psychol. Rep. 28: 575–580, 1971.
49. HUNT, G. M. and AZRIN, N. H. A community-reinforcement approach to alcoholism. Behav. Res. Ther. 11: 91–104, 1973.
50. MILLER, P. M. The use of behavioral contracting in the treatment of alcoholism; a case study. Behav. Ther. 3: 593–596, 1972.
51. POMERLEAU, O. F. and BRADY, J. P. Behavior modification in medical practice. Penn. Med. 78: 49–53, 1975.
52. SKOLODA, T. E., ALTERMAN, A. I., CORNELISON, F. S. and GOTTHEIL, E. Treatment outcome in a drinking decisions program. J. Stud. Alcohol 36: 365–380, 1975.
53. HEDBERG, A. G. and CAMPBELL, L., 3d. A comparison of four behavioral treatments of alcoholism. J. Behav. Ther. 5: 251–256, 1974.
54. ROHAN, W. P. Follow-up study of problem drinkers. Dis. Nerv. Syst. 33: 196–199, 1972.
55. HUNT, W. A. and GENERAL, W. R. Relapse rates after treatment for alcoholism. J. Community Psychol. 1: 66–68, 1973.
56. SOBELL, M. B. and SOBELL, L. C. Individualized behavior therapy for alcoholics; rationale, procedure, preliminary results and appendix. (California Mental Health Res. Monogr., No. 13.) Sacramento; Department of Mental Hygiene; 1972.
57. SOBELL, M. B. and SOBELL, L. C. Individualized behavior therapy for alcoholics. Behav. Ther. 4: 49–72, 1973.
58. SOBELL, M. B. and SOBELL, L. C. Second year treatment outcome of alcoholics treated by individualized behavior therapy; results. Behav. Res. Ther. 14: 195–215, 1976.
59. SOBELL, M. B. and SOBELL, L. C. A brief technical report on the MOBAT; an inexpensive portable test for determining blood alcohol concentration. J. Appl. Behav. Anal. 8: 117–120, 1975.
60. ROSALKI, S. B. and RAU, D. Serum gamma-glutamyl transpeptidase activity in alcoholism. Clin. Chim. Acta 39: 41–47, 1972.

61. LeBlanc, A. E. The disease concept of alcoholism. The Journal, Toronto 1 (No. 12): 4, 1973.
62. Roman, P. M. and Trice, H. M. The sick role, labelling theory, and the deviant drinker. Int. J. Social Psychiat. 14: 245–251, 1968.
63. Tiebout, H. M. The act of surrender in the therapeutic process; with special reference to alcoholism. Q. J. Stud. Alcohol 10: 48–58, 1949.

7

The Alcohologist's Addiction

Some Implications of Having Lost Control over the Disease Concept of Alcoholism[1]

David Robinson, Ph.D.

"Any label or definition is only a matter of convenience and convention. . . . the essential factor is the consistency in connotation."—E. M. Jellinek (1).

ATTEMPTS to spell out the nature of the relationship between alcohol consumption, alcoholism and disease have formed a well-established and lively debate. However, as Edwards (2) points out, "much of the necessary evidence on which to make a decision as to whether alcoholism is a disease is not yet available, and when all the relevant information on the causes of abnormal drinking has been gathered in, the decision as to alcoholism being a disease will still rest very much on the definition of 'alcoholism' on the one hand and of 'disease' on the other."

Edwards thus directs our attention to the crucial question for the sociologist, namely, the question of what counts as something for particular people in particular social situations and what are the implications of those definitions for social behavior. Ideas about what counts as alcoholism and what is the nature of its relationship to disease are constantly changing. There has been a discernible and well-documented shift over the past century from considering alcoholism as primarily a legal or moral problem to considering it primarily as one of medicine or public health. Jellinek's seminal contributions to the study of alcohol-related problems have played no

[1] Reprinted by permission from the QUARTERLY JOURNAL OF STUDIES ON ALCOHOL, Vol. 33, pp. 1028–1042, 1972. Copyright by Journal of Studies on Alcohol, Inc., New Brunswick, New Jersey 08903.

small part in focusing our attention on the core question of what it means to say that alcoholism is a disease.

In the present paper I describe certain consequences which could follow from operating with a wide-ranging disease concept of alcoholism. Jellinek's work is briefly discussed and particular developments of his position are identified. However, it is not my aim to suggest that Jellinek alone changed the world's ideas about the nature of alcoholism. Nor do I blame Jellinek for the fact that his ideas have been selectively plundered and unhelpfully interpreted. But since Jellinek has, with justification, been referred to as "primarily responsible for the great progress made in the understanding of and approach to alcoholism" (3), he must stand as at least representing a major body of thought on the nature of the relationship between alcohol consumption, alcoholism and disease and, as such, must be held partially responsible for the way in which "the disease concept of alcoholism" is now applied. How happy he would be with the various manifestations of its application is a quite separate question upon which we can merely speculate.

JELLINEK AND THE DISEASE CONCEPT OF ALCOHOLISM

In his much quoted 1952 article Jellinek (4) restricted the application of the disease conception to "addictive drinking"—"The disease concept of alcohol addiction," he wrote, "does not apply to the excessive drinking, but solely to the loss of control which occurs in only one group of alcoholics and then only after many years of excessive drinking. . . . the loss of control is a disease condition per se which results from a process that superimposes itself upon those abnormal . . . conditions of which excessive drinking is a symptom."

Not only was Jellinek clear about the precise nature of the disease conception of alcoholism but he was also clear about the need for a restricted definition of alcoholism itself and clear about the harmful consequences which would follow from the "unwarranted extension" of the conception to all excessive drinking. For "sooner or later," he believed, such a misapplication would "reflect on the legitimate use too and, more important, will tend to weaken the ethical basis of social sanctions against drunkenness" (4). Later, in *The World and its Bottle* (1), Jellinek again denied the usefulness of defining as "alcoholism" everything which, in any culture, is given that label. "If the term alcoholism is extended to occasional excessive drinkers, as is the case in many countries, one may say with justification that the nature of alcoholism shows marked differences throughout the world. According to the accepted ideas about alcoholism in the Anglo-Saxon countries and even in some Latin countries occasional excessive drinkers—such as weekend or Sunday drinkers who follow a cultural pattern, or 'celebrators,' and even the explosive occasional relief drinker—would never be regarded as alcoholics. . . . The extension of the term alcoholism to cover all forms of drinking which may occasion damage is not impossible," but "while such a broad connotation would perhaps eliminate much conflict in international communication on this subject, it would hardly be a useful means."

Perhaps because of his increasing involvement with organizations committed to "international communication," Jellinek later reneged on this position and in *The Disease Concept of Alcoholism* (5) used the term alcoholism to refer to "any use of alcoholic beverage that causes any damage to the individual or society." The utility of such a wide-ranging definition of alcoholism, claimed Jellinek, was that it "forces us to single out species of alcoholism and to speak of them in stringent terms." While such a strategy might have helped to solve some of Jellinek's problems in "international communication" it tended to cloud rather than illuminate other related issues. For instance, the five species of the genus alcoholism which Jellinek outlined do not in fact cover the whole range of alcoholism as he defined it. "The definition of alcoholism, namely that alcoholism is any drinking that leads to any damage, does not permit of designating as alcoholic all those who occasion some kind of damage through their use of alcoholic beverages. I would call alcoholics only those who manifest the alpha, beta, gamma, delta, and epsilon varieties of alcoholism." Because of the wide-ranging definition of alcoholism and the concomitant fact that "we cannot say that alcoholics are those who suffer from alcoholism" Jellinek concentrated his attention upon only certain of the alcoholisms when he addressed himself to the question of in what way alcoholism is a disease. His answer to this question was that only gamma "loss of control" and delta "inability to abstain" alcoholisms qualify as diseases, because only they are addictions in the pharmacological sense.

Having come to this conclusion Jellinek felt that the next challenging question should concern the pharmacological nature of addiction to which "the newer techniques in pharmacology, physiopathology and biochemistry" should be addressed. He considered it was the case that "if any physiological or biochemical anomaly —which in itself may not seem grave—can strip nervous tissue of its resistance to adaptation of its metabolism to a noxious substance then that adaptation with all its concomitant behavioral changes may be designated as a disease." This, then, was what Jellinek postulated as the disease nature of alcoholism.

Over the whole body of his writing Jellinek was quite consistent about the distinction which should be maintained between "alcoholism" as broadly defined and "the disease nature of alcoholism" restrictively defined as addictive alcoholism. Unfortunately his discussion of the topic made him appear less clear on intimately related points. The apparent lack of clarity was probably due to the fact that, in addition to setting out his own position in *The Disease Concept of Alcoholism*, he was also endeavoring to produce a short history and extensive contemporary description of how various countries, groups and associations defined alcoholism and how they saw the relationship between alcoholism and disease. On the latter point Jellinek maintained that, while ideas about the nature of the relationship between alcoholism and disease varied from group to group, "the indications for the great majority are that the accepted version is merely that 'alcoholism *is* a disease.' "

This is the crux of the problem. For if, as Jellinek pointed out, a steadily increasing majority of the medical profession, governments, voluntary associations and general publics accepted "merely that alcoholism *is* a disease" how helpful was it for him to extend his own definition of the broader term "alcoholism" to include "any use of alcoholic beverage that caused any damage to the individual or to society"? His justification for adopting the wide-ranging definition of alcoholism is acceptable in that it might force a careful scrutiny of the alcoholic. However, since he was readily recognized as an authority on alcohol-related problems and since so many people were, as he himself reported, unable to understand or at least maintain the distinction between alcoholism and the disease nature of alcoholism, Jellinek must be said to have contributed to the designation of an ever-widening set of conditions and behaviors as symptoms or diseases when, in fact, his own conception of the disease nature of alcoholism was just as restricted and clearly defined as ever. Certain consequences result from the adoption of a wide-ranging definition of alcoholism and a concomitant acceptance merely that "alcoholism *is* a disease." The remainder of this paper is devoted to the identification and discussion of such consequences.

CONSEQUENCES OF ACCEPTING A WIDE-RANGING DISEASE CONCEPT OF ALCOHOLISM

"The statement 'alcoholism is a disease' is now so widely heard in scientific and lay circles that one can hardly safely begin any undertaking in reference to alcoholism without first repeating it" (6).

The trouble with starting a popular book about alcoholism (7) with the declaration that "alcoholism is a disease" is that those who read it often have ill-defined notions not only of what counts as alcoholism but also of what counts as a disease. By accepting that "alcoholism is a disease" an increasing proportion of the general population may, in fact, adopt quite false and unhelpful expectations and beliefs about the nature of alcoholism and thus also about the nature and role of treatment and its outcome. How widespread particular ideas are is a researchable question. It is possible, however, to discuss certain consequences which follow from the general public's accepting the idea that alcoholism is a disease when their conception of what a disease is may be ill-defined, or at least significantly different from that with which the medical profession operates. A belief about some specific aspect of social life, such as that "alcoholism is a disease," may be widely held, but that it is widely held does not force any particular person to see the world in a certain way for, of course, man is not impotent to create his own meaningful account of the world about him and his own place within it. Widely held ideas do tend, however, to set limits to the range of expectations and beliefs which any person is likely to have about his own condition and about what counts as appropriate behavior in specific situations.

If an increasing number of people are coming to accept as axiomatic that "alcoholism is a disease" and are also defining as alcoholism "any use of alcoholic beverage that causes any damage to the individual or to society" then certain things are consequent.

These consequences, which have clear implications for those whose concern is with prevention, education and treatment, or with the provision of medical and social services associated with alcohol-related problems, are briefly discussed below. To an extent these consequences stem from the acceptance of *any* disease concept of alcoholism but clearly become more problematic and assume greater significance as a more wide-ranging disease conception is accepted.

Consequence 1: A person may define himself as an alcoholic, and thus his condition and behavior as a medical matter, when the medical profession does not define the situation in that way, and vice versa.

"The subjective meaning need not necessarily be the same for all the parties who are mutually oriented in the given social relationship. . . . in such cases the parties associate different meanings with their actions and the social relationship is in so far objectively asymmetrical from the points of view of the two parties" (8).

Whether the self-defined alcoholic's definition of himself is accepted as appropriate by the medical profession as a whole, or by the particular member of the profession to whom the matter is presented, will depend upon how inclusive their disease conception of alcoholism is and whether they operate with similar criteria of what counts as alcoholism. If members of the medical profession operate with a restricted definition of alcoholism and a stereotype of the alcoholic as a "down and out," recognizable by appearance, manners or loss of social position, then this has clear consequences for diagnosis and for their willingness to treat as legitimate the self-defined alcoholic's presented complaint. Blane et al. (9) have demonstrated that alcoholics not conforming to the popular Skid Row stereotype are missed diagnostically, while Pattison (10) reports that many doctors will not define as an alcoholic a person who is working and retaining his social and economic standards.

However, even if the medical profession's definition is less inclusive than that of a presenting "alcoholic," certain processes are likely to operate *in effect* to widen the disease conception in any particular case. These processes are inevitable, given the medical profession's ethics, the fact that doctors are human beings and thus have a commitment and a general readiness to conceive of any presented complaint as an illness to be treated or at least as an appeal for help to them as doctors to be dealt with in some way. A member of the medical profession may thus be drawn as a medical expert into an area which he may feel "in his bones" does not come within his competence to be expert about. However, the process does not stop here, for any intervention, however reluctant, will tend to reinforce an erroneous lay conception of the disease nature of alcoholism. For if, as Jellinek wrote (5), "a disease is what the medical profession recognizes as such," then from the layman's point of view it is perfectly reasonable to define as a disease "anything which the medical profession is seen to be willing to deal with in some way."

When the medical profession accepts a more inclusive definition of alcoholism than does the alcoholic this also has implications for diagnosis and treatment. In such a situation the patient is likely to resist any attempts to persuade him that he is an alcoholic, or is exhibiting early symptoms of the disease, if his behavior does not match up to *his* stereotype of an alcoholic. Thus if, for example, the patient's definition of the alcoholic is restricted to the Skid Row or down-and-out stereotype, then clearly a successful preventive or early treatment program will only be initiated with extreme difficulty, while the chances of obtaining help at what the medical profession might see as an early stage in the disease process will be remote.

Consequence 2: A person defined as an alcoholic by the medical profession may not be treatable because of the way he conceptualizes his responsibility for his disease.

"He may, of course, have carelessly exposed himself to danger of accident, but once injured he cannot, for example, mend a fractured leg by 'will power' " (11).

Both the general public and the medical profession tend to share certain assumptions about the relationship between disease and individual responsibility. These are that while the individual may have intentionally exposed himself to disease conditions, or behaved in some way which increased his likelihood of contracting a disease, it is not possible once the disease is contracted to get rid of it by will power. Parsons' discussion of the sick role (11) still informs the majority of sociological work in this field and has been shown to reflect widespread beliefs about the nature of being ill (12). Briefly, Parsons pointed out that whenever a person's illness condition is legitimized by the authority of the medical profession, of his intimates or of other people having influence over him, he assumes a special role. This role, the sick role, replaces or modifies his usual occupational, familial and other roles. It permits him special rights such as freedom from usual obligatory duties, requires him to observe certain rules such as cooperating with the doctor, and imposes special requirements on other people near to him, such as his family, friends and medical personnel.

On the crucial question of responsibility for the disease or illness condition Parsons has this to say in a section in which he outlines the relationship between illness and deviance: "By institutional definition of the sick role the person is helpless and therefore in need of help. If being sick is to be regarded as 'deviant,' as certainly in important respects it must, it is . . . distinguished from other deviant roles precisely by the fact that the sick person is not regarded as 'responsible' for his condition, 'he can't help it.' " Such assumptions are certainly appropriate when applied to a *restricted* definition of the alcoholism "disease." For, implied in the notion of "the addictive drinker" is the idea that once the disease has been contracted it can be arrested or cured only by outside intervention.

However, in the situation where the disease conception has been widened to cover other alcoholisms there are immediate implications for the alcoholic, the medical profession and, thus, for treatment. Let us assume that both the doctor and a nonaddictive drinker accept a wide-ranging definition of alcoholism along the lines of that set out by Jellinek, and also accept that alcoholism is a disease. Any attempt by the doctor to persuade the alcoholic to change his drinking habits is likely to fail since he will, by definition, believe himself incapable of doing so. In fact, if the doctor suggests any course of action for the alcoholic which is based upon expectations about the alcoholic's "will power" or the alcoholic having the right "motivation," then such a course of action is likely to be unsuccessful if the alcoholic defines out of court the notion of individual responsibility for his condition. Even in the event of the doctor and an addictive drinker sharing a restricted definition of alcoholism the problems for treatment are no less acute. As well as the patient being likely to define out of court the responsibility for his condition and drinking behavior, the expectation that will power is not sufficient to change drinking behavior is essentially implied in the very notion of "loss of control" or "inability to abstain" addictive drinking.

Siegler et al. (13) in their delineation of eight "models of alcoholism" stress the importance of the question of differing conceptualizations of individual responsibility for illness conditions. A belief in individual responsibility for a condition is one of the key distinctions between the "old" and the "new" medical models, while a major component of the Alcoholics Anonymous model as they present it is that it "lifts the burden of personal responsibility from the shoulders of the alcoholic by persuading him that alcoholism is bigger than he is." Nevertheless, many of those who attempt to treat addictive drinkers appear to demand that "the alcoholic" display the "correct motivation" prior to being allowed to embark on a treatment program, while a change in "motivation" is presented as an essential prerequisite to starting on an upward path to recovery, according to certain diagrammatic representations of alcohol addiction and recovery (e.g., 3).

Consequence 3: Different diseases might serve as models for different people's conception of the disease nature of alcoholism. Thus a disease which may appropriately serve as a model for addictive alcoholisms may be inappropriate as a model for a wider conception of the disease nature of alcoholism, and vice versa.

"It is highly important to realize that once the form of a language is established it can discover meanings for its speakers which are not simply traceable to the given quality of experience itself but must be explained to a large extent as the projection of potential meanings into the raw material of experience" (14).

Just as both laymen and professionals may differ in their beliefs about individual responsibility for any illness condition and thus about the nature of appropriate treatment, so they may also differ in their ideas about what other diseases alcoholism approximates and in what ways. Some people may operate with a quite inappropriate particular disease analogy and thus prejudice the likelihood or outcome of treatment or the possibility of recovery. For example, it would be legitimate but largely unhelpful to operate with an infectious-disease model of alcoholism. Expectations as to the course or outcome of alcoholism would clearly be inadequately informed by considering as analogous measles and alcoholism. Measles, as a model of alcoholism, is more appropriate than playing chess or milking a cow but perhaps not as appropriate as diabetes or cancer. The ideas which inform our behavior in any particular situation may be particular, specific and drawn from personal experience. It is quite reasonable therefore, in relation to such an ill-defined notion as alcoholism, for people to structure their experience in alcohol-related situations by reference to those diseases and disease features which they find manageable, understandable, and which have served them adequately in previous experiences with illness and disease. I shall not attempt to set out the implications of operating with every known disease as a model for alcoholism nor identify the range of particular disease models which implicitly or explicitly underlie the main body of medical and lay thought on alcoholism. Such challenging enterprises are quite beyond the scope of this paper. It is possible, however, to indicate, quite briefly, some of the incompatible notions about "alcoholism" and "the alcoholic" which could stem from the widespread use of specific disease models.

If, for instance, the measles model were adopted it would be reasonable to expect immunity from further attacks after one self-limiting bout of "alcoholism." If such a view were held, it would have definite implications for the alcoholic's readiness to consult initially, and also his readiness to give up drinking as part of any treatment or recovery program. For what would be the point of abstaining if immunity to the disease had been obtained? If, on the other hand, the alcoholic conceived of alcoholism as a disease like bronchitis, an acute attack, possibly culminating in a period of detoxication, might be thought to have weakened the tissues in some way and made the body more susceptible to subsequent acute attack. However, it is reasonable in the bronchitis case to assume that in the interval between acute attacks the person is free from the disease. This notion is strictly at variance with a basic tenet of, for example, the A.A. philosophy which encourages its members and the general public to believe that alcoholism is a disease which, once contracted, can never be cured. The most that can be hoped for is that the condition is arrested. As the subject of an article in a popular Sunday newspaper put it, "I'm still an alcoholic but it doesn't matter because I don't drink."[2] It appears that A.A. operates with the concept of alcoholism as a disease rather like cancer or diabetes which it is not in the individual's power to get rid of. Yet there is also the belief that if the individual acts in a particular way (takes a drink) then the disease will inevitably remanifest itself. While this view is largely consistent with the diabetes model it neither accords with the cancer conception of disease nor with the evidence concerning the many "alcoholics" who have returned to "normal drinking" (e.g., 15–17). The only way to square the latter incompatibility is to argue that such people were not *really* alcoholics. As in the case of any problem of definition or categorization such a tautology is hardly useful.

These few examples have been presented to emphasize the importance of teasing out and attempting to delineate the models of different peoples' disease conceptions of alcoholism. For only after this is done in any particular case are we likely to understand the way in which people behave toward the alcoholic and he behaves toward them. Only then shall we be in a position to consider offering "help" or "treatment."

Consequence 4: An ever-increasing range of conditions and behaviors may be conceptualized as related to stages in a disease process.

"Neither social reaction to deviance nor the process of becoming deviant can be studied apart from the economic, educational and class systems, institutions such as family and school, and leisure and patterns of power, conflict and diversity" (18).

If a member of the general public accepts that alcoholism, widely defined, is a disease then it will be perfectly reasonable for him to be on the lookout for signs or symptoms of early stages in an assumed disease process. Such a strategy is encouraged by charts like

---

[2] Quoted in VALENTINE, S. Horror of the teenage alcoholic. *News of the World*, London, 8 August 1971.

Jellinek's (4) and Glatt's (3) which foster the notion of alcoholism as a "developmental process" (3) marked by "phases and sequences of symptoms" (4). A member of the general public, thus bolstered in his strategy, is likely to assume that one stage in the "developmental process" follows inevitably after another. This assumption is reasonable since it is consistent with the way in which many people conceptualize disease processes; for instance, "once you've got it, it's got to run its course." Consequently, if one stage is believed to follow another and if, for example, "heavy habitual social drinking" is felt to be a symptom of one stage of the disease process (as it might be if a wide-ranging definition of alcoholism is accepted) then it is reasonable for the drinker to believe that there is no way of preventing his progression through the subsequent stages of the process until "rock bottom" is reached. This again is reasonable since "it has to get worse before it gets better" is a familiar and appropriate notion when applied to certain other diseases. It is hardly surprising, therefore, that the heavy social drinker should continue to drink if, first, he has been led to believe that an alcoholic cannot stop because he is addicted and, second, he believes that he is an alcoholic and has a disease in which stages inevitably follow one another until rock bottom is reached. There is no reason to suppose that such a self-fulfilling prophecy mechanism should not operate with respect to alcoholism in the same way as it has been so clearly demonstrated to operate in relation to streaming and scholastic attainment in the field of education (19).

It may certainly be the case that by operating with, and encouraging the general public to accept, the disease concept of alcoholism the medical profession and A.A. vitally aid the "rock bottom" alcoholic's progress toward an "interesting, happy, useful way of life" (3). On the other hand if an alcoholic who accepts the disease concept of alcoholism, and the concomitant need for total abstinence, actually has a drink, it would be perfectly reasonable for him to continue drinking—first, because it would follow that he would believe himself to be, by definition, "lost" and unable to stop drinking even if he wanted to, and second, because believing himself to be inevitably lost would be reason enough for him to drink himself to oblivion as quickly as possible. Unfortunately, since ideas cannot be locked away like drugs in a cupboard, the disease concept of alcoholism cannot be kept in a bottle until it is deemed fit to dispense it as a vital therapeutic tool.[3]

---

[3] Significantly, on Glatt's chart "learns alcoholism is a disease" comes after the "rock bottom" stage (3).

*Consequence 5: The medical profession will be considered to have compe-
tence in an ever-widening sphere of life.*

"The basic dilemma is that it is not within human capacity to
complete the task which medical and social services impose upon
themselves, but neither are we free to desist" (20).

Once the disease concept of alcoholism is extended to include
the behavior concomitant with the addiction or with the physical
damage caused by alcohol consumption then there will be an inevitable extension of medical competence into an ever-widening
sphere of life. This will take place under the heading of "preventive
medicine." It is implicit in such a phrase that the medical profession
will treat not only disease entities but behavior considered to be
part of a causal chain leading to the development of disease entities.
Once this position is accepted by the general population then the
medical profession is obliged to advise about, or intervene in relation to, any behavior which falls into such a category. In the case of
alcoholism, the medical profession would consider themselves, and
be considered by the general public, as the relevant authority to decide upon, for example, licensing laws or alcohol price policy if it
was shown that alcohol price increases and shorter licensing hours
were associated with a drop in alcohol consumption. The idea that a
time might come when a public health official would decide upon
the licensing hours in a particular area should not be thought of as
impossible or even extremely unlikely. For the idea that anything
which is considered to affect in some way the working of the body
or mind is "a medical problem" and thus within the jurisdiction of
the medical profession is happily applied in other spheres. Medicine
is readily seen to be a legitimate arbiter in cases of clashes of values
or political principle; witness the abortion controversy or the history of the fluoridation campaigns in the United States.[4]

Medical authorities do not actually have to make decisions in the
political or educational arena, or even lend their weight to one side
or the other, for decisions to be taken in their name. For there is
nothing like the phrase "for health reasons" for enhancing any proposal. The response to the "clacker" craze which swept Britain in
1971 was a fine example of the use of such a maneuver. In the au-
tumn of that year thousands of children plagued their parents and
schoolteachers with the awful row produced by knocking two small
plastic balls together at great speed. The problem which faced

[4] ZOLA, I. K. Medicine as an institution of social control. Presented at the British
Sociological Association Medical Sociology Conference, 1971.

school authorities was how to justify the banning of these noisy and irritating toys from school premises. There was, of course, no reasonable justification. Until, that is, someone reported that clackers had broken wristbones in a number of children. Overnight the "irritating toys" turned into "harmful and dangerous objects" and were banned on "health grounds" from schools in several areas. That other much more "harmful and dangerous" pastimes such as interschool football matches should be banned as well was not proposed.

I am not suggesting that the medical profession or the many other helping agencies concerned with alcohol-related problems are coolly calculating empire builders plotting to take control over vast areas of late 20th-century life. What is being maintained is that the general public and legislators are placing these agencies, and the medical profession in particular, in a position in which they are expected to exercise their discretionary powers and perform decision-making functions beyond their legitimate and willingly accepted brief.

CONCLUSION

"No area of medicine is so bedevilled by semantic confusion as is the field of alcoholism" (21).

Jellinek was very clear about what he considered to be the disease nature of alcoholism. He restricted the notion of disease to the loss-of-control and inability-to-abstain aspects of excessive drinking because they were addictions in the pharmacological sense. His definition of the broader concept of alcoholism was much more wide-ranging as time went on. In *The Disease Concept of Alcoholism* (5) it became "any use of alcoholic beverage that causes any damage to the individual or society." In addition, more and more people were coming to accept the view that "alcoholism *is* a disease." Since he was certainly an influential authority on alcohol-related problems Jellinek must be held partly responsible for a much more inclusive disease conception of alcoholism being held by the general public than he held himself. Certain consequences have been shown to follow from accepting a definition of alcoholism such as Jellinek's and from also accepting that alcoholism is a disease. These consequences are not presented as good or bad, for such questions are beyond the scope of this paper, but rather as social facts of current life.

If we are to understand and predict the nature of drinking behavior and subsequently provide effective treatment for those considered to need such help, this can only be done if we take into account the implications of people's differing conceptions of what counts as "alcoholism" and what counts as "disease." For typification—perceiving the world and structuring it by means of categorical types—is the essence of social communication and interaction. Thus, the aim of this paper has been, first, to suggest that we have, to a certain extent, "lost control" over the disease concept of alcoholism and, second, to indicate some of the implications of this "addiction" for the alcoholic, for the medical profession and for the wider society.

REFERENCES

1. JELLINEK, E. M. The world and its bottle. Wld Hlth 10 (No. 4): 4–6, 1957.
2. EDWARDS, G. The status of alcoholism as a disease. Pp. 140–161. In: PHILLIPSON, R. V., ed. Modern trends in drug dependence and alcoholism. New York; Appelton–Century–Crofts; 1970.
3. GLATT, M. M. The alcoholic and the help he needs. Pts. I and II. Royston, England; Priory; 1970.
4. JELLINEK, E. M. Phases of alcohol addiction. Q. J. Stud. Alcohol 13: 673–684, 1952.
5. JELLINEK, E. M. The disease concept of alcoholism. Highland Park, N.J.; Hillhouse Press; 1960.
6. SEELEY, J. R. Alcoholism is a disease; implications for social policy. Pp. 585–593. In: PITTMAN, D. J. and SNYDER, C. R., eds. Society, culture, and drinking patterns. New York; Wiley; 1962.
7. WILLIAMS, [E.] L. Alcoholism explained. Rev. ed. London; Evans Bros.; 1967.
8. WEBER, M. The theory of social and economic organisation. London; Oxford University Press; 1964.
9. BLANE, H. T., OVERTON, W. F., JR. and CHAFETZ, M. E. Social factors in the diagnosis of alcoholism. I. Characteristics of the patient. Q. J. Stud. Alcohol 24: 640–663, 1963.
10. PATTISON, E. M. A critique of alcoholism treatment concepts; with special reference to abstinence. Q. J. Stud. Alcohol 27: 49–71, 1966.
11. PARSONS, T. The social system. Chicago; Free Press; 1951.
12. ROBINSON, D. The process of becoming ill. London; Routledge & Kegan Paul; 1971.
13. SIEGLER, M., OSMOND, H. and NEWELL, S. Models of alcoholism. Q. J. Stud. Alcohol 29: 571–591, 1968.
14. SAPIR, E. Selected writings of Edward Sapir in language, culture and personality. Berkeley; University of California Press; 1949.
15. DAVIES, D. L. Normal drinking in recovered alcohol addicts. Q. J. Stud. Alcohol 23: 94–104, 1962.
16. KENDELL, R. E. Normal drinking by former alcohol addicts. Q. J. Stud. Alcohol 26: 247–257, 1965.
17. PATTISON, E. M., HEADLEY, E. B., GLESER, G. C. and GOTTSCHALK, L. A.

Abstinence and normal drinking; an assessment of changes in drinking patterns in alcoholics after treatment. Q. J. Stud. Alcohol 29: 610–633, 1968.

18. COHEN, S. Introduction. In: COHEN, S., ed. Images of deviance. Baltimore, Md.; Penguin; 1971.

19. DOUGLAS, W. J. B. The home and the school. London; MacGibbon & Kee; 1964.

20. KAHN, J. H. Beyond the determinancy principle. Appl. Soc. Stud. 1: 73–80, 1969.

21. DAVIES, D. L. The concept of alcoholism. Pp. 9–19. In: SCOTT, R. B. and WALKER, R. M., eds. The medical annual; a yearbook of treatment and practitioners' text. Bristol; Wright; 1969.

8

Bad Habits Are Not Diseases

A Refutation of the Claim That Alcoholism is a Disease[1]

Thomas S. Szasz, M.D.

MORRIS E. CHAFETZ, M.D., then director of the National Institute on Alcohol Abuse and Alcoholism, announced the promulgation of a "Bill of Rights for Alcoholic People," drafted for them by the Commissioners on Uniform State Laws at their annual meeting in August 1971. This bill, Dr. Chafetz explained, removes "the crime of public intoxication and the illness of alcoholism from the criminal codes and places them in the public health area where they rightfully belong." Since some people who drink do not consider themselves alcoholics and hence decline medical care, Dr. Chafetz added that the Uniform Alcoholism and Intoxication Treatment Act adopted by the Commission "guarantees, in those few instances where civil commitment is necessary, a right to treatment 'which is likely to be beneficial' " (1).

A subsequent editorial (2) warmly endorsed the creation of the institute headed by Dr. Chafetz, and concluded with this ringing exhortation:

"It is to be hoped that through government incentives, the support of medical students throughout the country, and the efforts of local medical societies together with the American Medical Association and other professional organizations, the medical schools will become much more aware of the need to equip tomorrow's physicians with the ability and imagination to cope with two of the most pressing problems of medical care facing the nation—alcoholism and drug dependence."

[1] Reprinted by permission from *Lancet*, Vol. 2, pp. 83–84, 1972. Copyright by The Lancet, 7 Adam Street, London, WC2N 6AD, England.

I submit that the foregoing views consist of an approximately equal mixture of mendacity and nonsense. As a teacher in a medical school, I believe it is my duty to teach facts and theories as I see them, and not as the state, the American Medical Association, Alcoholics Anonymous, the Woman's Christian Temperance Union, the liquor industry, or any other group of special interests see them. In my judgment, the view that alcoholism is a disease is false; and the programs sponsored by the state and supported by tax moneys to "cure" it are immoral and inconsistent with our political commitment to individual freedom and responsibility (3).

It is impossible, of course, to discuss what is and is not illness, without agreement on how we shall use the word "illness." First, then, we must distinguish—as do both physicians and patients, and as our language does—between bodily and mental illness.

When a person asserts that he is ill, he usually means two things: first, that he suffers, or that he believes he suffers, from an abnormality or malfunctioning of his body; and second, that he wants, or is at least willing to accept, medical help for it. Should the first of these conditions be absent, we would not consider the person to be physically ill; should the second be absent we would not consider him to be a medical patient. This is because the practice of modern Western medicine rests on the scientific premise that the physician's task is to diagnose and treat disorders of the human body; and on the moral premise that he can carry out these services only with the consent of his patient. Strictly speaking, then, disease or illness can affect only the body.

Accordingly, there can be no such thing as mental illness. The term "mental illness" is a metaphor. Bodily illness stands in the same relation to mental illness as a defective television set stands to a bad television program. Of course, the word "sick" is often used metaphorically. We call jokes "sick," economies "sick," sometimes even the whole world "sick"; but only when we call minds "sick" do we systematically mistake and strategically misinterpret metaphor for fact—and send for the doctor to "cure" the "illness"! It is as if a television viewer were to send for a TV repairman because he dislikes the program he sees on the screen.

With the foregoing definitions in mind, I offer the following observations about alcoholism and its relation to the medical profession.

(1) Drinking to excess may cause illness, but in itself is not a disease—in the ordinary sense of the word "disease." Excessive drinking is a habit. Ac-

cording to the person's values, he may consider it a good or a bad habit. If we choose to call bad habits "diseases," there is no limit to what we may define as "disease"—and "treat" involuntarily. The misuse of alcohol—whatever the reason for it—is no more an illness than is the misuse of any other product of human invention, from language to nuclear energy.

(2) Every individual, the alcoholic included, is capable of injuring or killing himself. This potentiality is a fundamental expression of man's freedom of action. Such conduct may be regarded as immoral or sinful or undisciplined, and penalized by means of informal sanctions. But it should not, in a free society, be regarded as either a crime or a disease, warranting the use of the police powers of the State for its control or suppression.

(3) Every individual, the alcoholic included, is also capable of injuring or killing others—both while under the influence of alcohol and while not under its influence. This potentiality, too, is a fundamental expression of man's freedom. Such conduct not only justifies self-defense by those attacked, but also often requires the formalized protection of society from the harmful individual by means of criminal laws and sanctions. In other words, the alcoholic should be left free to injure himself; those who wish to help him should be left free to offer their services to him, but should not be allowed to use force or fraud in their efforts to "help"; at the same time, the alcoholic should not be left free to injure others; nor should his alcoholism be accepted as an excuse for any criminal act he may have committed.

(4) It is one thing to maintain that a person is not responsible for being an alcoholic; it is quite another to maintain that he is not responsible for the interpersonal, occupational, economic and legal consequences of his actions. The former proposition implies only an unwillingness to punish a person for excessive drinking; the latter implies either giving the alcoholic an excuse for injuring others, or justifying legislation for controlling his alcoholism rather than his illegal behavior.

(5) If we regard alcoholism as a bona-fide disease—"like any other" —then we ought to let the alcoholic accept or reject treatment for it. Venereal diseases are now said to be of epidemic proportions. They are, moreover, genuine, bodily diseases for which we now possess efficacious and safe methods of treatment—yet such treatment is not compulsory. Advocating the compulsory "treatment" of alcoholics (and other "addicts") through what is euphemistically called "civil commitment," and calling such involuntary interventions a "Bill of Rights for Alcoholic People," are in my opinion, the manifestations of a state of affairs in American medicine and government far more alarming than the "diseases" against which such "cures" and their sordid justifications are invoked (4).

By a curious coincidence, in one of his most important short pieces, George Orwell compared the abuse of language with the abuse of alcohol. "A man may take to drink," he wrote, "because he feels himself to be a failure, and then fail all the more completely because he drinks. It is rather the same thing that is happening to the English language. It becomes ugly and inaccurate because our thoughts are foolish, but the slovenliness of our language makes it easier for us to have foolish thoughts" (5, *p. 355*).

When Dr. Chafetz asserts that alcoholism is an illness—without telling us what is "alcoholism" and what is "illness"; that "It is the task of the practicing physician to take the initiative in acting to provide adequate medical and follow-up care for alcoholic persons . . ." (1), when in fact his task is to offer care only to those persons who want it; when he calls giving physicians the power to imprison alcoholics a "Bill of Rights" for the victims; and when the American Medical Association uncritically and unqualifiedly endorses such humbug—we then stand before the very phenomenon Orwell described.

But, of course, Orwell did more than describe; he warned that ". . . if thought corrupts language, language can also corrupt thought" (5, *p. 364*). And he concluded that political language—and to this we may here add medical language—"is designed to make lies sound truthful and murder respectable, and to give an appearance of solidity to pure wind" (5, *p. 366*).

As an academician and a teacher, I believe our duty now is to stand up against the Lysenkoism that is sweeping the country. Whether we may want to dub it "Jaffeism," or "Chafetzism," or the "Crusade Against Alcoholism and Addiction," or by some other catchy phrase hardly matters; what matters is that as physicians and teachers we resist politically motivated and mandated redefinitions of (bad) habits as diseases; that we condemn and eschew involuntary medical and psychiatric interventions; and that, instead of joining and supporting the "holy war" on alcoholism and drug abuse, we actively repudiate this contemporary version of "popular delusion and crowd madness" (6).

In the past half-century, the medical sciences have advanced as never before in history; yet, morally, the medical profession has fallen upon bad times. Everywhere, it has allowed itself to be enslaved by the state; at the same time, it has encroached on the liberties of the patients, making them, in turn, the slaves of the doctors. But, as Montaigne, quoting Apollonius, observed: "It is for slaves to lie, and for free men to speak the truth" (7, *p. 208*). Where are the free men of medicine?

REFERENCES

1. CHAFETZ, M. E. A bill of rights for alcoholic people. J. Am. Med. Ass. **219:** 1471, 1972.
2. Education about drug abuse in medical schools. [Editorial.] J. Am. Med. Ass. **219:** 1757, 1972.
3. SZASZ, T. S. Alcoholism; a socio-ethical perspective. West. Med. 7: 15–21, 1966.
4. SZASZ, T. S. The ethics of addiction. Harper's Magazine, pp. 74–79, April 1972.
5. ORWELL, G. Politics and the English language. In: The Orwell reader, fiction, essays and reportage. New York; Harcourt, Brace; 1956.
6. MACKAY, C. Extraordinary popular delusions and the madness of crowds. New York; Noonday; 1962. [Orig. 1841.]
7. MONTAIGNE, M. E. DE. Essays. (COHEN, J. M., transl.) Baltimore, Md.; Penguin; 1967. [Orig. 1580.]

9

Alcoholism

Illness or Problem in Interaction?[1]

Donald G. Finlay, Ph.D.

TRADITIONALLY, the premise that alcoholism is an illness has guided helping professionals in their efforts to treat it (1). Several medical groups have officially sanctioned this view. The American Psychiatric Association, for example, acknowledges alcoholism as a mental disorder, defining alcoholics as persons ". . . whose alcohol intake is great enough to damage their physical health, or their personal and social functioning, or when it has become a prerequisite to normal functioning" (2, *p. 45*). Within this concept, the person who is labeled "alcoholic" becomes the identified patient. Work with significant others such as the spouse or other family members, if it is undertaken at all, becomes an adjunct to treatment directed at the alcoholic himself. Further, treatment goals usually are stated in individual terms, as the attainment of abstinence or relatively productive sobriety.

A more recent concept appearing in the literature on alcoholism regards excessive drinking from the viewpoint of communications, interactions and transactions within the social system. Within this general framework, the problem-for-solution is defined in interactional terms, and the target for change becomes not simply the alcoholic but the interactional system in which he is involved.

Excessive drinking or drunkenness is recognized as one facet of a life-style in which the person avoids responsibility on a global scale. This style is actively reinforced by the interactional style of

[1] Copyright 1974, National Association of Social Workers, Inc. Reprinted with permission from *Social Work*, Vol. 19, No. 4 (July 1974), pp. 398–405.

others—that is, the style is allowed to become stronger and more habitual because significant others do not constantly and effectively challenge or disrupt the alcoholic's modus vivendi (3, 4).

Such a concept does not negate the position of the medical model that excessive drinking can be a massive, rigid and chronic defense against anxiety. Neither does it question why most persons classified as alcoholics are unable to achieve effective control over their drinking, that is, cannot become social drinkers. The concept, however, indicates that it is important to modify a broader spectrum of individual functioning than the drug-oriented behavior. Moreover, applying a systems interpretation framework, the unit for both assessment and intervention becomes the alcoholic and significant others, not just the alcoholic himself.

This article explores empirical evidence that has emerged during the past decade with respect to treatment results of helping professionals with varying theoretical orientations to the problem of alcoholism. Basically, it considers the two theoretical perspectives already mentioned: (1) Alcoholism is a disease. (2) Alcoholism is an interactional problem—that is, excessive drinking is one manifestation of a generally problematic life-style shared and reinforced by significant others. The relative merits of these theoretical conceptions are identified by examining the treatment results of practitioners with these different orientations.

Five studies are reported in this article. Each involves some delineation of the theoretical premises about alcoholism that governed treatment efforts. In each, evidence is drawn from a sufficiently large sample to make potentially valid generalizations. Since there is considerable variation in the results obtained and since in one of the studies some control was achieved over such variables as worker experience and professional competence, some tentative conclusions can be advanced as to how a practitioner's theoretical stance vis à vis alcoholism relates to various measures of outcome. For the most part, the alcoholics in these studies were men, but effective treatment patterns apply to both sexes.

The first study basically sets the parameters within which the other studies can be evaluated. It identifies the merits of using a social systems approach to the treatment of alcoholism, regardless of theoretical orientation, as opposed to working exclusively with the alcoholic. The other four studies use a common social systems framework for assessment and intervention—the marital pair. They explore the efficacy of work with the alcoholic and his spouse when the counselor defines the problem-for-solution in one of the following two ways:

(1) Alcoholism is an illness; therefore the alcoholic is sick, and the spouse's behavior can be accounted for as that of a victim experiencing the stress of living with a sick husband.

(2) The current problem of alcoholism—regardless of whether it is the cause or result of a problematic relationship between husband and wife—is a mutual interactional one, with one of the marital pair exhibiting excessive drinking as the way of dealing with life while the other is displaying her own behavioral repertoire, which is problematic in its own right. That is, the wife may reinforce her husband's drinking and his avoidance of consequences by her own undue acceptance of consequences and her failure to confront him and demand that he change his habits.

Thus the studies compare the merits of a "one-up–one-down" view of interpersonal malfunctioning and an "everybody-in-the-same-boat-but-with-different-oars" perspective and consider their relative usefulness as designs for action. Further, these studies also provide some clues as to the effectiveness of working primarily with one member of the marital pair versus working with the marital pair itself as the unit of treatment—an implicit versus explicit interactional focus.

SOCIAL SYSTEMS APPROACH

Gerard and Saenger (5) report on a 5-year research study sponsored by the North American Association of Alcoholism Programs from February 1967 to June 1972. The study was carried out at 8 state-sponsored outpatient clinics in the eastern United States. It involved a sample of approximately 800 alcoholics whose cases were followed up 1 year after initial contact at the clinic. These patients were examined at the time of intake and follow-up, and improvement was determined by an over-all adjustment score designed to take into consideration a patient's adjustment in each of the following areas: drinking, health, social stability, social and family relationships and work adjustment. Gerard and Saenger state that ". . . although there were patients who had improved with respect to only one or another aspect of their functioning and adjustment, by and large, improvement in the total life situation tended to be interrelated with improvement in drinking" (5, *p. 129*).

Gerard and Saenger cite the following findings, which are relevant to the present discussion: First, "the involvement of collaterals (spouse or other relatives) in the evaluation of the patient enhanced his continuing attendance at the clinic." Second, for such patients, "there was a progressive increase in the proportion of improved patients as contacts with the clinic increased" (5, *pp. 138, 190*).

Thus some empirical evidence exists indicating that involvement of a spouse or other family members in an alcoholic's treatment is beneficial. Other studies corroborate this conclusion (6). In short, it would appear that an approach involving at least one facet of an alcoholic's social system in the undertaking of treatment is more effective than efforts directed solely toward the alcoholic. Even if the alcoholic remains the identified patient (an illness model) and others simply are regarded as collaterals, there is value in efforts that reach out to people besides the alcoholic.

All studies that follow embrace the notion of a social systems approach, if a narrowly defined one. It is not within the purview of this article to consider the utility of a more expanded arena for assessment and intervention. Rather, of interest are the varying ways in which the marital unit is viewed, the treatment approaches generated and the results achieved.

WORKERS' ORIENTATION

Cohen and Krause (7) report on a 4-year research and demonstration project conducted at the Family Service of the Cincinnati Area, 1962–1966. The project aimed to explore, develop and define treatment regimens that would effectively *(1)* keep the wives of alcoholics in treatment, *(2)* promote treatment of alcoholic husbands and *(3)* slow down or reverse the family's disintegration (7, *p. 4*). The project primarily tried to strengthen family functioning by identifying successful approaches for working with wives of alcoholics. A secondary aim was to engage and hold the alcoholic himself in treatment. Most of the work conducted was with the alcoholic's spouse.

Over a 17-month period, the agency assigned to the project 298 cases in which the husband's drinking was an identifiable problem. On an alternating basis after an intake interview, 50% of the cases were assigned to an experimental group and 50% to 2 types of control groups, which differed only in the workers' knowledge about whether their work was being scrutinized. However, this distinction became irrelevant since the groups were later combined for the major analysis of data. Therefore, it is possible to compare theoretical orientations of 2 groups of workers made up of practitioners matched in educational level, experience and competence.

The treatment approach of the experimental group was based on the following concepts: *(1)* Alcoholism is a disease. *(2)* Abstinence is a desired treatment goal. *(3)* Alcoholism constitutes a crisis for a man and his family. *(4)* The spouse's behavior with respect to her alcoholic mate is not neurotic in origin but is essentially a reaction of stress to the crisis of alcoholism. That is, her behavior is "an outgrowth of her efforts to handle the continuing stress created for all members of the family" (7, *p. 29*). Thus the concept of alcoholism as an illness and the view that the wife is a victim of the stresses of living with a diseased husband oriented the thinking and the activity of the experimental group workers.

Cohen and Krause describe the orientation of the control group workers as traditional. Workers were given no specific direction regarding the project's theoretical rationale or its treatment approach. Rather, they were expected to handle cases involving alcoholics in the agency's customary way, which Cohen and Krause cite simply as one in which alcoholism is viewed "as a symptom of other problems of the alcoholic and the members of his family" (7, *p. 29*). The distinguishing feature of this conceptualization is that the problem-for-solution appears to be more interactionally focused than in the usual traditional approach. Workers have a stronger sense that the two contributing participants in the marital and family systems have a mutually shared problem. Thus two otherwise comparable groups of workers express two theoretical orientations. Both primarily used individual interviews, and most work was with the alcoholic's spouse.

How did the two groups compare with respect to treatment results? According to the wives' reports to research interviewers at the end of treatment, workers with differing theoretical orientations made some indirect but comparable impact on the drinking pattern of the husbands. The study did not reveal the percentage of situations in which the wives reported that their husband's drinking pattern was modified and the indirect symptoms of drinking (poor appetite, work absences, sleeplessness, neglect of person) were reduced.

Cohen and Krause did indicate that illness-oriented workers evaluated reduction in drinking as occurring more frequently than did the interactionally focused workers (48% and 33%, respectively). However, they note that the wives themselves reported differences that were in the same direction but not statistically significant. Since Cohen and Krause report considerable pressure for success on the part of the experimental group workers, some bias may well have been introduced in the statements of the illness-oriented workers. This perhaps explains why the percentage of situations in which there was reduction of drinking in this group more closely approximated the percentage noted by the interactional workers.

In both groups, de facto separation of alcoholic husband and spouse existed in 30% of the cases at the end of treatment. Therefore, regardless of theoretical orientation, marital separation is a distinct possibility, at least when treatment efforts primarily take place with one member of the marital pair—the alcoholic's spouse.

When the marriage remained intact, the attainments of workers with an interactional focus emerged as superior. According to the evaluations at the end of treatment, the wives counseled by the more interactionally focused workers reported that changes in their husbands' drinking patterns brought about comparatively more sexual satisfaction in marriage, more satisfaction with their alcoholic spouse as a husband and father, and fewer employment problems. In contrast, the wives counseled by the illness-oriented workers reported only one area as being more favorable: the degree that the husband's drinking affected the family. The husbands who were interviewed favored the interactionally focused workers. They reported comparatively happier marriages, fewer problems with their children, better parental adjustment, better physical health and more positive feelings about the treatment experience.

Evaluations conducted at least 6 months after the treatment ended again favored the interactionally oriented workers. The wives reported that their husbands voluntarily obtained outside help for their drinking with significantly greater frequency and that they themselves experienced a significantly greater degree of sexual satisfaction. Hence workers buttressed by the theoretical rationale of a more interactional model—as opposed to an illness model—seem to have won a clear victory.

Cohen and Krause conclude that the work of the experimental group was "not more effective in the long run and on the average" than casework treatment given by the control group workers (7, p. 141). In his analysis of the findings, this author challenges such a conclusion. When analysis is restricted to clients' reports (as opposed to workers' subjective evaluations), the interactionally oriented group of workers emerges as superior.

UNIT OF TREATMENT

Since an interactional focus seems to have merit even when work is restricted primarily to one member of the marital pair—the alcoholic's spouse—the available literature was reviewed for studies in which an interactional concept of the problem-for-solution was translated into an explicit focus on the marital pair or the family as the unit of treatment (8). These were the questions of interest: What results emanate from ongoing work with the marital pair or the family as the unit of treatment? How do these results compare with those obtained by workers who have an interactional conception but are oriented to individual treatment?

Despite the voluminous literature in the field of alcoholism about marital and family dynamics, relatively few studies have been reported about treatment approaches that specifically address marital and family interaction as the unit of treatment. The predominant theoretical model, as has been the case in the fields of counseling and psychotherapy in general, is a medical one. Within such a concept one family member is labeled sick and becomes the identified patient. Work with significant others thus becomes an adjunct of treatment efforts with the named deviant. Given such a theoretical orientation, it undoubtedly is difficult to conduct ongoing treatment sessions with the marital pair or with the family as a unit. By definition, one member indeed is one-down while others are one-up. A therapist then either is entangled in conducting treatment of one person in the presence of one or more family members (thereby enforcing the one-down and one-up positions) or is straining the model's theoretical rationale to the breaking point by proclaiming that one is sick but both or all need help. As a consequence, it is not surprising that therapists in the field of alcoholism are generally reluctant to hold joint interviews and that, if held, they are primarily to assess rather than treat (7, *pp. 76–77*; 9, *p. 103*). Tulley (10), for example, although favoring individual treatment, indicates the value of joint interviews as a diagnostic tool in the early stages of casework. She suggests that they yield insight into the dynamics of the family relationships more quickly and more adequately—that is, they reveal to the worker who does what to whom (10, *p. 34*).

Reports of work with families as the unit of treatment are practically nonexistent. To my knowledge, only Esser (11) in the Netherlands and Meeks and Kelly (12) in Canada have done research on family therapy with alcoholics. While their samples are too small to yield anything but cautious conclusions, they do suggest that such therapy holds promise. Family therapy was restricted to the marital pair.

This author did not find any other reports of work done with the marital pair alone as the ongoing unit of treatment. Most counseling on alcoholism with an explicit interactional focus has been undertaken with groups of married couples in which one partner is alcoholic. The evidence on effectiveness suggests that the group couple is a preferred modality when compared with individual treatment that has an implicit interactional orientation. The answer to the question of whether treatment for group couples would be more effective than work with the marital pair as the unit of treatment currently remains unknown. The greater success of treating couples in groups may be because of the modality of treatment or because an interactional orientation is made explicit for all concerned. In any event, the approach has been sufficiently effective to merit reporting.

Burton and Kaplan (13), at the Marriage Council of Philadelphia, describe a project extending over a 6-year period (1959–1964) during which 47 couples received group counseling plus 1 or more initial individual sessions. Groups met weekly for 1½ hours and averaged 30 sessions per group. It was assumed that counseling would alleviate the marital problems of alcoholics and their nonalcoholic spouses and that this would have an effect on drinking behavior. Therapy specifically concentrated on the interaction between husband and wife rather than on "intrapsychic conflicts." The drinking problem was considered only in the context of the overt and covert roles it played in the interactional conflict.

Follow-up interviews conducted from 9 to 77 months after the final counseling session provided information on 39 of the 47 couples (83%) in the population of the study. At follow-up, 75% of the couples indicated they had fewer problems in their marriage. With respect to drinking, 55.6% of the couples reported that the alcoholic spouse's drinking had lessened, or his abstinence had been maintained—a higher percentage than that reported by either group of workers in the Cohen and Krause study (7, p. 138). Only 12.5% noted more marital difficulties, and only 16.7% said that drinking had increased. Burton and Kaplan conclude that improved marital relationships are associated with improved drinking behavior. They say counseling that focuses on the family pathology of alcoholics is therapeutic "not only with respect to the family and marriage problems, but with respect as well to the drinking problem" (7, p. 169). Thus the merits of a treatment approach that has an explicit interactional focus seem demonstrated.

In another study, Burton and Kaplan (14) contrasted results from group counseling with results from 131 couples who had individual marital counseling (primarily via one-to-one sessions) between 1953 and 1959. The 2 samples were roughly similar with respect to socioeconomic characteristics; those counseled in groups were about the same age but better educated than those counseled individually. Burton and Kaplan obtained data through follow-up interviews on 32% of those counseled individually and pointed out the following results: "The responses are revealing. Of the 149 responses from clients who had received individual counseling, 83 (57%) affirmed a positive experience for the respondent and/or spouse. For the group-counseled clients, on the other hand, 61 (76%) of the responses were affirmative" (14, *p.* 77). These two researchers suggest that for the limited comparison the data permit, group counseling is more successful than individual counseling. They argue convincingly that the group experience provides the alcoholic and his spouse an opportunity for training in communication—an opportunity to see how they respond characteristically to each other in self-defeating ways and to acquire more effective approaches for meeting their own needs, as well as those of the spouse.

ADDITIONAL STUDY

Gallant et al. (15) offer further evidence of the value of a group experience for alcoholics and their spouses. They cite a success rate of 45 to 56% in the treatment of 118 married couples at the New Orleans Alcoholism Clinic. The sample of their study included every discharged patient from the clinic's inpatient unit who was returning home to live with his spouse, in addition to an unstated number of outpatients and their spouses. The couples were seen in four marital groups from September 1967 to May 1969. Four to 7 couples participated in each group at any given time, and the groups met for a 2-hour session every 2 weeks. The goals of the treatment program were these: *(1)* penetration of the patient's severe denial mechanism in association with the goal of abstinence; *(2)* helping the couple to develop a satisfactory learning experience. "The primary goal is really to start the couple working on their marriage problems, but sobriety is required for this goal" (15, *p.* 42).

Follow-up interviews were conducted with the couples 2 to 20 months from the date they were admitted to the clinic. The couples were labeled a "success" if the alcoholic was completely abstinent and relating "reasonably well" to his wife or if he was experiencing "productive relative sobriety"—that is, if he was enjoying his family and his own personal existence and had not experienced more than two brief drinking episodes (15, *p. 42*). If the patient had more than 2 brief drinking episodes during the period prior to follow-up, he was rated a "failure." Patients were rated in the "unknown" category either if they dropped out of treatment and follow-up information could not be obtained or if the couple attended only one session and then dropped out.

Of the 118 couples, 53 were rated definite successes, 41 were failures and 24 were in the unknown category. Gallant et al. point out that when the category of unknowns is eliminated, the success rate is 56%. If all the unknowns are relegated to the failure group (even though at least 2 who dropped out after one group session were known to be doing well a year later), the success rate is 15%—"still a worthwhile result in the treatment of alcoholism" (15, *p. 42*). Further, it should be noted that only 3 of the couples were separated at the time of evaluation. This contrasts dramatically with the 30% figure reported by Cohen and Krause (7, *p. 137*).

Gallant et al. cite several possible reasons for the successful treatment of groups of marital couples. These are among the reasons: *(1)* the spouse of the patient helps to keep "pulling" the patient back to treatment; *(2)* the therapist obtains a more realistic picture of the marital interaction, and both he and the group can refuse to accept the distortions of both husband and wife; *(3)* with both partners present, being in the group eliminates minor bickering, and the important problems of the couple are directly faced.

Gallant et al. conclude that treatment of couples, whether counseling them as a marital pair or in a group, has distinct advantages over individual treatment. On the basis of their experience, these researchers specifically argue against separate interviews (and certainly against separate therapists) for an alcoholic husband and his wife. They state that separate treatment sessions "can magnify the distortions and misunderstandings between the partners, thus possibly bringing out a separation or divorce because of the unrealistic treatment structure" (15, *p. 43*).

SUMMARY

In exploring various approaches to treating alcoholism, the author has suggested that a social systems interventive model is more effective than an individualistic model and that an interactional conception of alcoholism offers a better design for action than an illness orientation. According to the results reported in the studies reviewed, using the marital pair as the unit of treatment, at least using the approach of treating couples in groups, is more profitable than working with only one of the pair. Thus an explicit interactional focus seems to have the greatest merit. And one study indicated that what practitioners think does make a difference in the results of treatment.

Although the illness model today governs most treatment efforts in the field of alcoholism, empirical evidence—in this author's view—effectively challenges the usefulness of the model as a design for action. Reinterpreting excessive drinking as one manifestation of an interactional style shows promise.

REFERENCES

1. JELLINEK, E. M. The disease concept of alcoholism. Highland Park, N.J.; Hillhouse Press; 1960.
2. COMMITTEE ON NOMENCLATURE AND STATISTICS. AMERICAN PSYCHIATRIC ASSOCIATION. Diagnostic and statistical manual of mental disorders. 2d ed. Washington, D.C.; 1968.
3. GORAD, S. L., McCOURT, W. F. and COBB, J. C. A communications approach to alcoholism. Q. J. Stud. Alcohol 32: 651–668, 1971.
4. GORAD, S. L. Communicational styles and interaction of alcoholics and their wives. Fam. Process, Balt. 10: 475–489, 1971.
5. GERARD, D. L. and SAENGER, G. Outpatient treatment of alcoholism; a study of outcome and its determinants. (Brookside Monogr., No. 4.) Toronto; University of Toronto Press; 1966.
6. SMITH, C. G. Alcoholics; their treatment and their wives. Br. J. Psychiat. 115: 1039–1042, 1969.
7. COHEN, P. C. and KRAUSE, M. S., eds. Casework with wives of alcoholics. New York; Family Service Association of America; 1971.
8. INFORMATION PLANNING ASSOCIATES, INC. Alcoholism treatment and rehabilitation; selected abstracts. Prepared for the National Institute on Alcohol Abuse and Alcoholism and the National Institute of Mental Health. (DHEW Publ. No. HSM-72-9136.) Washington, D.C.; U.S. Govt Print. Off.; 1972.
9. BAILEY, M. B. Alcoholism and family casework theory and practice. New York; Community Council of Greater New York; 1968.
10. TULLEY, R. Casework treatment for the problem drinker and his family; the view from a specialized public clinic. Pp. 30–44. In: UNIVERSITY OF CALIFORNIA. SOCIAL WELFARE EXTENSION. Treatment methods and milieus in social work with alcoholics. Berkeley; [1966].
11. ESSER, P. H. Evaluation of family therapy with alcoholics. Br. J. Addict. 66: 251–255, 1971.
12. MEEKS, D. E. and KELLY, C. Family therapy with the families of recovering alcoholics. Q. J. Stud. Alcohol 31: 399–413, 1970.
13. BURTON, G. and KAPLAN, H. M. Marriage counseling with alcoholics and their

spouses. II. The correlation of excessive drinking behavior with family pathology and social deterioration. Br. J. Addict. 63: 161–170, 1968.

14. BURTON, G. and KAPLAN, H. M. Group counseling in conflicted marriages where alcoholism is present; clients' evaluation of effectiveness. J. Marriage & Fam. 30: 74–79, 1968.

15. GALLANT, D. M., RICH, A., BEY, E. and TERRANOVA, L. Group psychotherapy with married couples; a successful technique in New Orleans alcoholism clinic patients. J. La St. Med. Soc. 122: 41–44, 1970.

10

Drugs, Drug Dependence and the Concept of Plasticity[1]

Griffith Edwards, M.D., M.R.C.P., D.P.M.

THIS ESSAY is a preliminary attempt to formulate a conceptual model within which may be placed some of the many interacting variables which determine the behavior of an individual who takes a drug. It endeavors to put drug taking in social and cultural context, and proposes explanations for a society's choice of permissible substances and the likelihood of breakdown in social control. The same model may also affect our understanding of relevant clinical syndromes and approaches to therapeutic behavior modification. It assumes that the dependent state is an important psychobiological reality, not a phenomenon comprehensible only in terms of social role or labeling; but the argument is able to proceed without any final assumptions as to the basic pathology of dependence, although a learning explanation would seem most apposite.

Model building can deteriorate all too easily into a self-indulgent academic game, embracing all known facts without fear of refutation, but remote from the happenings of the clinic or the street. It may therefore be wise to start our analysis of drug-taking behavior by considering as the raw material of evidence one particular unstructured, unplanned and indeed unwanted event from the world of everyday reality. Thus, anyone recently walking through the outpatient waiting area of a certain psychiatric hospital might have noticed a disturbance going on, a play being acted out. The hero is a very drunken man, shouting obscenities, threats, re-

[1] Reprinted by permission from the QUARTERLY JOURNAL OF STUDIES ON ALCOHOL, Vol. 35, pp. 176–195, 1974. Copyright by Journal of Studies on Alcohol, Inc., New Brunswick, New Jersey 08903.

proaches, taking a bottle of methylated spirits from his coat and leaning back unsteadily to swig from it. As he staggers about, a little cast of nurses try to persuade him to conform to the expectations of polite society, offering him a cup of tea and urging him to sit down quietly in a sideroom. The man makes it clear, however, that he has no taste for tea and certainly is not going in any direction which anyone might propose. Appeals to him to modify his tones and avoid distressing other people go unheeded. Asked not to drink on the premises, he takes another swig and proffers a drink to a passer-by. A hospital porter is punched. The hero staggers a whirling course around the hall, the other actors following him like the tail of a comet. Eventually the police are summoned, and a scuffling, shouting and very angry man is hoisted out the door. Everyone feels bad; there is no curtain-call.

What was the play about? The drama centered around the unsuccessful attempt to control and modify a particular man's unacceptable behavior. What baffled and distressed the supporting cast was that this man was not susceptible to any of the controlling influences which the environment brought to bear (other than the arm of the law): they could not mold his behavior. That particular matinée happened to be about alcohol, but it could as well have depicted any other drug-related behavior or indeed a wide variety of nondrug-related behaviors. Take, for example, a patient suffering from hypomania; if his condition is not too acute, he may easily be contained on an open psychiatric ward. The nurses know how to placate him, go along with his whims, and how to strike bargains with him to set limits. If, however, hypomania moves toward mania, the patient is increasingly less responsive to the ordinary stratagems and, from the angle of ward management, this lack of responsiveness is an essential dimension of the illness. In practical terms, the patient must be transferred to a closed ward.

Thus, model building which takes the notion of a behavior's responsiveness to modifying influences as of central importance is likely to be founded on an idea which the everyday world will find meaningful. Whether it is a drunken man, a psychotic or even a child in a temper tantrum, a fundamental question is the degree to which the behavior is malleable by other phenomena. The extent to which that drunken man in the outpatient department was able to respond to the persons seeking to mold his behavior determined whether he got treatment and was able to enter the sick role, or be taken off by the police and into the bad role.

Definitions and Questions

The notion of the inherent plasticity of any behavior is established on the basis of common sense. Translating common sense into acceptable scientific terms is not always easy, however, and the following definition should be considered entirely provisional: The *plasticity* of a phenomenon-related behavior is measured by the degree to which that behavior may be influenced by factors other than the original phenomenon.

The phenomenon-related behavior is really a very complex dimensional problem, however, which usually comprises a whole host of behavioral patterns. When drugs are concerned, we must distinguish the two fundamental elements: *(1)* The direct influence of the drug on the organism and the plasticity of the intoxicated behavior—whether the individual is active or sleepy, aggressive or friendly, convivial or withdrawn, laughing or crying, hallucinating or in contact with reality. *(2)* The drug-seeking behavior of the individual, and the degree of its plasticity—the quantity and frequency of drug taking, the settings and occasions, and the degree and circumstances in which he will give this behavior priority over other activities. For the sake of brevity we shall refer to drug-related behavior as those types subsumed under *(1)* and *(2)* together.

The word "plastic" was chosen to convey the immediately sensed reality confronting the outpatient nurse who is trying to persuade the drunken man to modify his behavior but who is also sensing that, in this instance, the behavior cannot be molded. The term "pathoplastic" to describe the modifying factors which bear on any disease entity was employed in 1923 by Birnbaum (1):

"The essential clinical phenomena which occur in any illness are, first, those which refer to the actual cause of the illness, which endow it with a specific character, its quality of being 'thus and no other': secondly, those which may be said to shape the disorder in that they give contour to individual illnesses whose basic form and character have already been etiologically established. The former group of phenomena I would call *pathogenic* (the word itself provides a sufficiently clear definition), the latter *pathoplastic*."[2]

What has been asserted so far is therefore only a slight rephrasing of conventional psychiatric wisdom. The argument must be taken a little further, however, than the familiar proposition that

---

[2] Translation by Miss H. Marshall, Librarian, Institute of Psychiatry.

drug-related behavior is the interaction between drug, personality and environment. Such truisms are the starting point, but in building the proposed model we then have to examine the following questions which stem from acceptance of the basic interactionist tenets:

(A) Whether Different Psychoactive Substances Are Inherently Capable (for Pharmacological Reasons) of Inducing Drug-Related Behaviors of Very Different Plasticity. The overlay of any apparent drug-related behavior by pathoplastic environmental and personality factors is often so great that one is tempted to overlook the fact that the drug itself still does have its own distinct properties both in terms of immediate influence on cerebral function and its potential as reinforcer of drug-seeking behavior. What the concept of plasticity proposes is that a fundamental property of any psychoactive substance is manifested in the degree to which its drug-related behavior is potentially susceptible to modification. The following propositions might be put forward:

(1) The plasticity of drug-related behavior is likely to depend on dose, and the dose–plasticity curve may vary for different substances and different dimensions of drug-related behavior.

(2) At least at high doses, depressant substances are likely to produce more plastic behavior than stimulants: alcohol and amphetamines provide obvious contrasts. This assertion is at present only speculative and perhaps runs contrary to conditioning theory (2): if data support the assertion, it would seem to imply that the type of learning relevant to an understanding of the plastic potential of drug-related behavior is not simply conditioning.

(3) Opiatelike substances might produce intoxication intermediate between the plasticity of the depressants and stimulants. The psychoactive effect on the habituated person may be minimal but, with increased dose, opiates generally produce increased lethargy; the subject may "coast" or "nod off," but he is to some extent responsive to his environment and his attention can be recaptured. The stereotyped behavior of opiate intoxication suggests pathoplastic potential less than that of alcohol; the person under the influence of a high dose of heroin can be predicted to behave like one type of drunken person (the sleepy one), rather than exhibit acting-out behavior. The plasticity of drug-seeking behavior for depressants and opiates may, however, be in reverse order to dimensions of intoxication-related behavior—the reinforcing properties of heroin may result in behavior far less plastic than the corresponding alcohol-seeking behavior.

(4) Cannabis and psychotomimetic substances produce behavior that is plastic par excellence: the content of a lysergide experience is so astonishingly at the play of personality and environmental factors that it is tempting to suppose that the actual core drug effect is almost nil. This interpretation would probably be faulty, however, and one closer to the truth might be that these substances tend to produce profound cerebral effects with consequent behavior so unusually plastic that the success of efforts to mold it are most unpredictable. The reinforcing properties of psychotomimetic substances do not generally set up strong drug-seeking drives; hence this behavior is likely to be responsive to environmental factors.

But again it must be stressed that these postulates as to the varying degree of plasticity related to different drugs are only speculative. Such speculation draws attention to the fact that an analysis of any particular drug's properties in terms of the plasticity of its drug-related behavior may be a useful supplement to the conventional notions that *(a)* the drug has primary psychobiological effects and *(b)* the drug's action may be modified by extraneous factors. What I am proposing is that the *degree* of modifiability is important and that the rules governing the process of modification may be worthy of study and susceptible to useful generalization. Such speculations should be investigated in laboratory experiments with both human and animal subjects. Understanding might be gained of the degree to which different substances inherently differ in respect to the plasticity of related behavior, the dose-relatedness of such responsiveness, the actual types of manipulation likely to be successful in different circumstances in establishing control over drug-related behavior, and also of the circumstances in which such responsiveness may break down.

(B) Personality as a Pathoplastic Factor. There is now a substantial literature on personality and drug effects. Useful reviews include those by Eysenck (3) and Shepherd et al. (4). Analysis concerned with neuroticism and extraversion has been fruitful, but more holistic aspects of personality organization need to be considered. Experiments on the influence of personality on lysergide response have been reviewed by Barr et al. (5), and these authors have added to that literature some original observations suggesting the manner in which aspects of ego organization can shape the lysergide experience.

Moreover, the type of personality fundamentally lacking in responsiveness to ordinary informal cues or more formal social control (psychopathy, sociopathy, or any of its rephrasings) will probably exhibit the same unresponsiveness in intoxicated and drug-seeking behavior. The conditions in which such unresponsiveness will be exacerbated or alleviated by a drug are clearly matters of great interest.

(C) Environmental Pathoplastic Influence on Drug-Related Behavior. Alcohol provides a persuasive example of the degree to which a drug-related behavior may be influenced by pathoplastic factors of the environment. In their important book MacAndrew and Edgerton (6) present a mass of anthropological data on this issue; in the quotations below, two contrasting societies are used as illustrations of how in one case intoxication may be associated with wild acting-out, while in another society the same drug produces no violation of social controls. The former type of society is exemplified by the Abipone people of the great plains of Paraguay from an account by Dobrizhoffer (7):

"The Abipones, in their whole deportment, preserve a decorum scarce credible to Europeans . . . they never break out into clamours, threats and reproaches, as is usual to certain people of Europe. These praises are justly due to the Abipones as long as they remain sober: but when intoxicated, they shake off the bridle of reason, become distracted, and quite unlike themselves. . . . It often happens that a contention between two [when intoxicated] implicates and incites them all, so that snatching up arms, and taking the part, some of one, some of the other, they furiously rush to attack and slay one another."

Secondly, MacAndrew and Edgerton quote a description by Heath (8) of the drinking behavior of the Camba, a mestizo people of eastern Bolivia:

"The behavioral patterns associated with drinking are so formalized as to constitute a secular ritual. Members of the group are seated in chairs in an approximate circle. . . . A bottle of *alcohol* and a single water glass rest on a tiny table which forms part of the circle. The 'sponsor' of the party pours a glassful (about 300 cc.) at the table, turns and walks to stand in front of whomever he wishes, nods and raises the glass slightly . . . drinks half of the glassful in a single quick draught, and hands it to the person he has toasted, who then repeats the toast and finishes the glass in one gulp. While the 'sponsor' returns to his seat, the recipient of the toast goes to the table to refill the glass and to repeat the ritual. . . . By the fourth hour there is little conversation; many people stare dumbly at the ground except when toasted, and a few who may have fallen asleep or 'passed out' are left undisturbed. . . . Among the Camba drinking does not lead to expressions of aggression in verbal or physical form. . . . Neither is there a heightening of sexual activity: obscene joking and sexual overtures are rarely associated with drinking."

The contrast between the "drunken comportment" of the Abipone and Camba people could hardly be more extreme. The implications fully support MacAndrew and Edgerton's contention that much which has been conventionally assumed to be an inevitable "disinhibiting" pharmacological effect of alcohol stands now in need of reappraisal in the light of cultural evidence.

Alcohol-related behavior is certainly not the only type which must be subjected to cultural analysis. A recent series of essays (9) on the use of hallucinogens from an anthropological perspective contains fascinating and highly relevant material. In his introduction, Furst (9) contrasts the use of psychomimetics within the cultural framework of highly organized non-Western cultures with the use of similar substances in the modern West:

". . . there are fundamental differences that set the traditional magico-religious use of hallucinogens apart. They have to do above all with a basic function of the psychedelic experience in non-Western cultures—to facilitate the integration of the individual into the total society and the values by which he lives, as opposed to the association of hallucinogens in Western cultures with alienation and rejection of the corrupted values of the parental generation."

Furst then quotes from Roszak (10) who argues that drug experience in the Western world has been

"laid hold of by a generation of youngsters who are pathetically acultural and who often bring nothing to the experience but a vacuous yearning. They have, in adolescent rebellion, thrown off the corrupted culture of their elders and, along with that soiled bath water, the very body of the Western heritage—at best, in favor of exotic traditions they only marginally understand; at worst, in favor of an introspective chaos in which the 17 or 18 years of their unformed lives float like atoms in a void."

What then are the actual devices available to society or culture with which to exploit the pathoplastic potential of a drug-related behavior? How do the Camba control so dangerous a substance as alcohol, and how did some Central and South American societies so successfully coexist with, indeed exploit the cultural usefulness of, the astonishing variety of psychomimetic substances which nature provides in those parts of the world? There is no simple answer to that question, and a wide variety of devices are "employed," from the simplest to the most complex. Learned expectation of the likely form which drug-related behavior will take may be an important way in which societies control behavior by suggestion. If the individual is told that the drug will make him aggressive, then the drug will probably do so; if he is told that it will make him sleepy, then he will probably experience sleepiness. Schachter and Singer (11) have reviewed the general influence of cognitive, social and physiological determinants of emotional states and adduce experimental work from a wide field to support their contention:

"Given a state of physiological arousal for which an individual has no immediate explanation, he will label this state and describe his feelings in terms of the cognitions available to him. To the extent that cognitive factors are potent determiners of emotional states, it should be anticipated that precisely the same state of physiological arousal could be labeled 'joy' or 'fury' or 'jealousy' or any of a great diversity of emotional labels depending on the cognitive aspects of the situation."

The bearing of such an argument on an understanding of the determinants of drug effects is close.

The literature on the placebo effect could be similarly interpreted as providing additional evidence for the reality of plasticity, and much of the experimental work in that area reveals processes which may just as well apply to "active" drug effects. For instance, Frankenhaeuser et al. (12) nicely illustrated the fact that the action of a placebo was to a considerable extent determined by whether the tablets were described as a "depressant" or "stimulant," and their evidence was in terms not only of subjective ratings of alertness, sleepiness, happiness and depression, but also along physiological parameters such as pulse rate and blood pressure. Merely calling a substance "a *drug*" in our society must set multifarious expectations.

But to suppose that straightforward suggestive mechanisms are the whole explanation would be too great a simplification: pathoplastic effect of culture on drug-related behavior is as complex as culture itself and as multitudinous in its elements. Snyder's (13) study of alcohol and the Jews illustrates some of these complex aspects of cultural control: the Jewish drinking pattern is not determined by attitudes toward alcohol per se; drinking takes place within the matrix of general Jewish cultural values, attitudes toward others and aspects of self-image which overtly have no immediate bearing on drinking behavior. He instances the fear of behavior which would let down the Jew in front of the outgroup and the fear of losing affective control, the valuing of more distant rather than proximate goals, with these and various other general cultural attributes "accidentally" bearing on drinking behavior. One could not hope to understand the English country gentleman's fox hunting simply by exploring his attitudes toward the fox.

DEPENDENCE AS DIMINISHED PLASTICITY

Postulated Nature of Dependence. As already mentioned, for the purposes of the present discussion it is not strictly necessary to take any particular position on the pathological basis of the dependent state. To an extent the concept of dependence can be conveniently "black boxed": we can postulate that there is such a state and then agree for the time being to set aside all questions relating to the possible psychophysiological basis. For present purposes the postulate seems sufficient, namely, that repeated exposure to a drug which has effective reinforcing properties may lead to increased drive toward drug-seeking behavior. As Kumar et al. (14) have put it: "The ability of certain drugs to induce powerful drives and the development of drug-centered behavior seem to be exceptions to the aphorism that drugs do not put anything new into behavior but only alter ongoing processes."

The precise nature of the learning process underlying the acquisition of drug dependence is unknown, e.g., whether the dependent state differs from the nondependent only in quantitative terms, or whether qualitatively different types of learning are involved. Dependence is seen here not as an all-or-none phenomenon, but as something which can exist in degrees.

Dependence as Loss of Plasticity. The bearing of the notion of plasticity on our understanding of dependence is that dependence to some degree robs drug-related behavior of its nondependent plasticity. To take the analysis further, the following points must be considered:

(*a*) An alcohol-dependent person is likely to drink toward higher levels of intoxication than the nondependent drinker and will be resistant to society's dictates as to what is the appropriate level of intoxication in any setting. To give a concrete example, an alcoholic is someone who when he drinks and drives will not easily observe society's expectations that he should keep his blood alcohol level below a certain limit.

(*b*) Drug-seeking behavior now acquires a salience and centrality which result in a need to satisfy that drive and a willingness to ignore the appropriateness of circumstances in which drug-taking behavior may be indulged. The nondependent cigarette smoker finds no difficulty in abstaining if he happens to be in a nonsmoking railway compartment whereas the dependent smoker even in that setting is likely to light a cigarette.

It may also be noted that if we accept the assumption that dependence is not an all-or-none phenomenon, then the degree of unresponsiveness seen at different stages of development in the dependence process will also be other than all-or-none. There are important differences between drugs.

Part of the environment's bafflement with the dependent person may stem from society's imperfect understanding of the implications of dependence, hence surprise (and annoyance) when someone is unresponsive to control. The wife expects the husband who drinks to modify his behavior in response to a variety of ordinary interpersonal manipulations: if she is angry when he gets home late from the pub, she expects him to be home earlier the following evening. She would normally consider a bit of cajoling, a few threats, a little sulkiness as legitimate and effective strategies for modifying drinking behavior or any other form of behavior which she deems to be mildly problematical. Such strategems might have been highly effective so far as nondependent drinking was concerned, but as the husband slips further and further into alcohol dependence these ordinary household remedies lose their power. The wife is gradually driven to up the odds and, rather than indulging in a little mild scolding, may stage first-class rows, resort to violence or leave for a few days. In the early stages of dependence such stratagems may effectively bear upon a behavior which is still somewhat responsive; but in the advanced stages of dependence, the extent to which plasticity has been lost almost guarantees the wife's continued bafflement.

The very notion of dependence as some sort of special state, whatever the psychobiological reality of that specialness, may also have expectation-inducing implications which will affect plasticity. This idea is inherent in the disease concept of alcoholism and its societal implications: that "loss of control" over drinking may be dictated in part by society legitimizing the idea that the illness of alcoholism robs the individual of control (15).[3]

Dependence and the Retention of Plasticity. Although dependence may generally imply loss of plasticity, and although this observation may increase our understanding of the social problems caused by dependence, it is equally necessary to observe that there are consequences which stem from the fact that dependent behavior always

---

[3] HERSHON, H. I. The disease concept of alcoholism: a reappraisal. Presented at the 30th International Congress on Alcoholism and Drug Dependence, Amsterdam, September 1972.

continues to exhibit some degree of plasticity. Failure to give due weight to this aspect of dependence has perhaps led to overvaluing the absoluteness of clinical typologies in alcoholism studies. Because alcohol-dependent behavior is plastic, it will show itself in a variety of molded forms in different cultures and with different personalities. Alcohol dependence in one country, or as it affects one type of personality, can be very unlike the alcohol dependence seen in another culture, or as it exhibits itself in a person of a different temperament. The open invitation is then to assume that there are fundamentally different pathologies. If, however, the matter is analyzed within terms of the concept of plasticity, we may instead deduce that there is one essential dependence pathology with behavioral forms which cluster into "types" under the impact of pathoplastic factors. Instead of truly distinct types of alcohol dependence, there may be one dependence with a variety of faces. Such an approach may aid clinical understanding of the individual case to a far greater extent than resort to the labels of a typology. It may enable us to see cultural varieties of alcohol dependence as related to sociocultural structures of a particular setting, or as related to our appreciation of the individual's personality. The approach may finally serve a useful purpose in stressing the idea that there is a core dependence state which, though plastic in its inferences, is not a will-of-the-wisp.

The analogies from general psychiatry are obvious. Lambo (16), in an analysis of the relationship between culture and the form and content of paranoia among people of the Yoruba tribe of Nigeria, found the psychosis among those in rural areas very different from that among members of the same tribe living in urbanized areas who have been exposed to Westernizing influences. Lambo nonetheless argued that it is essentially the same disease process with the face much influenced by pathoplastic cultural factors. Stengel (17) discusses, on the other hand, the influence of personality (obsessional characteristics) on psychotic reaction types. He sees the obsessional disposition as to some extent preserving the integrity of the personality from the threat of schizophrenic disintegration. If Lambo's and Stengel's articles are read together, they provide a model based on the plasticity of schizophrenic behavior and the influences on that plastic condition of both cultural and personality pathoplastic factors. The actual concept of the pathoplastic factor is indeed employed by both authors.

Thus, in suggesting that dependence states give rise to plastic forms of behavior, and that it may be profitable to analyze the influence of various cultural and personality pathoplastic factors, I am borrowing from an already established line of reasoning in general psychiatry which has certainly proved fruitful. To what extent can the influence of cultural and individual factors be identified in alcohol dependence?

When Jellinek (18) set up his typology of alcoholism (the alpha-epsilon categorization), he clearly stated that the difference between gamma (loss-of-control) and delta (inability-to-abstain) alcoholism might lie in part in cultural patterning: gamma alcoholism was typical in Anglo-Saxon countries, while delta alcoholism was more common in France and other countries with large wine consumption. He was uncertain whether epsilon alcoholism (bout drinking) was "a disease per se or the symptom of an underlying disease," and he added an interesting note on what he termed "pseudoperiodic alcoholism":

"I should like to point out that in the last 20 or 25 years a phenomenon which may be called pseudoperiodic alcoholism has turned up. It would appear that some gamma alcoholics who have not benefited to the full extent from the A.A. program or from therapy in clinics or by private psychiatrists are able to resist drinking for 3, 6 or 12 months, but then find no other solution than intoxication, after which they remorsefully return to 'sobriety.'"

The idea of a fundamental and unitary pathological process being molded by various secondary factors, so as to present different clinical pictures, is thus inherent in Jellinek's writing. The particular phrase Jellinek uses—"species" of alcoholism—is in some ways ambiguous, however: whether he saw the species as no more than behavioral clusterings resulting from the impact of pathoplastic factors on the fundamental "disease" state, or whether he saw his "species" as having more concrete and absolute meaning. It is possible that he wanted to leave the issue open, hence choosing the untendentious but ambiguous term intentionally. Jellinek himself was fully aware of the great variety of clinical presentations, and he made it abundantly clear that the five-item typology (two of which related to nondependent drinking) did not in any way exhaust the range of possibilities: "There are, of course, many other species of alcoholism—if it is defined as any drinking that causes any damage—and all the remaining 19 of the Greek and if necessary other alphabets are available for labeling them."

With regard to personality as a determinant of the form of alcoholism, Walton (19) has presented evidence to suggest that there are personality differences in a British population between the typical loss-of-control and typical inability-to-abstain alcoholic. Psychological tests indicated that the former tended to be more aggressive, more fearful of not being able to control their aggressive tendencies and more easily depressed over losses and disappointments, in contrast to the latter type. The same idea has been taken up by Mellor (20) who has suggested that "regular restrained drinkers" may be those who are more abnormally "sensitive."

The above citations in no way exhaust the very considerable body of writing bearing on the issue of plasticity; particular reference should be made, however, to a paper by Winokur et al. (21) which poses the specific question, "Is there more than one type of alcoholism?" and to the useful reports by Schuckit et al. (22) on the "bender alcoholic" and by Gottheil (23) as illustrating work which dissects the plasticity of alcoholics' drinking behavior in the setting of a research ward. The essential basis of the transactional position taken by Steiner (24), who sees alcoholism as "a game," might be reinterpreted as a statement that alcohol-related behavior exhibits plastic potential which can be exploited by the manipulations of the therapist. It may finally be noted that some data support the notion that even the withdrawal state may be seen as culturally plastic behavior. A report by Gross et al. (25) offers evidence that hallucinations in alcohol withdrawal are more common among the Black than White patients seen at a New York hospital, and the authors make the following interpretation:

"It remains to be determined whether this . . . is a result of culturally determined early patterns of child-rearing and its effects upon self–nonself differentiation and subsequent characteristics of ego boundaries, later factors such as cultural attitudes regarding the acceptability or even expectation of hallucinations and its effect upon the ego ideal, or a more general effect upon a culture such as deprivation and harsh reality predisposing to the enhancement of mental activity along the phantasy–hallucination continuum."

The bearing of Lambo's writing (16) on these findings is immediate and obvious.

Much the same analysis as has here been focused on the plastic nature of behavior related to alcohol dependence could be applied to the dependence condition associated with any other dependence-inducing drug. Similarities and some dissimilarities might be discerned. There is a need for broad principles. The rather surprising degree of separateness between professional groupings with prime interest centered largely on just a particular substance or type of substance (narcotics, say, as opposed to alcohol, or alcohol as opposed to tobacco) has, however, resulted in the unlikelihood of general principles being enunciated which could be usefully applied across a wide range of substances and enhance our understanding of the precise manner in which cultural and individual facts mold dependent behavior. There is perhaps something to be gained from comparing the delta alcoholic of Jellinek's classification with the "stabilized addict" described in the Rolleston Report (26), or the gamma alcoholic with the street addict of the Western world's more recent heroin experience. The conclusion might be that pathoplastic factors can lead in almost any dependence condition either to the individual's social integration or disintegration. The vital task would then be to identify the relevant pathoplastic factors across a range of drugs—greater or less "availability" of the substance in terms of price or situational factors; stigmatization or lack of it of the dependent person; the dose effect; whether the person whose drug hunger is fully satiated is more socially stable; the influence of different types of pathoplastic personality factors; the inherent properties of the drug.

THE MODEL: SUMMARY AND SOME FURTHER IMPLICATIONS

Up to this point a number of discrete postulates have been put forward and their immediate implications explored. It may now be useful to bring those postulates together since their articulation, one with another, constitutes the proposed model. Implications may also be summarized and certain wider implications identified.

The potential *degree* of plasticity of a drug-related behavior is a dimension which must be assessed if we are to comprehend the potential of pathoplastic influences. The commonly accepted premise that behavior is multifactorially determined should be elaborated into a series of postulates which propose quantification. The model proposes that drug-related behavior is plastic behavior, whether the individual is drug-dependent or not. Different drugs will induce behavior of different degrees of plasticity. The fact of dependence will rob the individual's drug-taking behavior of some of its plasticity; the degree will be determined by the degree to which the dependence has been established. Plasticity will be dose-related. Drug-taking behavior is multidimensional; different aspects may show different degrees of plasticity. Pathoplastic influences are also multidimensional and include the possible influence of other drugs taken concomitantly, the influence of variables within the individual (personality) and factors within the environment (multidimensional aspects of culture and social structure).

Implications for Society. The environment defines the drug-taking mores for any particular substance (the occasions on which it will be taken and the typical quantities used), but also has the potential to define the expected nature of the drug-taking experience, the expected consequences of drug-taking behavior and intoxication, and the role which the dependent person will adopt. Societies are more likely to legalize substances which induce highly pathoplastic behavior (depressants or psychomimetics) rather than those lacking this property (stimulants). As dependence robs behavior of its plasticity to some extent, societies are likely not to accept substances with strong dependence-inducing properties (narcotics). Complex cultures which imbue the individual with a strongly integrative sense of his oneness with that culture are needed for the control of drugs which produce hallucinatory and perceptual change (psychomimetics), whereas less complex cultural controls will be needed for depressants such as alcohol. Use of any psychoactive substance whatsoever results in behavior expressive of a dynamic equilibrium between the effects of that substance and of pathoplastic factors, and the equilibrium is invariably unstable to some degree. Breakdown of that equilibrium will occur in the following circumstances:

(a) When the culture itself is changing and loosening its control over individual members. The drinking of the Industrial Revolution is a prime example. It might be predicted that postindustrial cultures are going to be faced with similar but even larger problems, and that the changes in Western culture which will be consequent on increased wealth, breakdown of ordinary ties, the abandonment of ordinary forms of institutionalized belief and the questioning of many aspects of established ethic, will produce societies which are profoundly incompetent in their control of any form of drug use. Such controls as are exerted are more likely to be punitive and legalistic as the old cultural controls fade out.

(b) The sudden introduction of a substance with high dependence-inducing properties will pose a particular threat to an unprepared society. The narcotic epidemic in the United States is an example. The U.S. experience should be contrasted with the much more stable equilibrium between societies and opiates in the East. The failure of the West to exert similar controls is not entirely accounted for by the introduction of opiates in injectable form, although such advances in technology can also upset the balance.

(c) Control will be lost over the drug-taking behavior of individuals who are unresponsive to cultural influences. Such individuals are found in any culture, but their number may to a degree be culturally determined.

Thus the central implication here for society is that a "drug problem" is as likely to be a manifestation of inept social responses or an impoverished culture as the properties of the drug itself or the supposed "deviance" of individuals. This much of course is little more than a truism, but the model proposes the necessity for a close analysis of the way in which the complexities of culture are succeeding or failing to exploit the pathoplastic potential of drug-taking behavior: we need to get away from the feeling that such an assertion is mere truism, and explore objectively the relationship between aspects of culture and aspects of the pattern of drug-taking behavior. That we can establish a point-by-point congruence between the two sets of variables is probably too much to expect, but possibilities of research are nonetheless inviting, and such research might have a profound relevance to society's ability to tolerate certain recreational drugs and also avoid casualties.

Implications for the Individual. This model would seem to have implications for the individual both in terms of recreational drug use and of "pathology." The individual should be aware that what can be positively gained from a particular drug is determined only partly by its inherent properties; it is also highly dependent on his intrapsychic state and on his relationship to a culture. It is no accident that the cult of psychomimetic use should have grown to some extent hand-in-hand with a renewed interest in meditation, the emergence of latter-day religious cults and the rediscovery of mysticism. One might then propose that any typology of dependence on alcohol or on any other substance into discrete and discontinuous "species" is a less useful clinical analysis than one which seeks to establish the degree of dependence and identify the variety of pathoplastic factors in each individual case. A dimensional analysis is more useful than a typology, although a typology serves as some sort of guide to thinking.

Implications for Research. The most certain implication for research is that enquiries which will illuminate our understanding of drug-taking and dependence behavior can only be multidisciplinary. Research is required into the primary phenomena, into the core drug effects and the core nature of dependence pathology. The heavy emphasis which this model must place on the need to explore the interaction between pathoplastic factors and the primary phenomena should not lead to any neglect of those little understood primary drug phenomena. Neither pharmacology nor any of the social or behavioral sciences can provide complete understanding in isolation. Gove (27) has recently reviewed an analogous area relating to objective evidence for "societal reaction" as an explanation of mental illness, and he suggests that sociologists have tended to neglect the primary determinants of deviance in favor of the phenomena of secondary deviance. He quotes Becker (28):

> "Social groups create deviance by making rules whose infractions constitute deviance, and by applying those rules to particular people and labeling them as outsiders. From this point of view, deviance is not a quality of the act a person commits, but rather a consequence of the application by others of rules and sanctions to an 'offender.' The deviant is one to whom the label has successfully been applied: deviant behavior is behavior that people so label."

If we are to understand the power or the impotence of pathoplastic factors, it is vital that we continue to see them in terms of their bearing on the real and little understood primary pharmacological properties of drugs and the even less understood phenomena of dependence and plasticity.

BACK TO THE MAN WHO WAS DRUNK

This essay started with instancing a particular work-a-day happening—a man who was drunk in an outpatient department and the strivings of various actors to control his behavior. It is perhaps a rather unfair demand on a theoretical model that it should immediately illuminate the nature of such an event; the initial value of a model may rather be to clarify the nature of ignorance, to segment its areas, and define more closely what constitutes the legitimate material for study.

In terms of the model which this essay proposes, the happenings of that outpatient afternoon would suggest that we most certainly have to continue to focus on such traditional areas as the psychopharmacology of ethanol and invest heavily in research to dissect the psychobiological basis of alcohol dependence. The model suggests also other types of research: the laboratory worker might, for instance, wish to use the enormous potential of the animal paradigm to analyze precisely the degree to which intoxicated or dependent states interfere with responsiveness to a variety of cues, or lead to disruption of established behavior patterns. The social scientist might study the meaning of drunkenness, dependence and cultural belief as to the related plasticities—the beliefs of the nurses, the patient, the policeman. Research which focuses on the causes of that man's alcoholism has to look with new precision at the exact nature of social controls and the pathology of their breakdown. Treatment is in part a matter of discovering strategies which will make the individual responsive again to the cues of his environment, and a first stage of treatment might well be simply the intelligent molding of dependent behavior into less damaging dependent behavior.

Whatever the particular research focus, the model in short proposes, in terms which an artist or sculptor might use, that we have more than anything to sense the nature of the material.

REFERENCES

1. BIRNBAUM, K. Der Aufbau der Psychose. Berlin; Springer; 1923.
2. EYSENCK, H. J. The dynamics of anxiety and hysteria. London; Routledge & Kegan Paul; 1957.
3. EYSENCK, H. J. Experiments with drugs; studies in relation between personality, learning theory and drug action. Oxford; Pergamon; 1963.
4. SHEPHERD, M., LADER, M. and RODNIGHT, R. Clinical psychopharmacology. London; English Universities Press; 1968.
5. BARR, H. L., LANG, R. J., HOLT, R. R., GOLDBERGER, L. and KLEIN, G. S. LSD; personality and experience. New York; Interscience; 1972.
6. MACANDREW, C. and EDGERTON, R. B. Drunken comportment; a social explanation. Chicago; Aldine; 1969.
7. DORBRIZHOFFER, M. An account of the Abipones, an equestrian people of Paraguay. 3 vols. London; John Murray; 1822.
8. HEATH, D. B. Drinking patterns of the Bolivian Camba. Q. J. Stud. Alcohol 19: 491–508, 1958.
9. FURST, P. T., ed. Flesh of the gods; the ritual use of hallucinogens. London; Allen & Unwin; 1972.
10. ROSZAK, T. The making of a counter culture. New York; Doubleday; 1969.
11. SCHACHTER, S. and SINGER, J. Cognitive, social and physiological determinants of emotional state. Psychol. Rev. 69: 379–399, 1962.
12. FRANKENHAEUSER, M., JAERPE, G., SVAN, H. and WRANGSJOE, B. Psychophysiological reactions to two different placebo treatments. Scand. J. Psychol. 4: 245–250, 1963.
13. SNYDER, C. R. Alcohol and the Jews; a cultural study of drinking and sobriety. (Rutgers Center of Alcohol Studies, Monogr. No. 1.) New Brunswick, N.J.; 1958.
14. KUMAR, R., STOLERMAN, I. P. and STEINBERG, H. Psychopharmacology. Annu. Rev. Psychol. 21: 595–628, 1970.
15. ROBINSON, D. The alcohologist's addiction; some implications of having lost control over the disease concept of alcoholism. Q. J. Stud. Alcohol 33: 1028–1042, 1972.
16. LAMBO, T. A. The role of cultural factors in paranoid psychoses among the Yoruba tribe. J. Ment. Sci. 101: 239–266, 1955.
17. STENGEL, E. A study of some clinical aspects of the relationship between obsessional neurosis and psychotic reaction types. J. Ment. Sci. 91: 166–187, 1945.
18. JELLINEK, E. M. The disease concept of alcoholism. Highland Park, N.J.; Hillhouse Press; 1960.

19. WALTON, H. J. Personality as a determinant of the form of alcoholism. Br. J. Psychiat. 114: 761–766, 1968.
20. MELLOR, C. S. Drinking behaviour and its correlates in alcohol addicts. Ph.D. dissertation, University of Manchester; 1969.
21. WINOKUR, G., RIMMER, J. and REICH, T. Alcoholism. IV. Is there more than one type of alcoholism? Br. J. Psychiat. 118: 525–531, 1971.
22. SCHUCKIT, M. A., RIMMER, J., REICH, T. and WINOKUR, G. The bender alcoholic. Br. J. Psychiat. 119: 183–184, 1971.
23. GOTTHEIL, E. Research on fixed interval drinking decisions in an alcoholism treatment program. Proc. 2d Annu. Alcsm Conf., NIAAA, pp. 139–157, 1973.
24. STEINER, C. Games alcoholics play; the analysis of life scripts. New York; Grove; 1971.
25. GROSS, M. M., ROSENBLATT, S. M., LEWIS, E., MALENOWSKI, B. and BROMAN, M. Hallucinations and clouding of sensorium in acute alcohol withdrawal syndromes; dependent and independent relationships including evidence for cultural hallucinogenic mechanisms. Pp. 227–236. In: KEUP, W., ed. Origins and mechanisms of hallucinations; symposium. New York; Plenum; 1970.
26. GREAT BRITAIN. MINISTRY OF HEALTH, DEPARTMENTAL COMMITTEE ON MORPHINE AND HEROINE ADDICTION. Rolleston Report. London; H. M. Stat. Off.; 1926.
27. GOVE, R. W. Societal reaction as an explanation of mental illness; an evaluation. Am. Sociol. Rev. 35: 873–884, 1970.
28. BECKER, H. Outsiders; studies in the sociology of deviance. New York; Free Press; 1963.

Part III

INTERFACES BETWEEN ALCOHOLISM
AND PSYCHOPATHOLOGIES

In 1967 (and it is unlikely that the state of the science has since been significantly altered), Marconi (1) wrote, "The progress of a scientific discipline is measured by the quality of the method used in research. A realistic appraisal of the methodological rigor of psychopathological research shows that the discipline is at the same stage of development as was physics before 1638 when Galileo formulated the principles of the hypothetical–deductive method." Similarly, in his presidential address to the Canadian Psychiatric Association, Chalke (2) wrote of "the need for science in psychiatry," closing with a quotation from John Ruskin: "The work of science is to substitute facts for appearance, and demonstrations for impressions."

Both alcoholism and various forms of psychopathology have the appearance of extreme behavior and, to a degree, this is a societal perception. Even more specifically, some of their symptomatologies appear to be identical. The following section presents some facts about these appearances and considers possible interrelationships between alcoholism and various forms or manifestations of psychopathology. The nature of the relationships covers a broad spectrum because, as I (Chapter 11) noted in a review of alcoholism and schizophrenia, clinicians and researchers have sought "correlative or even more exclusive relationships" between alcoholism and other psychiatric disorders. Most desired, one presumes, would have been a clear-cut etiological relationship. This has been difficult to achieve, largely because of the heterogeneity characterizing both alcoholisms and mental illnesses. Alcoholism and other forms of psychopathology may also be secondarily related as manifestations, or they may coexist; multiple psychiatric diagnoses occur with some frequency.

Much of what I wrote about alcoholism and manic–depressive illness holds, too, for alcoholism's interfaces with other psychiatric diagnoses in more general terms:

"The relationship between manic–depressive disorders and alcoholism remains a significant area for thought and for exploration, at the very least because of the importance and tragic impact of the two psychopathological conditions involved. That their relationship is of consequence can be inferred from the many attempts by clinicians to link them either theoretically or dynamically. Surely, there are features of both which are strikingly similar. Whether these will prove to be superficial or fortuitously susceptible of comparison remains to be demonstrated. The inventiveness of the scientific community has been little taxed in highlighting the commonalities between the lability and the often-transient depressive and euphoric phases of affective disorder and alcoholism. Real ingenuity, however, will be necessary to establish more meaningful ties. What seems required is a more experimental approach to the questions involved. But there are implicit difficulties in this because one deals with independent (and dependent) variables which are not static but are inconstant and in flux: mania, depression, intoxication. Affective states are difficult to define and still harder to measure and they tend to overlap" (3, *p. 82*).

The difference between causal involvement and coincidental accompaniment of alcohol with other problems, however, highlights what Keller (4) has referred to as the "alcohol-and" approach. He did see alcohol-and-health problems as etiologically related, not just a sort of heterograft. Filkins and Mortimer (5) wrote, "We have argued metaphysically that alcohol abuse is not a neat, well-behaved entity which can be simplistically defined and dealt with as such, but rather a somewhat amorphous, generalized concept from which many undesirable behavioral manifestations derive." This was Williams's (6) "concept of individual alcoholism."

Lacking the ideal sort of attributable cause and effect paradigm, investigators often have settled for lesser clues, superficial and serendipitous comparisons or seeming parallels between psychiatric disorders and alcoholism. The motivation to find linking pins or fixed points from which comparisons can be drawn is understandable. Examples here would include commonality in the cyclical aspects of manic–depressive disturbance and of periodic inebriety, consideration of the stimulant and depressive phases of a drinking bout as a miniaturized manic–depressive episode, contrasting alcoholic delirium and hallucinosis with schizophrenic hallucinatory behavior, viewing alcohol and drug addictions as compulsions differing only in terms of the substance misused, etc. Gitlow (7), however, was impressed by the unique, unilateral, dominant role of alcoholism in determining clinical patterns. He noted that "although the alcoholic may start down the path of his illness from the vantage point of various psychiatric problems, he ends with a clinical picture dominated by his difficulty with alcohol, a circumstance playing a determinant role in both choice and efficacy of therapy. Thus, the neurotic, the sociopath, the manic–depressive and the schizophrenic with alcoholism may each pose singular and somewhat specific therapeutic problems, but all ultimately demand a surprisingly uniform therapeutic approach"—namely, in his view, abstinence. That all would not agree is manifest in the furor over the Rand Corporation report (8) on the need for abstinence in alcoholism treatment.

Mental health professionals are, perhaps, by virtue of their training and experiences, too attuned to psychopathological aspects of adjustment and not enough to correlates of normality. By the same token, nonabusive alcohol consumption and patterns of abstinence are too readily bypassed by alcohologists. By focusing largely on full-blown alcoholism, we are perhaps overly concerned with the morbidity of alcohol use, and, while such a focus may yield clues to pathogenesis, there are other, perhaps more appropriate, routes to learning about etiology, prognosis, management and prevention. In addition, we need to identify more comprehensively alcohol use which does not lead to morbidity statistics.

Maddox (9), writing about teen-agers and alcohol, noted that "we know very little about the persistently abstinent young person," indicating that "the needed research with regard to abstention as a facet of behavior and as a style of life remains to be done." Even though some data have been assembled by Cahalan and Room (10) on characteristics of adult abstainers and by Demone (11) on adolescents, by and large, Maddox's statement is still true. He added that "among social scientists, only historians have shown any substantial and sustained interest in abstainers and abstinence, and even they have been preoccupied with the Prohibition era." It is uncertain whether abstinence bespeaks a psychologically healthy attitude, but there is a need to address the relationships of alcohol vis à vis psychological health to the same degree that the relationships between alcohol and illness have been explored (12). Demone (11) concluded that the adolescent male "abstainer and pathological user are both removed from the mainstream of adolescent behavior," but Barry (13) called for studies of people who have predispositions against alcohol because they share a common failure to manifest the pathology of alcoholism. When asked whether he thought "it is possible for psychologically well-adjusted people to become alcoholics," Barry replied, "I would say 'no'; certainly not during the time that they are psychologically well-adjusted. . . . I see it very much as a psychiatric disorder; a person who is an alcoholic is ill psychiatrically." Whether he was ill psychiatrically before his alcoholism became manifest is a question that some sociologists (e.g., 14, 15) would seem to answer in the negative.

The articles presented here indicate that no single psychiatric disorder has "cornered the market" on alcohol problems nor do alcoholics all evidence specific psychological disturbances. Psychological problems may manifest themselves in alcoholism, and the literature is replete with references to the detrimental psycho-organic sequelae of alcoholism. While hypothesized etiological relationships for the former lack impressive evidence, there are data to support the latter concept of central nervous system impairment caused by alcohol (16).

An important interface clearly exists in the area of diagnosis, and, since diagnosis is but the precursor to treatment, therapy, too, becomes a bridge between alcoholism and mental illness. A recurrent issue, cutting across many lines of psychiatric classification, is that of symptom choice or manifestation. For the sake of pursuing a line of inquiry, let us assume that alcoholism is a symptom or expression of some underlying psychological problem, a traditional psychodynamic model (8). Then, the question becomes, why do some individuals "select" (albeit not consciously) this route of expression and why do others with the same underlying problem show depression, for example? The issue of symptom choice appears in discussions of alcoholism and other disturbances, both physical and emotional, respectively, masking one another. For instance, in his discussion of criminality and alcoholism, Guze (17) wrote that the association between antisocial personality and hysteria "is important because, coupled with the observation that hysteria is predominantly a disorder of women while antisocial personality is predominantly a disorder of men, it offers the interesting possibility that, depending upon the sex of the individual, the same etiologic and pathogenetic factors may lead to different, though sometimes overlapping, clinical pictures." The issue of symptom choice appears in considerations of alcohol addiction replacing drug addiction or vice versa (18) and in follow-up studies of the adjustment of patients discharged from mental hospitals. It is implicit in studies of symptom characteristics of newly admitted alcoholic and psychiatric patients and in discussions of the specificity theory of alcoholism. It is likewise implicit in life history studies which seek longitudinal data on frequency of alcoholism among former childhood or adolescent mental hygiene clinic patients, as well as in studies of the relationship of alcoholism to violent death (e.g., 19).

There is little doubt that with ever larger computer matrices, fortuitous and likely spurious correlations may be found between alcoholism variables and other dysfunctions within the mental health purview. Barring a common biological explanation (and although we are approaching such goals, they are still distant vistas), an underlying psychodynamic explication will be needed, even bearing in mind that correlation is not necessarily causation. Even with correlation, the possible relationships between alcoholism and mental health variables have to be examined with respect to another (and possibly independent) variable. Various theoretical frames of reference have been offered to date, but such contributions are often vague or contradictory and they almost universally have difficulty in handling heterogeneity. There would probably be little disagreement that psychiatric disorders and alcoholisms all are multifactorial (20).

The nature–nurture controversy, as applied to alcoholism, lives on in the work of biologists and geneticists and in terms of hypothesized environmental factors (21, 22). Nature and nurture interact most in families, and the role of the family in alcoholism and psychopathology is the subject of an increasing number of studies (e.g., 23, 24).

Close relationships between alcoholism and psychopathology have also been documented in studies of hospitalized alcoholic patients, but the meaning of such relationships is unclear. Tyndel (25), for example, found evidence of psychopathology in all 1017 alcoholics examined, and concluded that their alcoholism was "the outcome of a prolonged process of continuous or repeated attempts to deal with the discomfort caused by psychopathological processes and their associated social difficulties." Hoffman et al. (26), however, reported that "the measured manifestations of psychopathological behavior observed in this sample [of 282 alcoholics] are probably as diverse as one might encounter among a more heterogeneous psychiatric population." They wisely called for replications with other psychiatric and normal groups and, one might add, abstainers and nonproblem drinkers.

Myers et al. (27) reported a positive relationship between changes in the occurrence of life events and alterations in psychiatric symptomatology or impairment. Investigations directed specifically at alcoholism and life events might be fruitful in furthering understanding of the alcoholism–mental status interface. Thimann (28) believed that about 70% of the alcoholic population were mild psychoneurotics, the remaining 30% being mostly severe psychoneurotics and psychotics. It has been suggested, however, that alcoholics with a history of abnormal mental content might represent a clinical variant of schizophrenia (29).

Often the alcoholism–psychopathology borderland is conceptualized, and thus investigated, as a 2 × 2 design with alcohol problems and no alcohol problems or normative drinking (30) or degree of drinking versus adjustment and maladjustment (or infinite degrees or parameters of both). In studies of the prevalence of any one manifestation of psychopathology among alcoholic patients, Keller's Law (31) will prevail: "The investigation of any trait in alcoholics will show that they have either more or less of it." This tongue-in-cheek remark embodies a very serious lesson. It tells us, in effect, that alcoholics are different—different from the norm (and different from each other, too)—and we have used this difference as a raison d'etre to look for commonalities between alcoholics and other groups of individuals who are also "different." De Lint (32) also cautioned against viewing alcoholism (and, in this regard, one might add mental health) in dichotomous terms. The multivariate aspects of alcoholism and of a variety of psychopathologies, separately and as they interrelate, are the subject of the articles in this section. My review of the search for relationships between alcoholism and schizophrenia (Chapter 11) and Schuckit's essay (Chapter 12) on the relationships between alcoholism and sociopathy illustrate the approaches which have sought to clarify alcoholism's interactions with other psychiatric diagnoses. Underlying these attempts has been the assumption of a psychological predisposition, and Lisansky's classic article (Chapter 14) enumerates considerations involved in studying possible prealcoholic personality constellations. Chodorkoff's psychoanalytic thesis (Chapter 13) is that an alcoholic's drinking is related to psychological defense and adaptation, and that efforts to make up for ego deficiencies play a role in the development and maintenance of alcoholism.

REFERENCES

1. MARCONI, J. Scientific theory and operational definitions in psychopathology; with special reference to alcoholism. Q. J. Stud. Alcohol 28: 631–640, 1967.
2. CHALKE, F. C. Presidential address; the psychiatrist as scientist. Can. Psychiat. Ass. J. 19: 533–542, 1974.
3. FREED, E. X. Alcoholism and manic–depressive disorders; some perspectives. Q. J. Stud. Alcohol 31: 62–89, 1970.
4. KELLER, M. What are the problems around alcohol? StateWays 3 (No. 4): 25–26, 1974.
5. FILKINS, L. D. and MORTIMER, R. G. Exploring some common ground relative to alcohol abuse. Proc. Joint Conf. Alc. Abuse Alcsm, 21–23 February 1972, U.S. National Institute on Alcohol Abuse and Alcoholism, U.S. Law Enforcement Assistance Administration and U.S. National Highway Traffic Safety Administration (DHEW Publ. No. HSM-73-9051), pp. 24–41, 1972.
6. WILLIAMS, L. Who is qualified to treat the alcoholic? Comment on the Krystal-Moore discussion. Q. J. Stud. Alcohol 26: 118–120, 1965.
7. GITLOW, S. E. Alcoholism; a disease. Pp. 1–9. In: BOURNE, P. G. and FOX, R., eds. Alcoholism; progress in research and treatment. New York; Academic Press; 1973.
8. ARMOR, D. J., POLICH, J. M. and STAMBUL, H. B. Alcoholism and treatment. Prepared for the U.S. National Institute on Alcohol Abuse and Alcoholism. Santa Monica, Calif.; Rand Corp.; 1976.
9. MADDOX, G. L. Teenagers and alcohol; recent research. Ann. N.Y. Acad. Sci. 133: 856–865, 1966.
10. CAHALAN, D. and ROOM, R. Problem drinking among American men. (Rutgers Center of Alcohol Studies, Monogr. No. 7.) New Brunswick, N.J.; 1974.
11. DEMONE, H. W., JR. The nonuse and abuse of alcohol by the male adolescent. Proc. 2d Annu. Alcsm Conf. NIAAA, pp. 24–32, 1973.
12. KELLER, M. Alcohol in health and disease; some historical perspectives. Ann. N.Y. Acad. Sci. 133: 820–827, 1966.
13. BARRY, H., 3d. Personality and the alcoholic; personality of the individual vulnerable to alcoholism and associated characteristics. Proc. 1st Int. Med. Conf. Alcsm, London, 10–14 September 1973, pp. 43–56, 1974.
14. SARGENT, M. J. The conception of alcoholism as a mental illness; comment on the article by R. A. Moore, and a sociological alternative. Q. J. Stud. Alcohol 29: 974–978, 1968.
15. BACON, S. D. The process of addiction to alcohol; social aspects. Q. J. Stud. Alcohol 34: 1–27, 1973.
16. WALLGREN, H. and BARRY, H., 3d. Actions of alcohol. Vol. 2. Chronic and clinical aspects. Amsterdam; Elsevier; 1970.
17. GUZE, S. B. Criminality and psychiatric illness; the role of alcoholism. Proc. Joint Conf. Alc. Abuse Alcsm, 21–23 February 1972, U.S. National Institute on Alcohol Abuse and Alcoholism, U.S. Law Enforcement Assistance Administration and U.S. National Highway Traffic Safety Administration (DHEW Publ. No. HSM-73-9051), pp. 13–23, 1972.
18. FREED, E. X. Drug abuse by alcoholics; a review. Int. J. Addict. 8: 451–473, 1973.

19. GOODWIN, D. W. Alcohol in suicide and homicide. Q. J. Stud. Alcohol 34: 144–156, 1973.

20. CURNOW, R. N. and SMITH, C. Multifactorial models for family disease in man. J. R. Statist. Soc., Ser. A 138: 131–169, 1975.

21. STORM, T. and CUTLER, R. E. Alcohol consumption and personal resources; a general hypothesis and some implications. J. Stud. Alcohol 36: 917–924, 1975.

22. POPHAM, R. E., SCHMIDT, W. and DE LINT, J. The prevention of alcoholism; epidemiological studies of the effects of government control measures. Br. J. Addict. 70: 125–144, 1975.

23. GOODWIN, D. W. Is alcoholism hereditary? A review and critique. Archs Gen. Psychiat. 25: 545–549, 1971.

24. GOODWIN, D. W., SCHULSINGER, F., MØLLER, N., HERMANSEN, L., WINOKUR, G. and GUZE, S. B. Drinking problems in adopted and nonadopted sons of alcoholics. Archs Gen. Psychiat. 31: 164–169, 1974.

25. TYNDEL, M. Psychiatric study of one thousand alcoholic patients. Can. Psychiat. Ass. J. 19: 21–24, 1974.

26. HOFFMAN, H., JACKSON, D. N. and SKINNER, H. A. Dimensions of psychopathology among alcoholic patients. J. Stud. Alcohol 36: 825–837, 1975.

27. MYERS, J. K., LINDENTHAL, J. J. and PEPPER, M.P. Life events and psychiatric symptomatology. In: RICKS, D. F., THOMAS, A. and ROFF, M., eds. Life history research in psychopathology. Vol. 3. Minneapolis; University of Minnesota Press; 1974.

28. THIMANN, J. Who is qualified to treat the alcoholic? Comment on the Krystal-Moore discussion. Q. J. Stud. Alcohol 26: 310–311, 1965.

29. WOODRUFF, R. A., JR., GUZE, S. B. and CLAYTON, P. J. Alcoholics who see a psychiatrist compared with those who do not. Q. J. Stud. Alcohol 34: 1162–1171, 1973.

30. ROOM, R. Normative perspectives on alcohol use and problems. J. Drug Issues 5: 358–368, 1975.

31. KELLER, M. The oddities of alcoholics. Q. J. Stud. Alcohol 33: 1147–1148, 1972.

32. DE LINT, J. "The status of alcoholism as a disease"; a brief comment. Br. J. Addict. 66: 108–109, 1971.

11

Alcoholism and Schizophrenia: The Search for Perspectives

A Review[1]

Earl X. Freed, Ph.D.

STUDENTS of alcoholism often seek correlative or even more exclusive relationships between it and other psychiatric disorders. Sometimes superficial aspects lend themselves to serendipitous comparisons, and analogies are drawn in the hope of a known shedding light on an unknown. A review of research on psychotic problem drinkers revealed that little had been written on the subject although there was wide recognition of the "need for definitive research to explore the etiology of these conditions" (118). There are some characteristics of both alcoholism and schizophrenia meriting superficial comparison, but they illuminate neither. For example, there are seeming parallels between schizophrenic hallucinatory phenomena and the delirium and hallucinosis of alcoholics, and both disorders bespeak a loss of control (9, 86, 140). One may speculate that alcohol intoxication suppresses overt psychotic manifestations in persons whose underlying psychiatric problems rise to the fore following the abstinence imposed by hospitalization for alcoholism. On the other hand, there are many patients whose schizophrenia is overtly manifested by, among other symptoms, uncontrolled drinking. Some clinicians speculate that alcohol excess may be a precipitating factor in schizophrenia.

Despite inconclusive evidence about the relationship between alcoholism and schizophrenia, alcoholism is a behavior exhibited by

[1] Reprinted by permission from the JOURNAL OF STUDIES ON ALCOHOL, Vol. 36, pp. 853–881, 1975. Copyright by Journal of Studies on Alcohol, Inc., New Brunswick, New Jersey 08903.

many schizophrenics. Do such patients differ from schizophrenic abstainers, and does such consideration bear implications for prevention and treatment? This topic has received scant attention in the literature despite no dearth of alcoholism or schizophrenia. I hope that this historical review will stimulate some thought and research; at least, its purpose is to collate and summarize previous sources of information even if they are contradictory and inconclusive.

SOME DIAGNOSTIC PROBLEMS

Classification

Diagnostic issues are a major unclarified consideration (157). Thus, "many of the ambiguities and conflicting reports about alcoholism treatment in the literature may well be the result of the failure to establish such a diagnosis" (139). Thirty per cent of new admissions to a mental hospital were diagnosed as alcoholics, and an additional 19% were probably alcoholics, based on a review of their drinking histories (96). The American Psychiatric Association's (APA) *Diagnostic and Statistical Manual of Mental Disorders* (5) encouraged the diagnosis of alcoholism "even when it begins as a symptomatic expression of another disorder." Which of the two conditions should be regarded as the prime disorder is judgmental, with consideration going to the more serious condition. Unless the schizophrenic condition is acute, the sequelae of intoxication likely predominate on initial examination. Others and I (53) have observed that "The patient admitted to a psychiatric hospital with blatant and dramatic alcoholism symptomatology, such as delirium tremens, often poses a crisis situation which, it goes without saying, demands focus upon the alcoholism." Lawrence (90) felt that not only the severity but the very existence of possible underlying psychiatric disorders might be obscured by alcoholism symptomatology. On the other hand, Schwarz and Fjeld (154) made a good point in noting that patients diagnosed as psychotic in emergency rooms were typically assigned to psychiatric wards rather than to alcoholism units which generally afford patients more freedom. Blizard (25) found that schizophrenic and alcoholic case histories were most often considered examples of serious illness by a sample of urban New Zealanders, although a majority considered the diagnostic label, alcoholism, not serious.

The clinical consensus appears to be that if there is disguising or cloaking of psychopathology, alcoholism masks schizophrenia rather than vice versa (42, 126), even though Taylor et al. (168) concluded that many patients diagnosed as acutely schizophrenic actually had affective illness. Alcoholism's role as a dissembler suggests that admission diagnoses, where alcohol is involved, be tentative. The temporal factor is important. For example, Pottier (134) reported a case of a patient hospitalized because of alcoholism whose alcoholic symptomatology gradually gave way to true hebephrenia. Earlier, Diem (41) found 7 alcoholics among 19 patients with dementia simplex with alcoholism secondary to the psychosis, as did Williams and Long (181) much later. Again avoiding the pitfall of determining primacy, the findings of Norman's (120) retrospective study of 42 patients with diagnosed "chronic alcoholic hallucinosis" are fairly typical. Later, most, especially the younger patients, were found to be schizophrenic.

Lest it be concluded that alcoholism diagnoses are too liberally applied, Barchha et al. (12) found that the prevalence of alcoholism among general hospital ward patients was grossly underestimated, concluding that such diagnoses are "not appreciated by attending physicians." Combining their data with those of other general hospital patients (62, 128) and university service patients (119) yielded a 20% prevalence of alcoholism (plus an additional questionable 8%) among the men and 6.5% among the women patients. Not only are physicians loath to make a diagnosis of alcoholism, but patients show a similar reluctance to agree with the diagnosis and treatment for it (162). Hartocollis (72) also noted that alcoholics, when examined by a physician, tended to deny that they had a drinking problem. Labeling alcoholism as a disease has not helped. Rubington (147) saw treatment for alcoholism as a sanction, the end result of exposure and disapproval. Where patients were willing to accept their alcoholism (perhaps because it was less threatening than a disorder over which they felt they had even less control), their self-definition may or may not have been accepted by their physician depending on the latter's criteria for alcoholism and his readiness to make the diagnosis (142).

Jones and Helrich (82) pointed out that psychiatrists were less likely to diagnose problem drinkers as alcoholics and were prone to view alcoholism as a psychogenic symptom. Mayfield and Fowler (105) found that relatively few excessive drinkers received other diagnoses (including schizophrenia), concluding that the diagnosis of alcoholism tended to be arbitrary and to be assigned to a patient "who has an unsophisticated concept of his illness and motivation for passive involvement in nonspecific treatment." Kissin et al. (87) would have concurred for they felt that alcoholics tended to be "indiscriminately assigned to a treatment program" with little regard for the individual patient's needs and potential.

Not the least of diagnostic problems is that for some critics psychiatric diagnosis was perceived as nonproductive (47). Such views held that classification was overemphasized and treatment deemphasized. Unspecified as they are, the therapies for alcoholism and schizophrenia do differ; Fox (51) even suggested specialized therapy for the psychotic alcoholic. Diagnosis should serve to determine treatment, and it also should form one of the bases for composing groups for research comparisons. Increasingly adequate diagnostic techniques should serve to unmask underlying disorders. This is not to imply that schizophrenic and alcoholic disorders are mutually exclusive. It is not uncommon to see a diagnosis of "schizophrenia, manifested by alcoholism, etc.," but the obverse is not encountered. Blane (20) made an excellent point in stating that "if we hold to the conception that the architecture of adult personality is relatively stable and enduring, then it is absurdly whimsical . . . to contemplate the simultaneous existence in one individual of two personalities."

Regarding diagnosis, there have been separatist supporters for alcoholism. Lorr et al. (94) presented factor-analytic data showing that schizophrenic disorganization was a statistically independent syndrome. However, psychiatric disorders are rarely monosymptomatic. Thus, Wallerstein (180) examined notions that alcoholism might (a) be a phenomenon *sui generis* (isolated and distinct from mental illness), (b) be superimposed on the latter, (c) produce a liability to mental illness, or (d) flourish, given an individual already psychiatrically impaired. Diethelm (42) wrote that the majority of alcoholic patients could not be included in the usual diagnostic classifications. Criteria for inclusion in the schizophrenic category include disturbances in thinking, mood and behavior as well as a kind of gross disorganization. Criteria for alcoholism are less specific, with the exception that there be a great—and damaging —intake of alcohol and dependence on it (5). Roa (140), however, felt that "the relationship between schizophrenia and alcoholism could be clarified were it not for the prevalent idea that schizophrenia is a disease centered in thinking and affective disturbance." He focused, rather, on a patient's lack of vital purpose.

In conclusion, a state of irresolution exists, not the first for the mental health professions, concerning classification. This is abetted by the substantial overlap in symptomatology which is found in so many psychiatric disorders, especially if they are chronic in nature. Psychiatric disturbances do mimic one another.

Specificity Notions

A unitary pathogenesis for a psychiatric disorder has always been a tempting but elusive goal. The implications of specificity theories for detection, prevention and treatment are obvious, but current thought is in the direction of nonspecificity. Rothstein et al. (146) found clear adjustment, symptom and background differences between schizophrenics and alcoholics, as did Apperson (7) in the patients' childhood experiences.

Regarding alcoholism, I (53) have not been alone in concluding that "a wide variety of patients with as yet unelucidated underlying psychiatric conditions might be loosely grouped under the rubric of 'alcoholic,'" despite heterogeneity of symptomatology among alcoholics (54, 74). Schaefer (151) characterized alcoholics as a heterogeneous group drawn from a broader population subject to many different functional disorders; Johnson (80) viewed alcoholism as cutting across all behavioral diagnostic categories; and Lisansky-Gomberg (92) noted the failure to delineate a characteristic prealcoholic behavior structure. While denying that there is a specific alcoholic personality, Blane (20) emphasized the "3-D's of alcoholism: dependency, depression, and denial." On the other hand, Berry (17) found different premorbid characteristics among preschizophrenic and prealcoholic boys—the former were characterized by deficiency of self-value and the latter by group acting-out activities. Coleman (36), too, found that emergency-room patients with alcoholism represented a homogeneous group, discretely different from other psychiatric patients, and Fox (51) contended that alcoholics were prone to become alike in their behavior. Earlier, Fox (50) had delineated three types of patients in addition to the psychotic alcoholic. In this context, she noted, too, that some "symptomatic drinkers" might have an underlying psychosis. However, Thimann (169) had observed a category of patients who had a history of little preexisting emotional disturbance causally responsible for the alcoholic excess and Brotman (29), too, felt that alcoholism could develop in "normal" individuals. These views notwithstanding, by and large mental health professionals perceive alcoholism as symptomatic of an underlying emotional disturbance (43) and as nonspecific in terms of etiology.

This nonspecificity holds, too, in the latest views of schizophrenia which, for example, Bellak (15) called the "schizophrenic syndrome" and characterized as a shared commonality of a host of causative factors, a conception voiced by others (28, 44). However, Vincent et al. (177), studying physicians as psychiatric patients, introduced a somewhat different notion. Their proposition was that the greater the underlying personality disturbance the greater the possibility of addiction to alcohol. This would tend to negate specificity views of alcoholism, stressing, rather, the degree of psychopathology as a causative factor in excessive drinking. This has a quantitative, not qualitative, flavor. Others have also made reference to underlying or borderline psychosis. Fox (51) noted that individuals so diagnosed may turn to alcohol, and Andreyeva et al. (6) found that of 3 (of 800) alcoholics treated with disulfiram who developed psychoses, 2 had pretreatment schizophrenic conditions. In the same vein, there was a report of a "considerable schizophrenic gradient" in alcoholic patients who revealed psychotic tendencies after treatment with disulfiram, a gradient which might have become manifest during periods of prolonged abstinence (61).

Cause and Effect

While alcoholism and schizophrenia do not appear to interact in specific cause-and-effect relationships, there are some subtleties here. An extensive review (27) long ago concluded that excessive drinking per se did not produce psychosis. However, Sikorska-Godwod (160) attributed etiological significance to alcoholism in 13 alcoholic patients with schizophrenia-like psychoses who had begun their heavy drinking between the ages of 8 and 15. The APA diagnostic manual (5) also attributed some alcoholism to other mental disorders. In contradiction, Carney and Lawes (34) compared alcoholic and nonalcoholic psychiatric patients and found that the development of heavy drinking was not due to psychiatric illness. Also, Parker et al. (126) reported that intemperance was responsible for precipitating the conditions which eventuated in hospitalization for "quite a few" of 33 alcoholic schizophrenics. Schizophrenia has been viewed as intensified by heavy drinking (159), and the schizophrenic's alcoholism has been seen as "secondary to or symptomatic of the preexisting psychiatric illness, but even this remains to be demonstrated" (153). The latter study included 2 cases of alcoholism where the patients had preexisting schizophrenia. Similar views of alcoholism as symptomatic of another psychosis were propounded by Bleuler (21): "I have not yet seen a case where the schizophrenia appeared subsequent to alcoholism." Noyes and Kolb (121) also regarded alcohol as the releasor of a reaction which was primarily psychogenic and intrinsic to the individual's personality structure.

Personality as a predisposing condition for alcoholism was emphasized by Sanford (150) in an effort to point out that susceptibility to alcoholism is not solely biological. Jones (81) also stressed this when, using longitudinal study data, she showed that some alcohol-related behaviors, expressions of deep-seated personality tendencies, predated the onset of drinking patterns.

THE UTILITY OF ALCOHOL TO THE SCHIZOPHRENIC

Alcohol as a Defense

That alcohol can stimulate release is attested clinically, experimentally and anecdotally by 6000 years of drinking. Many have commented on this effect of alcohol in different terms. Hallay (68) saw alcohol as possibly producing a "social" amelioration of schizophrenic symptoms; Pollack (133) referred to use of alcohol as a tool to reestablish emotional homeostasis; Tähkä (166) conceptualized the psychodynamic function of alcohol to be that of a "regressive regulator of self-esteem"; Blume and Sheppard (26) characterized alcohol as a drug utilized "to achieve a particular psychological effect or personality change"; and Sherfey (158) speculated that alcohol permits emotional release, thus forestalling a full-blown psychotic breakdown. The effects of alcohol on mood and affect have been reviewed (53); many psychiatric patients apparently employ alcohol as a self-prescribed mood regulator, especially as an attenuator of depression (52). This follows for schizophrenics, too, if, as Blinder (24) held, some clinicians believe that all schizophrenia has its onset as depression. Additionally, Noyes and Kolb (121) saw affect as the major problem in schizophrenia. Since many schizophrenics experience affective blunting and mood disturbances, it is possible that alcohol has utility for them in this regard. One wonders, too, why the schizophrenic, with an already fairly well-fixed set of defenses, turns to alcohol, another line of defense so to speak. Still, Markham (102) emphasized the defensive nature of drinking for the schizophrenic.

Are schizophrenics who drink heavily those with the most tenuous schizophrenic defenses? If so, they would have the best prognosis, precisely the hypothesis advanced by Kardos and Mária (84), and exactly opposite to that of Tomsovic (171). Sherfey (158) noted in her follow-up of alcoholic paranoid schizophrenics that they had neither better nor worse prognoses than nonalcoholic schizophrenics. One research possibility would be a study of hospital length of stay, hypothesizing that schizophrenic excessive drinkers are discharged earlier than schizophrenics who do not drink heavily. A control would be that the former group's admissions had not been precipitated by drinking alone.

The Drive for Release

Enigmatic, too, is the fact that psychoanalysts (106, 136) have long depicted the craving for alcohol as a drive for release. Does the alcoholic schizophrenic, with his already poor reality testing and shaky self-control, seek further release or is the release which is sought an escape from the threat and vulnerability engendered by the schizophrenia? For example, McGuire et al. (97) hypothesized that alcoholics functioned with better ego integration when intoxicated than when sober, and DeVito et al. (40) described just such a phenomenon in a schizophrenic who preserved ego integrity by the prolonged consumption of alcohol, but who became overtly psychotic when detoxicated. These authors suggested that alcohol served a defensive function against anxiety. Alpert and Silvers (4) found that some schizophrenics reported that alcohol reduced the discomfort caused by hallucinations. A demurrer to this notion of alcohol's utility was Milano (109) who saw little evidence that alcoholism in schizophrenia was explicable in terms of an attempt to escape failure in social or interpersonal relationships. However, of 15 catatonics treated with alcohol to attain a blood alcohol concentration of 0.2%, 4 improved and became more communicative and socially accessible (83). In 7, however, the improvement lasted only as long as significant levels of intoxication were maintained. One may question, then, whether alcohol abets schizophrenic regression or counteracts it.

A final comment about alcohol's utility derives from the observation (89) that alcoholics have poor self-concepts, feel empty and perhaps drink because it is "better to be an alcoholic than nothing at all." Could this also be extrapolated to the schizophrenic with his unfulfilled sense of self? For example, might the whole ritual which surrounds drinking be a kind of affirmation of reality for the schizophrenic, might it make him "feel," even though for others the very opposite seemingly results when intoxication is achieved? Such questions bear a relationship to the vexed broader issue of symptom choice.

STATISTICAL EVIDENCE

Diethelm's (42) claim that alcoholism may hide psychotic manifestations in chronic schizophrenics for years is borne out by the citations in Table 1 in which other (notably schizophrenic) diagnostic data on alcoholic subjects are presented. These data underscore Diethelm's recommendation that the alcoholism receive treatment "but only as part of the treatment of the schizophrenic illness."

There is no controversy about the fact that some schizophrenics drink heavily although they are akin to Desdemona who averred, "I have very poor and unhappy brains for drinking." Table 2 presents a summary of data gathered on the intemperance of some schizophrenic samples. Roa (140) claimed that such data were misleading because only overt schizophrenics enter psychiatric hospitals, the sites for most data collection. On the other hand, the problem is compounded by the finding (57) that general hospitals do not admit grossly psychotic patients.

Some data, not quantitative, are based on statistical summations of clinical observations. For example, Gross (63) wrote that schizophrenia occurs in alcoholics ("Most observers report an incidence of about 14 percent which confirms our own experience") and Sherfey (158) noted that "probably all psychiatrists in practice have had some experience with the schizophrenic who is a heavy drinker and is often considered a chronic alcoholic until the schizophrenic symptomatology becomes obvious." However, Åmark (1) concluded that there was no greater risk of the development of schizophrenia among alcoholics than among the general population. Summarizing earlier research, it was estimated (139) that as many as 70% of alcoholics studied also presented other significant psychiatric symptomatology. Rathod and Thomson (138) also sought data on associated mental disorders of women alcoholics, reporting mainly affective disturbances, but Milano (109) claimed that schizophrenic forms of alcoholism were the most frequent syndrome. Earlier, Bleuler (21) wrote that nearly 10% of the alcoholics whom he had studied were schizophrenics. Epidemiological evidence (60) showed that many alcoholics had previously received treatment for another

TABLE 1.—*Other Diagnostic Data on Alcoholics*

Author	Year	Subjects	Other Diagnoses
Adell (3)	1938	39 alcoholics admitted to institution for antisocials	9 (23%) simple schizophrenics
Barrett (13)	1943	100 hospitalized alcoholics	2 (2%) paranoid dementia praecox
Binswanger (18)	1935	174 patients diagnosed as pathologically intoxicated	6 (4%) schizophrenics
Carney (33)	1970	40 psychiatric inpatient alcoholics	5 (13%) paranoid schizophrenics
Feeney et al. (48)	1955	50 workhouse patients with charges of inebriety	14% schizophrenics; 18% borderline schizophrenics
		50 outpatient alcoholics	8% schizophrenics; 28% borderline schizophrenics
Gillis and Keet (57)	1969	797 inpatient alcoholics	9 (1%) schizophrenics at follow-up
Gorwitz et al. (60)	1970	1171 identified alcoholics who had received another nonalcoholic diagnosis	385 (33%) schizophrenics
		1024 Maryland residents with a reported drinking problem and a nonalcoholic diagnosis	23% schizophrenics
Guze et al. (67)	1962	Case report of 1 alcoholic	also diagnosed schizophrenic before drinking
Hallay (69)	1940	Patient with acute alcoholic psychosis	schizophrenic on earlier admission
Lederer (91)	1953	32 patients admitted to hospital with history of alcoholism	10 (31%) schizophrenic reaction
Minski (111)	1938	50 hospitalized alcoholics	31 suffered from "psychopathy"; none schizophrenic

Study	Year	Sample	Findings
Moore and Ramseur (114)	1960	100 alcoholics in open-ward hospital	9 (9%) schizophrenics
Panepinto et al. (125)	1970	340 patients assigned to supportive drug therapy program	60 (18%) schizophrenics
Peters (129)	1956	120 patients in hospital ward for alcoholics	8.3% primarily psychotic
Rimmer et al. (139)	1972	259 hospitalized alcoholics	32% primary psychiatric problems independent of symptomatic drinking; only 4 schizophrenics
Scott (156)	1966	24 alcoholics in clinic	all schizophrenics
Sherfey (158)	1955	161 hospitalized alcoholics	14 (8%) paranoid schizophrenics
Smart et al. (161)	1966	30 alcoholics	1 (3%) pseudoneurotic schizophrenic
Tidmarsh (170)	1970	117 alcoholics in mental hospital	5% primary diagnosis of schizophrenia
Tomsovic (171)	1968	411 alcoholic patients in V.A. hospital	19% schizophrenics; another 13% possible schizophrenics
Tomsovic and Edwards (172)	1970	233 alcoholic patients in V.A. hospital	113 (49%) had diagnosis of schizophrenia
Van Dusen et al. (174)	1967	68 female alcoholics	2 (3%) schizophrenics
Vorontsova (178)	1959	60 patients with atypical hallucinatory-delirious psychoses	1 clear, 3 possible history of schizophrenia; 5 schizoid traits
Wolfensberger (185)	1923	16 patients hospitalized with alcoholic hallucinosis	10 (63%) developed schizophrenia

TABLE 2.—Data on Intemperance of Schizophrenic Patients

Author	Year	Subjects	Intemperance
Alpert and Silvers (4)	1970	9 schizophrenics	all heavy alcohol abusers
Csekey (37)	1925	1 schizophrenic patient	abused alcohol
Johanson (79)	1958	100 male schizophrenics	35 (35%) have "more notable" alcohol consumption
Malzberg (99)	1955	dementia praecox patients admitted to N.Y. State mental hospitals, 1939–41	14.7% of Black and 7.1% of White patients were intemperate
Malzberg (101)	1960	dementia praecox first admissions to N.Y. State mental hospitals	0.9% of Jewish and 8.7% of non-Jewish patients used alcohol intemperately
Markham (102)	1957	1 schizophrenic woman	had pronounced alcoholism
Moon and Patton (113)	1963	schizophrenic first admissions to N.Y. State mental hospitals, 1955–60	11% were intemperate users of alcohol
Opler (123)	1957	30 hospitalized schizophrenic patients of Irish extraction	19 (63%) were alcoholics
		30 schizophrenics, Italian extraction	1 (3%) alcoholic
Parker et al. (126)	1960	150 hospitalized schizophrenics	22% alcoholics
Strauss (165)	1950	7 schizophrenic women in hospital	alcoholism was symptom or determining factor in psychosis in all
Winship (184)	1957	1 chronic schizophrenic	was alcoholic

stated psychiatric diagnosis. An 8-year follow-up study (59) of convicted felons diagnosed as alcoholics in prison revealed that about 10% had hallucinations and paranoid ideation not attributable to drinking. Also, Benedetti (16) found that 13 of 23 patients with chronic alcoholic hallucinosis developed typical schizophrenic patterns. He suggested that they might have developed blatant schizophrenia had they not become alcoholics. By the same token, 9.6% of first admissions with alcoholic psychoses to all hospitals for mental disease in New York State from 1949 to 1951 had a schizoid personality make-up (100). Binswanger (19) reported in 1920 that 8 alcoholics who showed no overt schizophrenia were schizoid personalities. On the other hand, 113 patients, recovered from acute episodes of alcoholic hallucinosis, showed neither premorbid nor postintoxication schizophrenic personalities (16). Benedetti concluded (16) that chronic hallucinosis might result in schizophrenic dementia. Shumakov (159) studied a group of schizophrenics who drank excessively: when 43 of 85 stopped their intemperance, in only 7 cases was there a concomitant improvement in mental status.

Statistical studies have accomplished their purpose with convincing evidence that a not insignificant proportion of schizophrenics are intemperate and that many alcoholics suffer an underlying schizophrenia. Further studies should be aware of the need for a careful and probing history as well as for establishing a comprehensive diagnosis.

There is need for identification of drinking patterns in schizophrenics. Schizophrenic alcoholics "generally seemed nonresponsive to therapeutic measures" (126), although a later report of a 3-year special treatment program for schizophrenic alcoholics (156) seemed encouraging.

SOME COMPARISONS OF ALCOHOLISM AND SCHIZOPHRENIA

Similarities and Differences

Alcoholics and schizophrenics have been compared on a number of dimensions, few of which meet stringent requirements for research into schizophrenia (11). Darrohn (38) found a "remarkable" but statistically insignificant similarity in the prepsychotic personality traits of patients with dementia praecox and alcoholism. Nearly all of 150 "deteriorated alcoholics" or schizophrenics with a variety of incapacitating symptoms improved as a result of perphenazine treatment (149). Rapp (137) noted that nicotinamide had been an effective therapy for schizophrenia and that the unjustifiable assumption that alcoholics were basically schizophrenic had caused the drug to be recommended in the treatment of alcoholism. Dennehy (39) found that both alcoholics and schizophrenics suffered significant childhood bereavement and this parental deprivation was hypothesized to result in difficulties in coping with stresses in adulthood (73). Bleuler (23), however, tended to deny this in a sense, maintaining that alcoholics reacted to increased stress with increased frequency of alcoholism, not of schizophrenia. Kardos and Mária (84) saw a number of possible interactions between alcoholism and schizophrenia.

Differences between the syndromes have also been stressed. For example, if factor-analyzed neurotic and psychotic symptomatologies are plotted (45), then alcoholic and schizophrenic syndromes do not coincide. This conclusion would follow from a report (163) that the scores of alcoholics on the Minnesota Multiphasic Personality Inventory schizophrenia scale were not particularly elevated but more closely resembled a neurotic pattern. A possible metabolic difference between alcoholics and schizophrenics was pointed out by Gus'kov (65) who administered alcohol to both and found that in many schizophrenics, especially hebephrenics and catatonics, reducing substances were initially higher and times to maximum blood alcohol concentration and total alcohol oxidation were longer than in normals or alcoholics. Not only did alcohol appear to be metabolized differently by the two groups, they apparently also responded differently when anticipating drinking. Menaker (108) found that alcoholics reacted with significantly increased anxiety when anticipating drinking; schizophrenics' anxieties decreased. Rorschach assessment of genetic level of development[2] yielded significant differences between schizophrenics and both reactive and essential alcoholics.

Alcoholic Hallucinosis

Although a chronic pattern and life style of alcoholism seems to lend itself to a diagnosis of schizophrenia (54), the alcoholic hallucinosis accompanying an episode of acute intoxication has presented a

---

[2] REILLY, D. H. and MESSINGER, L. R. A specific Rorschach index for assessing genetic maturity. Presented at the Eastern Psychological Association Meeting, Boston, 6–8 April 1967.

close parallel to schizophrenia for many observers.[3] This phenomenon has stirred arguments pro and con. Hallucinatory behavior occurs with some frequency—according to Mott et al. (116) in 76% of the schizophrenics and 84% of the alcoholics in one sample.

There are proponents of the theory that alcoholic hallucinosis is not a purely alcoholic disorder but has a schizophrenic basis (22, 70, 76, 121, 185)—alcoholic hallucinosis is symptomatic of an underlying schizophrenic syndrome and does not represent an alcoholic psychosis. Additionally, Martín-Santos (103) categorized authentic delirious perceptions of alcoholics as characteristic of schizophrenia, as did Rosenberg (143) with three types of delirium tremens.

Gross and his colleagues (64) took a more moderate stance, seeing some, not all, cases of acute hallucinosis as schizophrenic. The acute–chronic dichotomy seems to be a crucial differentiating feature. Later, Gross (63) moved to a farther position, claiming that evidence that alcoholic hallucinosis was a manifestation of an underlying paranoid schizophrenia was lacking. In essential agreement with the view that alcoholic hallucinosis is a nonschizophrenic disturbance were Burton-Bradley (32), who found that in only 4 of 41 patients with alcoholic hallucinosis did the condition develop into schizophrenia, Orthmayr (124), who regarded alcoholic paranoid psychoses as a separate and distinct entity, and Moefes (112), who saw alcoholic paranoia as not purely psychogenic but due to alcohol. Alpert and Silvers (4) tried to differentiate between alcoholic hallucinations that were more frequent and localized in space, and schizophrenic hallucinations that were poorly localized, subject to emotional arousal and cognitively tainted. Freeman (55) differentiated the two types of hallucinatory syndromes largely in terms of other aspects of the patient's total life and Auersperg and Cid-Araneda (8) conceived of the fears of the metalcoholic psychotic as being very specific, those of the schizophrenic more general. Finally, Victor and Hope (176) studied 70 patients with 76 episodes of auditory alcoholic hallucinosis. No significant relationship to schizophrenia was noted in 68 of the episodes and few of the patients could be categorized as schizothymes.

Between the extreme positions that alcoholic hallucinosis and schizophrenia are either unitary or represent dichotomous catego-

---

[3] For early reviews, see Meggendorfer (107) and Zehner (186).

ries lies a middle ground. For example, Huber (75) had difficulty in differentiating whether alcoholic hallucinosis was purely exogenous or whether it required alcohol plus a schizophrenic predisposition. Harder (71) classified the acute form of alcoholic hallucinosis as exogenous, the chronic type as a form of paranoid schizophrenia. Goodwin et al. (58) found that hallucinations were nonspecific and appeared in conjunction with a variety of psychiatric disorders. As evidence of this, schizoid hallucinosis was described, a condition intermediate between schizophrenia with alcoholism and hallucinosis of schizoid origin (93).

Genetic and Family History Approaches

Early reviews (30, 31, 77) noted hereditary and family history relationships between alcoholism and schizophrenia. Parents and siblings of alcoholics were found to have a higher morbidity risk for psychogenic psychoses than the general population (1). There appeared to be a greater incidence of alcoholism and mental disorders in general in the families of alcoholics than was anticipated in the general population (166). This was supported by other reports of alcoholics (66, 88, 132, 155, 182, 183), but in none of these was there any outstanding relationship between alcoholism and schizophrenia per se among family members. Bleuler (23) studied the relatives of 50 alcoholics, finding no greater incidence of schizophrenia than in the "average population" of equivalent socioeconomic status, and Sherfey (158) found that 14 alcoholics with well-defined paranoid schizophrenia had family histories replete with mental illness but a relatively low incidence of alcoholism. Other reports, however, did suggest a more specific correlation. Thus, schizophrenia was found more frequently among the families of patients with alcoholic hallucinosis (117) and a 31% incidence of alcoholism was found in families of schizophrenics compared with 1% in the general population (115). Although one interpretation was that similar stresses such as sex-role confusion (95) led to both dysfunctions, the high incidence of alcoholism in the families of schizophrenics led Vaziri (175) to infer a possible hereditary disposition, a hypothesis carried to an extreme in considering the question of compulsive sterilization for alcoholism and schizophrenia because of their assumed inheritability (14).

Berry (17) emphasized the role of family influences in the development of later psychopathology. He studied the family patterns of boys seen in a child guidance center who were later hospitalized for schizophrenia or alcoholism. He found distinctive differences: homes of preschizophrenics tended to be severely chaotic, of pre-alcoholics less disorganized and including parents who stimulated socially deviant behaviors. This kind of longitudinal study gathered data which are much more precise than a more general family history overview, the latter traditionally lending itself readily to broad generalization in terms of inheritance.

Regarding familial studies of alcoholics, a good suggestion was made long ago—that family histories of alcoholics other than those who present themselves for treatment at clinics and hospitals be studied (30).

SOME RESEARCH CONSIDERATIONS

Subject Selection

There has been a plethora of research in schizophrenia as well as in alcoholism. In the case of the latter, there is a trend to study the "pure" alcoholic, eliminating as subjects those whose alcoholism is complicated by psychosis. For example, Tomsovic (171) attempted to screen alcoholics with diagnosed or possible schizophrenia out of his study although 134 such patients out of 411 were included in his final sample. The rationale for their exclusion was that they were prognostically difficult patients compared with nonschizophrenic alcoholics. In a comparison of two treatment programs for alcoholics, the diagnosis of "nuclear" schizophrenia was one of the criteria for absolute exclusion of alcoholic subjects (131). Mayfield and Allen (104) screened alcoholics for schizophrenia in a psychopharmacological study; others (57, 110) conducted alcoholism treatment programs which rejected psychotic patients. Earlier, Oltman and Friedman (122) referred to the diagnosis of "simple alcoholism." In a slight reversal of the aforementioned exclusivity, Menaker (108) eliminated schizophrenics with a history of drinking problems from his study.

All of the foregoing seemed to be based on the notion that there were unadulterated, as well as tainted (by combination), varieties of alcoholism and schizophrenia. If so, then one approach would be to include all such subjects (identified, of course) in, for example, treatment programs to try to discern differential responses to various modalities. This might help to identify basic differences and their origins between the types of patients studied. On the other hand, such investigations could possibly show a lack of significant differences, findings which cannot result from an experimental policy based on exclusion.

The Search for a Meaningful Variable

Classification of patients into the nosological groups, alcoholism or schizophrenia, has not seemed to yield fruitful research. Perhaps these broad groups should be refined into better differentiated subgroups (127) or in terms of some independent third variable. Other working classifications might include "acute" versus "chronic" alcoholism; Pugh's (135) notions that there were more general and more specific psychiatric disorders and that alcoholism was among the former; Rudie and McGaughran's (148) elaboration of essential and reactive alcoholism; Garmezy's (56) interpretations of process and reactive schizophrenia; Robins and Guze's (141) separation of schizophrenics in terms of favorable and unfavorable prognostic factors; and Katz's (85) interpretation that there were several distinct varieties of paranoid schizophrenia. Suggested variables for study might include, for example, age. Schizophrenia traditionally has been regarded as a disorder of early life while alcoholism takes more time to develop, requiring years of heavy drinking. Thus, Sikorska-Godwod's (160) description of a sample of alcoholics who began drinking very early in life and who developed a schizophrenia-like psychosis suggested less pathology than descriptions of full-blown schizophrenia, hinting that perhaps early alcoholism blunted the psychosis. One research possibility might be to pursue this lead, identifying early problem drinkers for later follow-up. A corollary hypothesis might be that, in a retrospective study, patients with an early onset of schizophrenia would have a lower incidence of alcoholism than those with a later onset because alcoholism required time to develop, because other (psychotic) defense mechanisms had primacy, or because alcoholism required effort, energy expenditure and more goal-directed behavior than a schizophrenic can garner. Follow-up studies would appear to be a sine qua non. The fate of recovered alcoholics and schizophrenics is important to determine, with frequency counts made of those who show decided switches to manifestations of the other disorder.

Other possible differentiating variables include personality test performance although there is little previous success to encourage optimism here. For example, overlap in score distributions between a variety of psychiatric patient groups has been a traditional finding.

A recent example utilizing the MacAndrew Alcoholism Scale found overlap between alcoholics and a nonalcoholic group of 56 patients which included 17 schizophrenics (173). However, Rorschach investigations of psychopathological perception and developmental level (130)[2] have not been exhausted. Other methodologies are available in the areas of learning and thinking. Aaronson et al. (2) reported that schizophrenics performed worse than alcoholics on tasks of incidental learning, and Wahl and Wishner (179) found schizophrenic thinking more concrete and regressive than that of alcoholics. A caution in such comparisons of alcoholics and schizophrenics concerns the possible prevalence of organic disorder. Thus, Schéda and Timár (152) raised the question of whether cerebral atrophy in alcoholism might result in psychosis, and Mabry-Hall (98) interpreted the deviant perceptions of alcoholics as a reflection of cortical pathology.

Social Factors

As is true with other factors, data on social parameters in alcoholism and schizophrenia are contradictory. An early report (46) found the highest rates of alcoholic psychoses and of schizophrenia in the zone of transition near the center of the city. Although the Midtown Manhattan Study (164) concluded that there were individuals vulnerable to schizophrenia in all socioeconomic status origin groups, recent data (144) confirmed that patients hospitalized with alcohol withdrawal syndromes tended to come from urban areas characterized by overcrowding, low income, etc. Opler (123) found, as did Bagley and Binitie (10), that alcoholism among schizophrenics had a cultural correlation. In general, it appears that the best that can be said about the manifestations and etiologies of alcoholism (78) and schizophrenia (145) is that they are multivariate and heterogeneous.

There are two recent notable attempts to outline diagnostic and prognostic criteria to enable psychiatric researchers to compose more homogeneous patient groups: Taylor's (167) advocacy of first-rank symptoms (35) and prognostic signs with schizophrenics and criteria (49) for the whole range of psychiatric diagnoses. However, even in the latter, two criteria for the diagnosis of schizophrenia are the "absence of alcoholism . . . within one year of onset of psychosis" and an onset prior to the age of 40, a relatively early age, which again tends to exclude some alcoholism.

BIBLIOGRAPHY

1. ÅMARK, C. A study in alcoholism; clinical, social-psychiatric and genetic investigations. Acta Psychiat., Suppl. No. 70, 1951.

2. AARONSON, B. S., SUGERMAN, A. A. and HAFETZ, M. R. Incidental learning in chronic schizophrenics, alcoholics and normals. Proc. 74th Conv. Amer. Psychol. Ass., pp. 181–182, 1966.

3. ADELL, G. Psychiatric examinations of certain male vagrants and alcoholics in Sweden in the year 1938. Acta Psychiat. 13: 447–462, 1938.

4. ALPERT, M. and SILVERS, K. N. Perceptual characteristics distinguishing auditory hallucinations in schizophrenia and acute alcoholic psychoses. Am. J. Psychiat. 127: 298–302, 1970.

5. AMERICAN PSYCHIATRIC ASSOCIATION. Diagnostic and statistical manual of mental disorders. 2d ed. Washington, D.C.; 1968.

6. ANDREYEVA, V. A., GAVRILOVA, L. V., LEVIN, V. M. and RESHETNIKOVA, Zh. V. K voprosu ob ostrykh psikhoticheskikh sostoyaniyakh, voznikayushchikh vo vremya lecheniya antabusom bol'nykh khronicheskim alkogolizmom. (The problem of acute psychotic conditions occurring during Antabuse treatment of patients with chronic alcoholism.) Zh. Nevropat. 59: 674–679, 1959.

7. APPERSON, L. B. Childhood experiences of schizophrenics and alcoholics. J. Genet. Psychol. 106: 301–313, 1965.

8. AUERSPERG, A. and CID-ARANEDA, A. Bedrohungsdelir und Verfolgungswahn; zur Unterscheidung metalkoholischer und schizophrener Halluzinosen. Nervenarzt 41: 209–214, 1970.

9. BACON, S. D. The process of addiction to alcohol. Q. J. Stud. Alcohol 34: 1–27, 1973.

10. BAGLEY, C. and BINITIE, A. Alcoholism and schizophrenia in Irishmen in London. Br. J. Addict. 65: 3–7, 1970.

11. BANNISTER, D. The logical requirements of research into schizophrenia. Br. J. Psychiat. 114: 181–188, 1968.

12. BARCHHA, R., STEWART, M. A. and GUZE, S. B. The prevalence of alcoholism among general hospital ward patients. Am. J. Psychiat. 125: 681–684, 1968.

13. BARRETT, T. M. Chronic alcoholism in veterans. Q. J. Stud. Alcohol 4: 68–78, 1943.

14. DE BARROS, M. Consideracioes sobre eugenia a propósito da esquizofrenia e do alcoolismo crónico. J. Méd. Porto 44: 217–221, 1961.

15. BELLAK, L. Introduction, personal reflections and a brief review. In: BELLAK, L. and LOEB, L., eds. The schizophrenic syndrome. New York; Grune & Stratton; 1969.

16. BENEDETTI, G. Die Alkoholhalluzinosen. Stuttgart; Thieme; 1952.

17. BERRY, J. C. Antecedents of schizophrenia, impulsive character, and alcoholism in males. Ph.D. dissertation, Columbia University; 1967.

18. BINSWANGER, H. Klinische und charakterologische Untersuchungen an pathologisch Berauschten. Z. Ges. Neurol. Psychiat. 152: 703–737, 1935.
19. BINSWANGER, K. Ueber schizoide Alkoholiker. Z. Ges. Neurol. Psychiat. 60: 127–159, 1920.
20. BLANE, H. T. The personality of the alcoholic; guises of dependency. New York; Harper & Row; 1968.
21. BLEULER, E. Dementia praecox or the group of schizophrenias. (ZINKEN, J., transl.) New York; International Universities Press; 1950.
22. BLEULER, E. Textbook of psychiatry. New York; Dover; 1951.
23. BLEULER, M. Familial and personal background of chronic alcoholics. Pp. 110–166. In: DIETHELM, O., ed. Etiology of chronic alcoholism. Springfield, Ill.; Thomas; 1955.
24. BLINDER, M. G. The pragmatic classification of depression. Am. J. Psychiat. 123: 259–269, 1966.
25. BLIZARD, P. J. The public image and social rejection of the alcoholic in New Zealand. Q. J. Stud. Alcohol 30: 686–700, 1969.
26. BLUME, S. B. and SHEPPARD, C. The changing effects of drinking on the changing personalities of alcoholics. Q. J. Stud. Alcohol 28: 436–443, 1967.
27. BOWMAN, K. M. and JELLINEK, E. M. Alcoholic mental disorders. Q. J. Stud. Alcohol 2: 312–390, 1941.
28. BRILL, N. W. General biological studies. In: BELLAK, L. and LOEB, L., eds. The schizophrenic syndrome. New York; Grune & Stratton; 1969.
29. BROTMAN, R. Total treatment. Int. J. Psychiat. 5: 45–46, 1968.
30. BRUGGER, C. Familienuntersuchungen bei chronischen Alkoholikern. Z. Ges. Neurol. Psychiat. 151: 103–129, 1934.
31. BRUGGER, C. Familienuntersuchungen bei Alkoholdeliranten. Z. Ges. Neurol. Psychiat. 151: 740–788, 1934.
32. BURTON-BRADLEY, B. G. Aspects of alcoholic hallucinosis. Med. J. Aust. 2: 8–11, 1958.
33. CARNEY, M. W. P. Serum folate and cyanocobalamin in alcoholics. Q. J. Stud. Alcohol 31: 816–822, 1970.
34. CARNEY, M. W. P. and LAWES, T. G. G. The etiology of alcoholism in the English upper social classes. Q. J. Stud. Alcohol 28: 59–69, 1967.
35. CARPENTER, W. T. and STRAUSS, J. S. Cross-cultural evaluation of Schneider's first-rank symptoms of schizophrenia; a report from the International Pilot Study of Schizophrenia. Am. J. Psychiat. 131: 682–687, 1974.
36. COLEMAN, J. V. Research in walk-in psychiatric services in general hospitals. Am. J. Psychiat. 124: 1668–1673, 1968.
37. CSEKEY, L. Az alkoholos elmeállapotok az elmebaj fölépítese szempontjából. (Alcoholic mental states from the viewpoint of the structure of the disorder.) Orv. Hetil. 69: 171–172, 1925.
38. DARROHN, L. D. The pre-psychotic personality traits of alcoholic patients as compared with dementia praecox and manic-depressive patients. Smith Coll. Stud. Social Work 10: 142–144, 1939.
39. DENNEHY, C. M. Childhood bereavement and psychiatric illness. Br. J. Psychiat. 112: 1049–1069, 1966.

40. DEVITO, R. A., FLAHERTY, L. A. and MOZDZIERZ, G. J. Toward a psycho-dynamic theory of alcoholism. Dis. Nerv. Syst. 31: 43–49, 1970.

41. DIEM, O. Die einfach demente Form der Dementia Praecox (Dementia Simplex). Archs Psychiat. 37: 111–187, 1903.

42. DIETHELM, O. Some fundamental considerations in the treatment of chronic alcoholism. Pp. 191–198. In: HIMWICH, H. E., ed. Alcoholism, basic aspects and treatment. (American Association for the Advancement of Science, Publ. No. 47.) Washington, D.C.; 1957.

43. DITMAN, K. S. Do we have a specific treatment for alcoholism? Int. J. Psychiat. 5: 48–53, 1968.

44. DONLON, P. T. The enigma of the schizophrenias. Psychosomatics 13: 272–275, 1972.

45. EYSENCK, H. J. Classification and the problems of diagnosis. In: EYSENCK, H. J., ed. Handbook of abnormal psychology. New York; Basic Books; 1961.

46. FARIS, R. E. L. and DUNHAM, H. W. Concentration of alcoholic psychoses. Pp. 110–119. In: Mental disorders in urban areas. Chicago: University of Chicago Press; 1939.

47. FARNSWORTH, D. L. Medical perspectives on alcoholism and around-the-clock psychiatric services. Am. J. Psychiat. 124: 1659–1663, 1968.

48. FEENEY, F. E., MINDLIN, D. F., MINEAR, V. H. and SHORT, E. E. The challenge of the Skid Row alcoholic; a social, psychological and psychiatric comparison of chronically jailed alcoholics and cooperative alcoholic clinic patients. Q. J. Stud. Alcohol 16: 645–667, 1955.

49. FEIGHNER, J. R., ROBINS, E., GUZE, S. B., WOODRUFF, R. A., JR., WINOKUR, G. and MUNOZ, R. Diagnostic criteria for use in psychiatric research. Archs Gen. Psychiat. 26: 57–63, 1972.

50. FOX, R. Treatment of alcoholism. Pp. 163–172. In: HIMWICH, H. E., ed. Alcoholism, basic aspects and treatment. (American Association for the Advancement of Science, Publ. No. 47.) Washington, D.C.; 1957.

51. FOX, R. A multidisciplinary approach to the treatment of alcoholism. Am. J. Psychiat. 123: 769–778, 1967.

52. FREED, E. X. Alcohol abuse by manic patients. Psychol. Rep. 25: 280, 1969.

53. FREED, E. X. Alcoholism and manic–depressive disorders; some perspectives. Q. J. Stud. Alcohol 31: 62–89, 1970.

54. FREED, E. X., TRIPLETT, D. G. and FREEMAN, E. P. Characteristics of male alcoholics. J. Med. Soc. New Jers. 68: 1011–1013, 1971.

55. FREEMAN, T. Symptomatology, diagnosis, and clinical course. In: BELLAK, L. and LOEB, L., eds. The schizophrenic syndrome. New York; Grune & Stratton; 1969.

56. GARMEZY, N. Process and reactive schizophrenia; some conceptions and issues. Pp. 419–466. In: KATZ, M. M., COLE, J. O. and BARTON, W. E., eds. The role and methodology of classification in psychiatry and psychopathology. (U.S. Publ. Hlth Service, Publ. No. 1584.) Washington, D.C.; U.S. Govt Print. Off.; 1968.

57. GILLIS, L. S. and KEET, M. Prognostic factors and treatment results in hospitalized alcoholics. Q. J. Stud. Alcohol 30: 426–437, 1969.

58. GOODWIN, D. W., ALDERSON, P. and ROSENTHAL, R. Clinical significance of hallucinations in psychiatric disorders; a study of 116 hallucinatory patients. Archs Gen. Psychiat. 24: 76–80, 1971.

59. GOODWIN, D. W., CRANE, J. B. and GUZE, S. B. Felons who drink; an 8-year follow-up. Q. J. Stud. Alcohol 32: 136–147, 1971.

60. GORWITZ, K., BAHN, A., WARTHEN, F. J. and COOPER, M. Some epidemiological data on alcoholism in Maryland; based on admissions to psychiatric facilities. Q. J. Stud. Alcohol 31: 423–443, 1970.

61. GOTTESFELD, B. H., LASSER, L. M., CONWAY, E. J. and MANN, N. M. Psychiatric implications of the treatment of alcoholism with tetraethylthiuram disulfide; a preliminary report. Q. J. Stud. Alcohol 12: 184–205, 1951.

62. GREEN, J. R. The incidence of alcoholism in patients admitted to medical wards of a hospital. Med. J. Aust. 1: 465–466, 1965.

63. GROSS, M. M. Management of acute alcohol withdrawal states. Q. J. Stud. Alcohol 28: 655–666, 1967.

64. GROSS, M. M., HALPERT, E. and SABOT, L. Some comments on Bleuler's concept of acute alcoholic hallucinosis. Q. J. Stud. Alcohol 24: 54–60, 1963.

65. GUS'KOV, V. S. Osobennosti okisleniya alkogolya pri shizofrenii. (Characteristics of alcohol oxidation in schizophrenia.) Trud. Gos. Inst. Psikhiat. 27: 138–146, 1961.

66. GUZE, S. B., GOODWIN, D. W. and CRANE, J. B. Criminality and psychiatric disorders. Archs Gen. Psychiat. 20: 583–591, 1969.

67. GUZE, S. B., TUASON, V. B., GATEFIELD, P. D., STEWART, M. A. and PICKEN, B. Psychiatric illness and crime, with particular reference to alcoholism; a study of 223 criminals. J. Nerv. Ment. Dis. 134: 512–521, 1962.

68. HALLAY, L. I. Alcohol and schizophrenia. J. Med. Cincinnati 18: 23–28, 1937.

69. HALLAY, L. I. Schizophrenia modified by alcohol. Va Med. Mon. 67: 111–112, 1940.

70. HAMPTON, P. J. A descriptive portrait of the drinker. J. Social Psychol. 25: 69–132, 151–170, 1947.

71. HARDER, A. Das Wesen der Alkoholhalluzinose. Schweizer Arch. Neurol. Psychiat. 58: 102–129, 1946.

72. HARTOCOLLIS, P. Denial of illness in alcoholism. Bull. Menninger Clin. 32: 47–53, 1968.

73. HILGARD, J. R. and NEWMAN, M. F. Early parental deprivation as a functional factor in the etiology of schizophrenia and alcoholism. Am. J. Orthopsychiat. 33: 409–420, 1963.

74. HORN, J. L. and WANBERG, K. W. Symptom patterns related to excessive use of alcohol. Q. J. Stud. Alcohol 30: 35–58, 1969.

75. HUBER, K. Über die Alkoholhalluzinose und ihre Beziehungen zur Schizophrenie. Schweizer Arch. Neurol. Psychiat. 44: 43–68, 1939.

76. HUDOLIN, V. Acute complications of alcoholism. Pp. 140–159. In: POPHAM, R. E., ed. Alcohol and alcoholism. Toronto; University of Toronto Press; 1970.

77. JELLIFFE, S. E. Predementia praecox; hereditary and constitutional features of dementia praecox make-up. J. Nerv. Ment. Dis. **38**: 1–26, 1911.

78. JELLINEK, E. M. The disease concept of alcoholism. Highland Park, N.J.; Hillhouse Press; 1960.

79. JOHANSON, E. A Study of schizophrenia in the male; a psychiatric and social study based on 138 cases with follow-up. Acta Psychiat. Neurol. Scand. Vol. 33, Suppl. No. 125, 1958.

80. JOHNSON, F. G. Personality characteristics of the alcoholic. Appl. Ther. **7**: 821–825, 1965.

81. JONES, M. C. Personality correlates and antecedents of drinking patterns in adult males. J. Cons. Clin. Psychol. **32**: 2–12, 1968.

82. JONES, R. W. and HELRICH, A. R. Treatment of alcoholism by physicians in private practice; a national survey. Q. J. Stud. Alcohol **33**: 117–131, 1972.

83. KANTOROVICH, N. V. and CONSTANTINOVICH, S. K. The effect of alcohol in catatonic syndromes; preliminary report. Am. J. Psychiat. **92**: 651–654, 1935.

84. KARDOS, G. and MÁRIA, B. Alkoholizmus és endogen psychosisok. (Alcoholism and endogenous psychoses.) Ideggyógy. Szle **20**: 117–127, 1967.

85. KATZ, N. M. A phenomenological typology of schizophrenia. Pp. 300–320. In: KATZ, N. M., COLE, J. O. and BARTON, W. E., eds. The role and methodology of classification in psychiatry and psychopathology. (U.S. Publ. Hlth Service, Publ. No. 1584.) Washington, D.C.; U.S. Govt Print. Off.; 1968.

86. KELLER, M. The definition of alcoholism and the estimation of its prevalence. Pp. 310–329. In: PITTMAN, D. J. and SNYDER, C. R., eds. Society, culture, and drinking patterns. New York; Wiley; 1962.

87. KISSIN, B., ROSENBLATT, S. M. and MACHOVER, S. Prognostic factors in alcoholism. Psychiat. Res. Rep. **24**: 22–43, 1968.

88. KOS, M., KRYSPIN-EXNER, K. and ZAPOTOCZKY, H. G. Untersuchungen zur psychischen Situation der Kinder Alkoholkranker. Wien Z. Nervheilk. **26**: 197–212, 1968.

89. LANGE, G., ASCHER, J., TAINE, D., LASSELIN, M. and FONTAN, M. Personnalités d'alcooliques ou personnalité alcoolique. Lille Méd. **15**: 860–866, 1970.

90. LAWRENCE, F. E. The outpatient management of the alcoholic. Q. J. Stud. Alcohol, Suppl. No. 1, pp. 117–128, 1961.

91. LEDERER, H. E. Treatment and prognosis of alcoholism. Delaware St. Med. J. **25**: 221–222, 1953.

92. LISANSKY-GOMBERG, E. S. Etiology of alcoholism. J. Consult. Clin. Psychol. **32**: 18–20, 1968.

93. LÓPEZ-ZANÓN, A., LÓPEZ-PEÑALVER-GONZÁLEZ, J. L., CAÑADA-ZUBÍA, L. and GONZÁLEZ-ELIPE-NIETO-SANDOVAL, J. Psicoses alcohólicas agudas. Acta Luso-españ. Neurol. Psiquiat. **25**: 33–39, 1966.

94. LORR, M., KLETT, C. J. and MCNAIR, D. M. Syndromes of psychosis. Oxford; Pergamon; 1962.

95. MABRY-HALL, M. Aberrant Rorschach perceptions of alcoholics. Q. J. Stud. Alcohol **28**: 255–266, 1967.

96. McCORD, J. Etiological factors in alcoholism; family and personal characteristics. Q. J. Stud. Alcohol 33: 1020–1027, 1972.

97. McCOURT, W. F., WILLIAMS, A. F. and SCHNEIDER, L. Incidence of alcoholism in a state mental hospital population. Q. J. Stud. Alcohol 32: 1085–1088, 1971.

98. McGUIRE, M. T., STEIN, S. and MENDELSON, J. H. Comparative psychosocial studies of alcoholic and nonalcoholic subjects undergoing experimentally induced ethanol intoxication. Psychosom. Med. 28: 13–26, 1966.

99. MALZBERG, B. Use of alcohol among White and Negro mental patients; comparative statistics of first admissions to New York State hospitals for mental disease, 1939–1941. Q. J. Stud. Alcohol 16: 668–674, 1955.

100. MALZBERG, B. The alcoholic psychoses; demographic aspects at midcentury in New York State. New Brunswick, N.J.; Publications Division, Rutgers Center of Alcohol Studies; 1960.

101. MALZBERG, B. Mental disease among Jews in New York State. New York; Intercontinental Medical Book Corp.; 1960.

102. MARKHAM, J. Casework treatment of an alcoholic woman with severe underlying pathology. Q. J. Stud. Alcohol 18: 475–491, 1957.

103. MARTÍN-SANTOS, L. Ideas delirantes primarias, esquizofrenia y psicosis alcohólica aguda. Acta Luso-españ. Neurol. Psiquiat. 11: 322–333, 1952.

104. MAYFIELD, D. G. and ALLEN, D. Alcohol and affect; a psychopharmacological study. Am. J. Psychiat. 123: 1346–1351, 1967.

105. MAYFIELD, D. G. and FOWLER, D. R. Diagnosed and undiagnosed alcoholism. Sth. Med. J. 63: 593–596, 1970.

106. MEERLOO, J. A. M. Artificial ecstasy; a study of the psychosomatic aspects of drug addiction. J. Nerv. Ment. Dis. 115: 246–266, 1952.

107. MEGGENDORFER, F. Intoxikationspsychosen. Pp. 165–286. In: BUMKE, O., ed. Handbuch der Geisteskrankheiten. Vol. 7. Pt. 3. Berlin; Springer; 1928.

108. MENAKER, T. Anxiety about drinking in alcoholics. J. Abnorm. Psychol. 72: 43–49, 1967.

109. MILANO, T. Incidenza dell'alcoolismo nelle malattie mentali. Rass. Neuropsich. 19: 792–812, 1965.

110. MILLER, B. A., POKORNY, A. D. and HANSON, P. G. A study of dropouts in an in-patient alcoholism treatment program. Dis. Nerv. Syst. 29: 91–99, 1968.

111. MINSKI, L. Psychopathy and psychoses associated with alcohol. J. Ment. Sci. 84: 985–990, 1938.

112. MOEFES, S. M. O strukture alkogol'nogo paranoida. (On the structure of alcoholic paranoia.) Zh. Nevropat. 66: 428–432, 1966.

113. MOON, L. E. and PATTON, R. E. The alcoholic psychotic in the New York State mental hospitals, 1951–1960. Q. J. Stud. Alcohol 24: 664–681, 1963.

114. MOORE, R. A. and RAMSEUR, F. Effects of psychotherapy in an open-ward hospital on patients with alcoholism. Q. J. Stud. Alcohol 21: 233–252, 1960.

115. MORIĆ-PETROVIĆ, S. and MILOSAVIJEVIĆ, P. Alkoholizam u porodieama bolesnika iz schizofrene grupe. (Alcoholism as hereditary factor in schizophrenia.) Medski. Glasn. 20: 189–191, 1966.

116. MOTT, R. H., SMALL, I. F. and ANDERSON, J. M. A comparative study of hal-
      lucinations. Archs Gen. Psychiat. 12: 595–601, 1965.
117. NAGAO, S. Clinico-genetic study of chronic alcoholism. [Japanese text.] Jap.
      J. Hum. Genet. 9: 111–135, 1964.
118. NICHOLS, S., PIKE, A. W., RICHTER, M. H. and SCULTHORPE, W. B. Foster-
      home placement of psychotic patients with histories of problem drinking.
      Q. J. Stud. Alcohol 22: 298–311, 1961.
119. NOLAN, J. P. Alcohol as a factor in the illness of university service patients.
      Am. J. Med. Sci. 249: 135–142, 1965.
120. NORMAN, J. P. Alcoholic hallucinatory states. Q. J. Stud. Alcohol 5:
      563–574, 1945.
121. NOYES, A. P. and KOLB, L. C. Modern clinical psychiatry. 5th ed.
      Philadelphia; Saunders; 1958.
122. OLTMAN, J. E. and FRIEDMAN, S. Trends in admissions to a state hospital,
      1942–1964. Archs Gen. Psychiat. 13: 544–551, 1965.
123. OPLER, M. K. Schizophrenia and culture. Sci. Am. 197(No. 2): 103–110,
      1957.
124. ORTHMAYR, A. Az alkoholizmussal kapcsolatos psychosisokról. (Psychoses at-
      tributable to alcoholism.) Pp. 41–50. In: TARISKA, I., GERÉBY, G. and
      KARDOS, G., eds. Tanulmányok az alkoholizmus pszichiátriai következményeiröl. (Results of psychiatric study of alcoholism.) Budapest;
      Alkoholizmus Elleni Országos Bizottság; 1969.
125. PANEPINTO, W. C., HIGGINS, M. J., KEANE-DAWES, W. Y. and SMITH, D.
      Underlying psychiatric diagnosis as an indicator of participation in alcohol-
      ism therapy. Q. J. Stud. Alcohol 31: 950–956, 1970.
126. PARKER, J. B., JR., MEILLER, R. M. and ANDREWS, G. W. Major psychiatric
      disorders masquerading as alcoholism. Sth. Med. J. 53: 560–564, 1960.
127. PARTINGTON, J. T. and JOHNSON, F. G. Personality types among alcoholics.
      Q. J. Stud. Alcohol 30: 21–34, 1969.
128. PEARSON, W. S. The "hidden" alcoholic in the general hospital; a study of
      "hidden" alcoholism in White male patients admitted for unrelated com-
      plaints. N. Carol. Med. J. 23: 6–10, 1962.
129. PETERS, G. A., JR. Emotional and intellectual concomitants of advanced
      chronic alcoholism. J. Consult. Psychol. 20: 390, 1956.
130. PHILLIPS, L., KADEN, S. and WALDMAN, M. Rorschach indices of develop-
      mental level. J. Genet. Psychol. 94: 267–285, 1959.
131. PITTMAN, D. J. and TATE, R. L. A comparison of two treatment programs for
      alcoholics. Q. J. Stud. Alcohol 30: 888–899, 1969.
132. PITTS, F. N., JR. and WINOKUR, G. Affective disorder. VII. Alcoholism and
      affective disorder. J. Psychiat. Res. 4: 37–50, 1966.
133. POLLACK, D. Experimental intoxication of alcoholics and normals; some psy-
      chological changes. Ph.D. dissertation, University of California; 1965.
134. POTTIER, C. Démence précoce consécutive à une intoxication éthylique chro-
      nique. Ann. Méd.-Psychol. 100: 230–235, 1942.
135. PUGH, T. F. An alternate way of grouping psychiatric diagnoses. J. Nerv.
      Ment. Dis. 143: 248–251, 1966.

136. RADO, S. The psychoanalysis of pharmacothymia (drug addiction). Psychoanal. Q. 2: 1–23, 1933.

137. RAPP, M. S. Use and abuse of drugs. Can. Med. Ass. J. 98: 922, 1968.

138. RATHOD, N. H. and THOMSON, I. G. Women alcoholics; a clinical study. Q. J. Stud. Alcohol 32: 45–52, 1971.

139. RIMMER, J., REICH, T. and WINOKUR, G. Alcoholism. V. Diagnosis and clinical variation among alcoholics. Q. J. Stud. Alcohol 33: 658–666, 1972.

140. ROA, A. Alcoholism and endogenous psychosis. Pp. 121–125. In: POPHAM, R. E., ed. Alcohol and alcoholism. Toronto; University of Toronto Press; 1970.

141. ROBINS, E. and GUZE, S. B. Establishment of diagnostic validity in psychiatric illness; its application to schizophrenia. Am. J. Psychiat. 126: 983–987, 1970.

142. ROBINSON, D. The alcohologist's addiction; some implications of having lost control over the disease concept of alcoholism. Q. J. Stud. Alcohol 33: 1028–1042, 1972.

143. ROSENBERG, R. Psychogenesis in delirium tremens. Psychiat. Q. 19: 316–321, 1945.

144. ROSENBLATT, S. M., GROSS, M. M., BROMAN, M., LEWIS, E. and MALENOWSKI, B. Patients admitted for treatment of alcohol withdrawal syndromes; an epidemiological study. Q. J. Stud. Alcohol 32: 104–115, 1971.

145. ROSENTHAL, D. The heredity-environment issue in schizophrenia. In: ROSENTHAL, D. and KETY, S. S., eds. The transmission of schizophrenia. London; Pergamon; 1968.

146. ROTHSTEIN, C., ZELTZERMAN, I. and SIEGEL, P. Non-specificity versus specificity in alcoholism. J. Maine Med. Ass. 57: 129–132, 1966.

147. RUBINGTON, E. The hidden alcoholic. Q. J. Stud. Alcohol 33: 667–683, 1972.

148. RUDIE, R. R. and McGAUGHRAN, L. S. Differences in developmental experience, defensiveness and personality organization between two classes of problem drinkers. J. Abnorm. Soc. Psychol. 62: 659–665, 1961.

149. SALZBERGER, G. J. Perphenazine treatment of patients with acute alcoholism or schizophrenia. Clin. Med. 71: 1565–1570, 1964.

150. SANFORD, N. Personality and patterns of alcohol consumption. J. Consult. Clin. Psychol. 32: 13–17, 1968.

151. SCHAEFER, E. S. Personality structure of alcoholics in outpatient psychotherapy. Q. J. Stud. Alcohol 15: 304–319, 1954.

152. SCHÉDA, W. and TIMÁR, I. Pneumoenzephalographische Untersuchungen an chronischen Alkoholikern. Psychiat. Neurol. Med. Psychol. 17: 338–340, 1965.

153. SCHUCKIT, M., PITTS, F. N., JR., REICH, T., KING, L. J. and WINOKUR, G. Alcoholism. I. Two types of alcoholism in women. Archs Gen. Psychiat. 20: 301–306, 1969.

154. SCHWARZ, L. and FJELD, S. P. The alcoholic patient in the psychiatric hospital emergency room. Q. J. Stud. Alcohol 30: 104–111, 1969.

155. SCOTT, D. F. Alcoholic hallucinosis; an aetiological study. Br. J. Addict. 62: 113–125, 1967.

156. SCOTT, E. M. Group therapy for schizophrenic alcoholics in a state-operated outpatient clinic; with hypnosis as an integrated adjunct. Int. J. Clin. Exp. Hypnosis 14: 232–242, 1966.

157. SELZER, M. L. Problems encountered in the treatment of alcoholism. Univ. Mich. Med. Center J. 33: 58–63, 1967.

158. SHERFEY, M. J. Psychopathology and character structure in chronic alcoholism. Pp. 16–42. In: DIETHELM, O., ed. Etiology of chronic alcoholism. Springfield, Ill.; Thomas; 1955.

159. SHUMAKOV, V. M. Alkogolizm u bol'nykh shizofreniyei. (Alcoholism in schizophrenic patients.) Zh. Nevropat. 70: 435–443, 1970.

160. SIKORSKA-GODWOD, C. O niektórych zespolach schizofrenopodobnych w przebiegu alkoholizmu przewleklego wezesnego. (On some schizophrenia-like syndromes in early chronic alcoholism.) Neurol. Neurochir. Psychiat. Polska 6: 923–932, 1956.

161. SMART, R. G., STORM, T., BAKER, E. F. W. and SOLURSH, L. A controlled study of lysergide in the treatment of alcoholism. I. The effects on drinking behavior. Q. J. Stud. Alcohol 27: 469–482, 1966.

162. SMITH, J. A. Problems in the treatment of the alcoholic. Q. J. Stud. Alcohol, Suppl. No. 1, pp. 129–137, 1961.

163. SOSKIN, R. A. Personality and attitude change after two alcoholism treatment programs; comparative contributions of lysergide and human relations training. Q. J. Stud. Alcohol 31: 920–931, 1970.

164. SROLE, L., LANGNER, T. S., MICHAEL, S. T., OPLER, M. K. and RENNIE, T. A. C. Mental health in the metropolis. New York; McGraw-Hill; 1962.

165. STRAUSS, E. El papel del alcoholismo en enfermedades mentales del sexo femenino en Panamá. Archs Neurol. Psychiat., Habana 5(No. 3): 163–165, 1950.

166. TÄHKÄ, V. The alcoholic personality; a clinical study. (Finnish Foundation for Alcohol Studies, Publ. No. 13.) Helsinki; 1966.

167. TAYLOR, M. A. Schneiderian first-rank symptoms and clinical prognostic features in schizophrenia. Archs Gen. Psychiat. 26: 64–67, 1972.

168. TAYLOR, M. A., GAZTANAGA, P. and ABRAMS, R. Manic-depressive illness and acute schizophrenia; a clinical, family history, and treatment-response study. Am. J. Psychiat. 131: 678–682, 1974.

169. THIMANN, J. Reflections on Dr. Fox's paper. Int. J. Psychiat. 5: 56–59, 1968.

170. TIDMARSH, D. Some sociological characteristics of male alcoholic patients from London admitted to a mental hospital. Br. J. Addict. 64: 333–346, 1970.

171. TOMSOVIC, M. Hospitalized alcoholic patients. I. A two-year study of medical, social and psychological characteristics. Hosp. Community Psychiat. 19: 197–203, 1968.

172. TOMSOVIC, M. and EDWARDS, R. V. Lysergide treatment of schizophrenic and nonschizophrenic alcoholics; a controlled evaluation. Q. J. Stud. Alcohol 31: 932–949, 1970.

173. UECKER, A. E. Differentiating male alcoholics from other psychiatric inpatients; validity of the MacAndrew Scale. Q. J. Stud. Alcohol 31: 379–383, 1970.

174. VAN DUSEN, W., WILSON, W., MINERS, W. and HOOK, H. Treatment of alcoholism with lysergide. Q. J. Stud. Alcohol 28: 295–304, 1967.

175. VAZIRI, H. Fréquence de l'oligophrénie, de la psychopathie et de l'alcoolisme dans 79 familles de schizophrènes. Schweizer Arch. Neurol. Psychiat. 87: 160–177, 1961.

176. VICTOR, M. and HOPE, J. M. The phenomenon of auditory hallucinations in chronic alcoholism; a critical evaluation of the status of alcoholic hallucinosis. J. Nerv. Ment. Dis. 126: 451–481, 1958.

177. VINCENT, M. O., ROBINSON, E. A. and LATT, L. Physicians as patients; private psychiatric hospital experience. Can. Med. Ass. J. 100: 403–412, 1969.

178. VORONTSOVA, G. A. Ob atipichnykh alkogol'nykh psikhozakh. (On atypical alcoholic psychoses.) Zh. Nevropat. 59: 657–667, 1959.

179. WAHL, O. and WISHNER, J. Schizophrenic thinking as measured by developmental tests. J. Nerv. Ment. Dis. 155: 232–244, 1972.

180. WALLERSTEIN, R. S. Alcoholism; symptom or disease? Int. J. Psychiat. 5: 59–65, 1968.

181. WILLIAMS, E. L. and LONG, R. The clinical problem and management of alcoholism. Practitioner 200: 205–214, 1968.

182. WINOKUR, G. and CLAYTON, P. J. Family history studies. IV. Comparison of male and female alcoholics. Q. J. Stud. Alcohol 29: 885–891, 1968.

183. WINOKUR, G., REICH, T., RIMMER, J. and PITTS, F. N., JR. Alcoholism. III. Diagnosis and familial psychiatric illness in 259 alcoholic probands. Archs Gen. Psychiat. 23: 104–111, 1970.

184. WINSHIP, G. M. Disulfiram as an aid to psychotherapy in the case of an impulsive drinker. Q. J. Stud. Alcohol 18: 666–672, 1957.

185. WOLFENSBERGER, M. Der Alkoholwahnsinn (akute Hallucinose der Trinker) und seine Beziehungen zu den Schizophrenien (an Hand der Kasuistik der Zürcher Psychiatrischen Klinik 1898–1921). Z. Ges. Neurol. Psychiat. 82: 385–418, 1923.

186. ZEHNER, L. Ueber die chronischen Psychosen nach Alkoholmissbrauch. (Ein Referat über den gegenwärtigen Stand der Frage.) Thesis, University of Bonn; 1930.

12

Alcoholism and Sociopathy— Diagnostic Confusion[1]

Marc A. Schuckit, M.D.

ALCOHOL ABUSE often occurs in persons showing antisocial behavior. The diagnostic categories of alcoholism and antisocial personality are frequently confused. Despite some similarities in the natural history of the two problems, they represent distinct entities with different prognoses. The present discussion outlines the similarities and differences between alcoholism and sociopathy and describes the confusion that can result when the two problems occur in the same individual.

BACKGROUND

The paradigm of a pattern of symptoms as either a primary illness or a secondary manifestation of another problem is not unique to alcoholism or to psychiatry. In general medicine the symptom complex of cough, fever, malaise and lung congestion can be primary pneumococcal pneumonia, or a pneumonitis complicating a general immune deficiency. Both illnesses are pneumonias, but their treatment and the prognoses are different. In psychiatry, a similar situation occurs with obsessions. Obsessions can represent a prominent feature of another morbid process, such as depression, or may indicate a diagnosis of obsessive–compulsive neurosis (1).

It may be valid to conceptualize two major types in alcohol abuse, primary alcoholism and secondary alcoholism (2–4). The primary alcoholic begins his problem drinking with a history clear of all other major psychiatric problems while the secondary alcoholic becomes an alcohol abuser only after a history of another psychiatric illness. (This distinction is based on symptom development and is not meant to imply an etiology.) The major

[1] Reprinted by permission from the QUARTERLY JOURNAL OF STUDIES ON ALCOHOL, Vol. 34, pp. 157–164, 1973. Copyright by Journal of Studies on Alcohol, Inc., New Brunswick, New Jersey 08903.

types of secondary alcoholism are depressive alcoholism, the form more likely to be seen in women, and sociopathic alcoholism, seen mostly in men.

Through this reasoning process, a group of women alcoholics have been divided into those with primary alcoholism and those with depressive alcoholism (3, 4). The latter group comprised 27% of the women studied on an alcoholism ward at a state mental hospital. When compared with the primary alcoholics, the depressive women alcoholics were younger and had been alcoholics fewer years, and their close female relatives showed enhanced rates of depression. They also evidenced higher rates of suicide attempts and showed more improvement over a 3-year follow-up (3).

The same pattern of reasoning may be followed to investigate the relationship between the antisocial personality and alcohol abuse. As sociopathy is predominantly a problem in men, the correlation between alcoholism and sociopathy is best tested in a group of men (5). Presented here is a review of some of the pertinent literature outlining the relationship between alcoholism and sociopathy within predominantly male samples.

DEFINITIONS

Alcoholism is here defined as drinking that interferes with the individual's way of life as evidenced by any one of the following occurring in relation to alcohol abuse: a job loss or lay-off, a marital separation or divorce, two or more nontraffic arrests, or a hospitalization for physical or mental consequences (4). *Primary alcoholics* are those with no history of any psychiatric disorder antedating alcohol abuse (3). This definition, in using objectively measured consequences of alcohol abuse, probably excludes the early problem drinkers who have not yet experienced severe consequences.

Sociopathy or *antisocial personality* is here defined as a chronic disorder, with onset prior to age 15, and manifesting at least four of the following problems: (1) repeated truancy, suspension or expulsion from school, or recurrent fighting at school; (2) repeated running away from home for at least overnight; (3) two or more nontraffic police offenses, four or more arrests of any type, or at least one felony conviction; (4) a work history characterized by repeatedly being dismissed or frequent impulsive job changes; (5) repeated outbursts of rage or fighting; (6) flagrant sexual promiscuity (e.g., 100 sexual partners reported), prostitution or pimping; (7) a period of wanderlust with 6 months or more of wandering with no arranged job or fixed abode; (8) persistent and repeated lying or use of an alias.

The manifestation of some antisocial behavior is not synonymous with a diagnosis of antisocial personality. The preceding diagnostic framework for sociopathy uses objectively measurable phenomena and is not based on etiological assumptions. The schema is used independently of the relationship of the antisocial personality to intelligence, socioeconomic status, race or ethnic background.

The diagnosis of *sociopathic alcoholism* involves the onset of alcohol abuse as defined above in a person with ongoing *antisocial personality or sociopathy* (5). Whereas sociopathy is recognizable by age 15 and the average male alcoholic is well into his 20s when alcohol abuse begins (5), the sociopathic alcoholic usually has up to 10 years of prior severe antisocial behavior. The diagnosis depends on a good chronological history of symptom development showing a full-blown antisocial history antedating alcohol abuse.

RELATIONSHIP BETWEEN ALCOHOLISM AND SOCIOPATHY

Many alcoholics engage in criminal activities (6–9). Tardif (10) in 1968 reported that 27% of the violent crimes in Montreal were committed by intoxicated persons. King et al. (11), in a study in 1969 of Black ghetto men, found a direct relationship between recent alcohol problems and crimes, including those against persons. Kant (12) in 1927 reported in Germany that 41% of 230 male alcoholics had been arrested for major crimes.

There is also evidence that convicted criminals have had a high rate of alcohol abuse (13–17). Banay (18) in 1942 classified almost half of the inmates at Sing Sing Prison as alcoholics. Guze and his associates (19, 20) classified 43% of a consecutive series of 223 convicted male felons as alcoholics and another 11% as questionable alcoholics, while Roth et al. (21) found that 29% of the inmates in a California prison had alcohol problems. The relationship between prisoner status and alcohol abuse should be viewed with caution. Drinking while attempting to carry out a crime may increase the chances of the perpetrator getting caught. Consequently, sociopathic prisoners may have a higher rate of alcohol abuse than the general sociopathic population.

There is, nonetheless, a close relationship between alcohol abuse and antisocial behavior. Alcoholics are likely to participate in antisocial activities; and criminals, most of whom are sociopaths, tend to engage in heavy drinking. The relationship between antisocial behavior and excessive drinking is most marked in men alcoholics with an early onset of excessive drinking.

In a study of a group of alcoholics in Australia aged 30 or less, Rosenberg (22) found 28% heavily engaged in antisocial behavior. In addition, these young alcoholics showed enhanced use of drugs other than alcohol. The propensity for men with a younger onset of alcohol abuse to show increased antisocial behavior is borne out by the observations of Foulds and Hassall (23) and of Schuckit et al. (24). In the former study, the authors noted that those who became excessive drinkers prior to the age of 30 showed more job, family and police problems, a picture that might indicate a group with sociopathy.

These findings may suggest that all alcoholics who begin drinking at an early age are sociopaths. In an attempt to evaluate this hypothesis, Schuckit et al. (24) studied a group of men alcoholics from which all probands with a diagnosis of sociopathy had been carefully excluded. They still found more antisocial behavior in those with an onset of alcohol abuse prior to age 20 than in those with an onset after age 30. The authors pointed out that even though more antisocial behavior was present, it was mild or moderate in extent and did not meet the criteria for a diagnosis of sociopathy or antisocial personality; among other things the onset of antisocial problems in this group was not evident by age 15.

Through careful history-taking, outlining the chronology of development of antisocial problems and alcohol abuse, it is possible to segregate the sociopath who drinks heavily from the alcohol abuser who engages in a limited sphere of antisocial acts. This distinction becomes important when one compares the prognoses of primary alcoholism and sociopathic alcoholism.

Alcoholism and sociopathy seem to occur in the same families (25, 26). This appearance may result from not separating primary alcoholic and sociopathic alcoholic subjects prior to family studies. If all alcoholics with antisocial problems are called sociopaths, or all sociopaths with drinking difficulties are classified as alcoholics, no distinct family patterns will be uncovered. The practice of including in alcoholic subject groups all people admitted to an alcoholism ward[2] does little to clear up this issue. When alcoholism and sociopathy are more clearly defined and separated by investigators, the degree of familial overlap between the two problems may become much less striking.

In this light, Winokur and his associates (5, 25) compared the rates of sociopathy among close male relatives of primary alcoholics with those of close male relatives of sociopathic alcoholics. Sociopa-

[2] This has been dealt with in SCHUCKIT, M. The woman alcoholic. Presented at the American Psychiatric Association Meeting, Washington, D.C., May 1971.

thy was seen in less than 4% of the close male relatives of primary alcoholics, and in 22% of the close male relatives of sociopathic alcoholics ($p < .005$). These findings indicate that while sociopathy is found in the families of alcoholics, the most striking rate occurs in the families of alcoholics with a diagnosis of sociopathic alcoholism.

THE SOCIOPATHIC ALCOHOLIC

Sociopathic alcoholics make up a large percentage of the alcoholics admitted to an alcoholism facility. Winokur et al. (25), in a series of 259 men and women alcoholics, found that 31 of the 156 men showed sociopathic alcoholism. The sociopathic alcoholic men were younger than the others at onset of alcohol abuse (18 versus 24 years) and younger at the time of the study (32 versus 34 years). By definition, they also had much more antisocial behavior than the primary alcoholics.

While making up a large percentage of men alcoholics, the sociopathic alcoholics were easily distinguished by their early history. Those thus designated also evidenced major differences in the natural history of their drinking problems.

There are many indications that sociopathic alcoholics have a poorer prognosis than do primary alcoholics. Wilkinson et al. (27), in a short follow-up of 132 male alcoholic veterans, found a good outcome in those who were less aggressive, less hostile, had more stable marital and job histories, and showed better emotional control. The alcoholics with the best prognosis in that study were the antithesis of the sociopathic alcoholics. Panepinto et al. (28) found the poorest outcome in alcoholics with personality disorders, and Diethelm (29) found the worst prognosis in psychopaths. McCance and McCance (30) described the poor-risk alcoholic as having no home or steady job, being single and possessing a record of police arrests. In a limited follow-up of four sociopathic women alcoholics, Schuckit and Winokur (31) found a poor prognosis in three.

The combination of alcoholism and true sociopathy indicates a poor prognosis. Ross (32) studied a group of alcoholics in prison and found that routine treatment methods for alcoholism were ineffective with this group. Goodwin et al. (20) also found an enhanced rate of criminal recidivism in sociopaths with alcohol problems.

DISCUSSION

The strong relationship between sociopathy and alcoholism may occur because (*a*) many alcoholics are sociopaths; (*b*) there is a third factor X underlying both alcoholism and sociopathy; or (*c*) many sociopaths abuse alcohol as part of their antisocial behavior (33).

Alcoholics do engage in antisocial behavior especially if the abuse of alcohol begins before age 30 (24). The criminal behavior is not as severe as in sociopathy (1, 7), begins at a later age (24), and is often committed in direct relation to alcohol abuse (13). Such crimes as assault, vagrancy, sexual deviation—especially indecent exposure—are often noted (13). It appears that alcoholics committing crimes differ markedly in past history from sociopaths. Alcohol abusers with a late onset of antisocial behavior should probably be excluded from any discussion of the interaction of sociopathy and alcoholism. They are alcoholics, not sociopaths.

The second hypothesis is more difficult to evaluate. There may be a third factor, such as impulsiveness or perhaps a genetically mediated biochemical abnormality, underlying both problems. In this schema, alcoholism and sociopathy are considered part of a spectrum, with the latter the more severe problem as evidenced by its earlier age of onset and more malignant course. More objective, sensitive and clinically applicable testing procedures are needed to test the validity of this view.

At the present stage of knowledge, a likely theory is that sociopathic alcoholism is a form of the first-appearing illness, sociopathy. Sociopaths engage in many forms of overindulgence, including alcohol and other drug abuse. Alcoholism, when added to the already established life style of the sociopath, complicates an already complex picture and makes treatment most difficult. A more appropriate term for this syndrome might be alcoholic sociopathy.

Alcoholism and crime, therefore, probably interact in two ways. First, some alcoholics commit crimes of a limited nature; the underlying problem is alcohol abuse and the confusion occurs only when the committing of a crime is erroneously equated with sociopathy. Second, many sociopaths abuse alcohol; the major problem is sociopathy, and severe disorder probably remains when alcohol abuse is stopped.

Many studies have dealt with the sociopathic alcoholic; but perhaps due to the confusions outlined, no clear picture of the syndrome has emerged. These caveats notwithstanding, the data available at present have been used herein to give some general guidelines as a stimulus to further research.

REFERENCES

1. FEIGHNER, J. P., ROBINS, E., GUZE, S. B., WOODRUFF, R. A., WINOKUR, G. and MUNOZ, R. Diagnostic criteria for use in psychiatric research. Archs Gen. Psychiat. 26: 57–63, 1972.
2. BACON, S. D. Alcohol, alcoholism, and crime. Crime & Delinq. 9: 1–14, 1963.
3. SCHUCKIT, M. A. Depression and alcoholism in women. Proc. 1st Annu. Alcsm Conf. NIAAA, pp. 355–363, 1973.
4. SCHUCKIT, M. A., PITTS, F. N., JR., REICH, T., KING, L. and WINOKUR, G. Alcoholism; two types of alcoholism in women. Archs Gen. Psychiat. 20: 301–306, 1969.
5. WINOKUR, G., RIMMER, J. and REICH, T. Alcoholism. IV. Is there more than one type of alcoholism? Br. J. Psychiat. 118: 525–531, 1971.
6. WOLFGANG, M. E. and STROHM, R. B. The relationship between alcohol and criminal homicide. Q. J. Stud. Alcohol 17: 411–425, 1956.
7. BARTHOLOMEW, A. A. and KELLEY, M. F. The incidence of a criminal record in 1,000 consecutive alcoholics. Br. J. Crim. 5: 143–149, 1965.
8. ELLERMANN, M. Social and clinical features of chronic alcoholism; based on a study of 231 male patients. J. Nerv. Ment. Dis. 107: 556–568, 1948.
9. HASSALL, C. A controlled study of the characteristics of young male alcoholics. Br. J. Addict. 63: 193–201, 1968.
10. TARDIF, G. Alcoolisme et violence. Toxicomanies 1: 125–134, 1968.
11. KING, L. J., MURPHY, G. E., ROBINS, L. N. and DARVISH, H. Alcohol abuse; a crucial factor in the social problems of Negro men. Am. J. Psychiat. 125: 1682–1690, 1969.
12. KANT, F. Die Süchtigen. Archs Psychiat., Berlin 80: 91–105, 1927.
13. WINKLER, E. G., WEISSMAN, M. and McDERMAID, G. Alcoholism and anti-social behavior; statistical analysis. Psychiat. Q., Suppl. No. 28, pp. 242–254, 1954.
14. GRAY, M. G. and MOORE, M. The incidence and significance of alcoholism in the history of criminals. Am. J. Psychiat. 98: 347–353, 1941.
15. TRIPKOVIĆ, D. Problem drinkers in the penitentiary at Sremska Mitrovica. Q. J. Stud. Alcohol 28: 738–741, 1967.
16. MAULE, H. G. and COOPER, J. Alcoholism and crime; a study of the drinking and criminal habits of 50 discharged prisoners. Br. J. Addict. 61: 201–212, 1966.
17. HANSEN, H. A. and TEILMANN, K. A treatment of criminal alcoholics in Denmark. Q. J. Stud. Alcohol 15: 246–287, 1954.
18. BANAY, R. S. Alcoholism and crime. Q. J. Stud. Alcohol 2: 686–716, 1942.
19. GUZE, S. B., WOLFGRAM, E. D., McKINNEY, J. K. and CANTWELL, D. P. Delinquency, social maladjustment and crime; the role of alcoholism. Dis. Nerv. Syst. 29: 238–243, 1968.

20. GOODWIN, D. W., CRANE, J. B. and GUZE, S. B. Felons who drink; an 8-year follow-up. Q. J. Stud. Alcohol 32: 136–147, 1971.

21. ROTH, L. H., ROSENBERG, N. and LEVINSON, R. B. Prison adjustment of alcoholic felons. Q. J. Stud. Alcohol 32: 136–147, 1971.

22. ROSENBERG, C. M. Young alcoholics. Br. J. Psychiat. 115: 181–188, 1969.

23. FOULDS, G. A. and HASSALL, C. The significance of age of onset of excessive drinking in male alcoholics. Br. J. Psychiat. 115: 1027–1032, 1969.

24. SCHUCKIT, M. A., RIMMER, J., REICH, T. and WINOKUR, G. Alcoholism; antisocial traits in male alcoholics. Br. J. Psychiat. 117: 575–576, 1970.

25. WINOKUR, G., REICH, T., RIMMER, J. and PITTS, F. N., JR. Alcoholism. III. Diagnosis and familial psychiatric illness in 259 alcoholic probands. Archs Gen. Psychiat. 23: 104–111, 1970.

26. ÅMARK, C. A study in alcoholism; clinical, social-psychiatric and genetic investigations. (BURTON, D., transl.) Acta Psychiat. Scand., Suppl. No. 70, pp. 1–283, 1951.

27. WILKINSON, A. E., PRADO, W. M., WILLIAMS, W. O. and SCHNADT, F. W. Psychological test characteristics and length of stay in alcoholism treatment. Q. J. Stud. Alcohol 32: 60–65, 1971.

28. PANEPINTO, W. C., HIGGINS, M. J., KEANE-DAWES, W. Y. and SCHNADT, F. W. Underlying psychiatric diagnosis as an indicator of participation in alcoholism therapy. Q. J. Stud. Alcohol 31: 950–956, 1970.

29. DIETHELM, O. Etiology of chronic alcoholism. Springfield, Ill.; Thomas; 1955.

30. MCCANCE, C. and MCCANCE, P. F. Alcoholism in north-east Scotland; its treatment and outcome. Br. J. Psychiat. 115: 189–198, 1969.

31. SCHUCKIT, M. and WINOKUR, G. A short-term follow-up of women alcoholics. Dis. Nerv. Syst. 33: 672–678, 1972.

32. ROSS, C. F. J. Comparison of hospital and prison alcoholics. Br. J. Psychiat. 118: 75–78, 1971.

33. PODOLSKY, E. The sociopathic alcoholic. Q. J. Stud. Alcohol 21: 292–297, 1960.

13

Alcoholism and Ego Function[1]

Bernard Chodorkoff, M.D., Ph.D.

THE DEVELOPMENT of an addiction, it is generally agreed, is a
complex and multidetermined affair (1–12). Constitution, heredity,
drugs, cultural, psychological and social conditions, all have been
implicated as causative factors (1–13). Psychoanalytic theorists have
traditionally interpreted addiction in terms of its symbolic meaning,
i.e., as an attempt on the part of the addict to provide himself with
instinctual gratification (1, 3, 10). Recently some relatively new
points of view have appeared in the literature (2, 6, 9, 11).

Chessick (2), for example, was able to demonstrate a relationship
between the psychological dynamics of addiction and its physiological concomitants. The verbal reports and fantasy productions of the
addicts he studied supported a formulation based on Shur's hypothesis (9). Shur pointed out that an individual's ego capacity to use
secondary process and to neutralize energy guarantees the
desomatization of reponses. Secondary process here refers to a psychological mode of functioning characteristically mature in that it
includes logical thinking, respect for reality demands, and ability to
delay impulse gratification. The ability to neutralize energy is associated with secondary process: drive energy which would ordinarily
seek immediate discharge is, instead, made available to the ego for
carrying out the above mature functions. Body manifestations are
minimal when the ego makes use of secondary process and neutral-
izes energy, and this would be referred to as desomatization of responses.

[1] Reprinted by permission from the QUARTERLY JOURNAL OF STUDIES ON AL-
COHOL, Vol. 25, pp. 292–299, 1964. Copyright by Journal of Studies on Alcohol,
Inc., New Brunswick, New Jersey 08903.

Primary process refers to relatively immature modes of psychological functioning and is associated with circumstances of non-neutralized drive energy. Body manifestations tend to appear as related phenomena and these are referred to as response somatization. Somatic discharge phenomena, characteristically infantile in nature, are included. When the addict experiences potential or actual danger (for example, in the form of loss of primal love) the panic that occurs produces regression. This includes physiological regression or recurring somatization of responses (i.e., resomatization), in addition to primary-process thinking and the acting out of archaic impulses. Furthermore, somatization is correlated with an exaggerated state of physiological tension. Drug intake serves to relieve the tension, partly because of its symbolic equivalence to the introjection of the ambivalently loved mother. It results in satisfaction of a primal love aim (much as when the breast is placed in the mouth of the infant and satisfaction after feeding occurs). The addicts studied described experiencing individual and characteristic "pharmacogenic orgasm." This varied from individual to individual in its components. These were: physiological reduction of sexual and aggressive drives, epileptic-like central nervous system discharge in the alimentary region, and a fantasied state of intrapsychic destruction of and fusion of the mother, where she is tucked safely inside the patient. Satiation of passive aims in this way restored primal love and the threat of loss of primal love was warded off.

Krystal (6), in cases of narcotic withdrawal, noted specific physiological occurrences which supported the notion of resomatization responses in the addict, i.e., exaggerated somatic expression of anxiety and depression. These observations were interpreted as supporting the hypothesis that the addict uses the drug to block the somatic expression of anxiety and depression.

Thus it can be seen that even these relatively new viewpoints tend to emphasize the role of the ego in the development of addiction along the lines previously described in the psychoanalytic literature; that is, in terms of regression characterized by passive–narcissistic aims. Szasz (11) has developed the significance of the role of the ego in the formation and function of addiction. He pointed out that although addicts are generally considered orally fixated and therefore vulnerable to regression from genital to oral mechanisms of tension discharge, this emphasis on the importance of instinctual gratification as a central determinant in addiction is misleading. He writes (11, *p. 316*):

"For example, stressing the great pleasure which the addict derives from alcohol or other drugs is reminiscent of the popular belief about the unusual pleasure which 'perverts' obtain from their practices. We recognize in this belief a distortion created by the observer, who reacts as does the child in the face of forbidden adult activities, like smoking, drinking or sexual activity. Not only does this result in an overestimation of the pleasure component ('forbidden fruit tastes sweeter'), but it also tends to obscure any other meaning and function of that particular activity. In the case of perversions, for example, we know that the symptom not only serves to discharge and gratify pregenital sexual impulses but also that it functions as a defense against certain aspects of genital sexuality. Or we could say that the patient is sexual in one way, in order not to be sexual in another way. Exclusive emphasis on the sexual gratification afforded by the symptom would be misleading."

Szasz offered case examples which illustrated a counterphobic mechanism in addiction and, by so doing, established specific ego activity or function as a developmental factor (11, *p. 324*):

"The symptom [addiction] represents a repetitive ('dramatic') re-enactment of a situation of danger (e.g., fear of instinct, of helplessness, or fearful fantasies of bodily damage in connection with pregnancy). The ego deliberately exposes itself to this situation in the hope of achieving mastery. The gratification associated with this process derives from the knowledge that one has been through the danger and has emerged unharmed. Interference with the symptom exposes the ego more directly to the underlying phobic, hypochondriacal and paranoid anxieties."

In the present paper I shall consider the role of ego function in alcohol addiction. Physiological processes associated with alcohol ingestion will be viewed in terms of the adaptive use which the ego makes of them.

Present Formulation

The alcoholic is assumed to be an individual whose ego functions are deficient. Alcohol is resorted to in an effort to make up for such deficiencies. One of the signs of ego deficiency is disturbances in object relationships. Alcoholics generally have a poor capacity for sound relationships. This may result either from a loss of object (probably early in life, to which the ego reacts by a withdrawal from personal objects, i.e., regression), or from an absence, in early development, of an impetus to seek object relationships. The former case probably defines the neurotic or psychotic alcoholic, while the latter defines the so-called character disorder. In this sense the character disorder is truly a deficiency disease; parental-environmental or constitutional factors make it impossible for the growing ego to develop the need for or means of establishing object attachments.

In an effort to adapt, the individual who later becomes an alcoholic relates to his own body in a characteristic way. His ego takes the body as an object which is relatively available and to which it can relate with some measure of safety. The establishment of such an ego–body relationship is not necessarily unique to the alcoholic. Szasz (13) has insightfully described its occurrence in schizophrenic, hypochondriac and paranoiac patients. Two features differentiate it in the individual who becomes an alcoholic. In the first place, this ego–body relationship lacks stability and is not a solidly founded one. This too is a consequence of the ego deficiency assumed to be present. In the second place, the prealcoholic individual must provide himself with some way of acknowledging the continuing existence of this relationship, or of reassuring himself of its maintenance. Alcohol intoxication serves to produce physiological changes which the individual experiences as assurance of the continued maintenance of the ego–body relationship. Such assurance provides him with a feeling of safety (i.e., ego safety). Without the continuing maintenance of the ego–body relationship, and the feeling of safety, threat of personal disintegration, or ego annihilation, appears. Psychological survival requires that personal disintegration and ego annihilation be prevented, and so the prealcoholic constantly seeks to reexperience his physiological responses. He drinks, and drinks again to intoxication; thus does alcoholism develop.

Whenever the already inadequate ego of the alcoholic is suddenly overwhelmed, he is left little choice other than desperately to seek to reexperience ego–body relatedness, or its physiological equivalent. Drinking to intoxication accomplishes this, and serves to reestablish some stability. It wards off the dissolution of the ego, which the disruption of the ego–body relationship would imply.

It has been noted that the drinking behavior of many alcoholics, either over an extended period of time or during a binge, appears to be "suicidal." This is partly true. The alcoholic initially drinks not in an effort to annihilate his physical being, but to experience its presence with greater certainty and intensity. Unfortunately, physiological adaptation to the drug, together with the fact that the use of alcohol prevents other social means of accomplishing what the alcoholic seeks, eventually lead him to experience less and less physiological effect and thereby less and less object (here, body) attachment. He therefore experiences the ego–body relationship as a progressively fading one, and one that is likely to be lost. The ego views the body as an object in danger of being lost; hence the dissolution of the ego seems imminent. Paradoxically, in an effort to prevent this dissolution, the alcoholic ego ceases to seek or maintain its previous interest in the body; in fact, it now seeks to destroy the body. Pain from the constant reminder of object loss is avoided in this way. The alcoholic chooses alcohol as his means to suicide because he sees alcohol as the drug that is destroying him, rather than as the drug that used to provide bodily sensations but no longer does. The question arises why the alcoholic does not give up alcohol for something else. Many alcoholics try to do just this. They add new addictions, or seek temporary rehabilitation, hoping that following the "cure" they will once again be able to experience the ego–body (object) relationship via alcohol ingestion. But many are unable to recognize or acknowledge that the drug no longer works. Their anger and frustration mount. They "drink with a vengeance" as though the very liquid they consume is what they are angry at: they express their anger by incorporating large quantities of the very substance which they both love and hate.

The alcoholic is frequently depressed, although he rarely experiences depressive affects. His significant object loss occurred early in development. Since then the depression has been much attenuated and denied by the choice of his own body as an object. To experience grief would be to acknowledge the original object loss. The choice of alcohol unfortunately serves constantly to decrease the degree of ego–body relatedness. This, it will be recalled, was described above as a consequence of physiological adaptation. The loss of the body as object is a constant threat. Hence, there is the threat of the return of the severe depression from original object loss.

The alcoholic's ego cathexis of (or attachment to) his own body apparently makes it very difficult for him to relate to another person's body, whether male or female. The alcoholic imposes upon other bodies the image of his own in an effort to make his ego–body cathexis more secure. Heterosexual behavior and development have remained immature. He relates to others of the same or opposite sex, not as such, but rather as projections of his own body. The problem of homosexuality in the alcoholic should be seen in these terms. Frequently the alcoholic is unable to impose his own image upon a member of the opposite sex. He then turns from women and seeks more the company of other men.

A final consideration of importance is the pharmacological effect which alcohol produces: it serves to remove the alcoholic from external objects. It is as though after experiencing early object loss, or never possessing objects, he dares not venture forth to re-establish old or establish new ones. Alcohol produces a genuine withdrawal from the outside world. In addition, this withdrawal serves to enhance the seeming importance and figural quality of the ego–body attachments.

CLINICAL OBSERVATIONS

Clinical or laboratory verification of these views will be easier if we restate its various features:

(a) The alcoholic is a person who experienced difficulty in establishing satisfactory human object relationships.

(b) The ego of the alcoholic-to-be therefore cathects his own body as an object in an effort to deal with the absence of other relationships.

(c) However, even this ego–body relationship (object attachment) cannot be securely established; he easily experiences threat of personal disintegration and ego dissolution.

(d) The alcoholic relies on the physiological effects of alcohol to provide assurance of the maintenance of an ego–body relationship, and thus the experience of personal or ego safety.

This formulation does not exclude or contradict earlier interpretations of alcoholism and other addictions. Within the context of such ego activity there may also be narcissistic regression, instinctual gratification, pharmacogenic orgasm, and the many fantasies that may appear as concomitant events.

The following clinical vignettes are illustrative:

1. A single woman in her 50's began drinking heavily following the onset of menopause. She was a "lone drinker" in the quiet of her small apartment. She described pervasive feelings of loneliness and expressed "feeling a change" when she drank. Drinking made her feel as though she "had something or someone."

2. A hospitalized woman alcoholic had been abstinent for the 7 years of her marriage. Her husband died and she began to drink excessively again. The only way she could avoid feeling depressed and that she had no one was by drinking. She experienced sensations then which she interpreted to mean that she was not alone.

3. A patient phoned at his appointment time and stated that he was drinking at a local bar. He invited his therapist to join him and explained that if the therapist were interested in him, he could now see his real self.

He explained that he felt like himself only when he drank, and that there was in essence no substance to himself when he didn't drink.

4. An alcoholic, a man in his 50's with angina pectoris, had intense fear of imminent death. He and his son, also an alcoholic, went on a hunting trip for a week, during which time the patient did nothing but drink. His behavior could justifiably be considered suicidal in that it nearly produced death. Yet, the patient explained later, he felt reassured when he drank because then he felt as though he had "something to hold on to." He therefore continued to drink for fear of losing this "something to hold on to."

This patient would usually stop at a bar for a beer or two before each treatment session. He described with relish how much he enjoyed these. Later he described his concern about needing the therapist and being dependent upon him. When he drank he didn't need his therapist as much and, by implication, was safer.

5. Chessick (2) noted that many alcoholic patients reported feeling lonely much of the time. Drinking dispelled this feeling and the associated fantasy was about one of their parents. Some patients feared death if they should stop the use of drugs. They associated this fear with loss of a parent. He also noted that addiction frequently occurs following a death in the family and replaces the mourning process. Object loss was thus denied and the body as an object was substituted for the lost object.

Summary

The alcoholic is a person whose ego functions are deficient. Alcoholics generally have a poor capacity for sound relationships as the result either of an early object loss or of an absence, in early development, of an impetus to seek object relationships. The prealcoholic resorts to alcohol in an effort to make up for such deficiencies. In an effort to adapt he chooses his body as a safe object to which to relate. Alcohol intoxication serves to produce physiological changes which he experiences as assurance of the continued maintenance of this ego–body relationship, providing him with a feeling of ego safety. Without this feeling, threat of personal disintegration and ego annihilation appears, so that he constantly seeks to reexperience his physiological responses. He drinks and drinks again to intoxication; thus does alcoholism develop. Drinking to intoxication enables the alcoholic to prevent the disruption of the ego–body relatedness and to ward off dissolution of the ego.

While the alcoholic's drinking appears to be suicidal, initially he drinks not to annihilate his physical being but to experience its presence. But, with physiological adaptation to alcohol, he experiences the ego–body relationship as a progressively fading one, and to prevent this dissolution, paradoxically, the alcoholic ego seeks to destroy the body. He chooses alcohol as his means to suicide because he sees alcohol as the drug that is destroying him. The alcoholic's depression, resulting from an early object loss, is denied by the choice of his body as an object. With physiological adaptation, the ego–body relatedness is decreased and he is threatened with the return of severe depression from original object loss.

Because of the alcoholic's attachment to his own body he imposes on other bodies the image of his own. He relates to others not as such, but as projections of his own body. Frequently he is unable to impose his own image on a person of the opposite sex, so he turns from women to men.

The pharmacological effect of alcohol produces a withdrawal from the outside world which enhances the seeming importance and figural quality of the ego–body attachment.

Some clinical notes are presented to verify these views.

REFERENCES

1. ABRAHAM, K. The psychological relation between sexuality and alcoholism. Pp. 80–89. In: JONES, E., ed. Selected papers of Karl Abraham. 4th ed. London; Hogarth; 1949.
2. CHESSICK, R. D. The "pharmacogenic orgasm" in the drug addict. Archs Gen. Psychiat. 3: 545–556, 1960.
3. CROWLEY, R. M. Psychoanalytic literature on drug addiction and alcoholism. Psychoanal. Rev. 26: 39–54, 1939.
4. ISBELL, H. Medical aspects of opiate addiction. Bull. N.Y. Acad. Med. 31: 886–901, 1955.
5. KOLB, L. and HIMMELSBACH, C. Clinical studies of drug addiction. Am. J. Psychiat. 94: 1–15, 1938.
6. KRYSTAL, H. A study of the syndrome of withdrawal from narcotics as a state of stress. Presented at the annual meeting of the American Psychiatric Association, May 1961.
7. RADÓ, S. The psychic effects of intoxicants; an attempt to evolve a psychoanalytic theory of morbid cravings. Int. J. Psycho-Analysis 7: 396–402, 1926.
8. RADÓ, S. The psychoanalysis of pharmacothymia (drug addiction). Psychoanal. Q. 2: 1–23, 1933.
9. SHUR, M. Comments on the metapsychology of somatization. Psychoanal. Study Child 10: 119–164, 1955.
10. SIMMEL, E. Alcoholism and addiction. Psychoanal. Q. 17: 6–31, 1948.
11. SZASZ, T. S. The role of the counterphobic mechanism in addiction. J. Am. Psychoanal. Ass. 6: 309–325, 1958.
12. THORNER, I. Ascetic Protestantism and alcoholism. Psychiatry 16: 167–176, 1953.
13. SZASZ, T. S. Pain and pleasure. London; Tavistock; 1957.

14

The Etiology of Alcoholism

The Role of Psychological Predisposition[1]

Edith S. Lisansky (Edith S. Gomberg), Ph.D.

A BASIC QUESTION that must be posed before considering the problem of personality variables involved in alcoholism is whether alcoholism[2] is a diagnostic entity in and of itself or only a syndrome or symptom. Patients may be diagnosed as manifesting an anxiety reaction, paranoid schizophrenia or compulsion neurosis, and it may be noted somewhere in the case record that they also have drinking problems. But these patients do have in common a loss of control over their drinking and it is important, in treatment and study, that they be distinguished from others who have the same diagnoses but not the drinking problems. If we call these patients alcoholics, the diagnoses then become double diagnoses, e.g., anxiety reaction with alcoholism. Specialized clinics throughout the country see many patients whose outstanding clinical characteristic is their alcoholism although they present other psychopathology as well. For them, too, double diagnoses seem best.

Any diagnostic solution presents its own problems. On the one hand it is unrealistic to minimize or ignore the alcoholism. On the other hand, diagnosing such patients exclusively as alcoholics and ignoring other behaviors and symptoms results in an artificial

---

[1] Reprinted by permission from the QUARTERLY JOURNAL OF STUDIES ON ALCOHOL, Vol. 21, pp. 314–343, 1960. Copyright by Journal of Studies on Alcohol, Inc., New Brunswick, New Jersey 08903.

[2] The definition of alcoholism assumed throughout this paper is one in which loss of control over drinking is the central feature. It is the definition elaborated in the report of the Alcoholism Subcommittee of the World Health Organization (WHO) Expert Committee on Mental Health (1). It has recently been seriously challenged (2).

grouping of all alcoholics by their common disorder and losing sight of the differences among them.

The controversy whether alcoholism is a symptom or a disease has diverted a lot of energy and effort. The question is not, at the present state of knowledge, a resolvable one. Symptom or disease, the major question is whether people who present this behavior disorder, this loss of control over their drinking, have some personality deviation or some psychodynamics in common. That is the subject of the present paper.

The search for the "alcoholic personality" is, according to many, a blind alley. This is concluded realistically enough because several research starts have led nowhere. Thus, after two different reviews of the psychological test literature on alcoholism (3, 4), the conclusion that ". . . there is no warrant for concluding that persons of one type are more likely to become alcoholics than another type. . ." (4) is not unreasonable. The results of psychological test studies have been ambiguous and inconclusive.

The view of the Alcoholism Subcommittee of the WHO Expert Committee on Mental Health does not encourage the search for the "alcoholic personality," for though it posits "a few traits in common" it states clearly: "There does not seem to emerge . . . any specific personality trait or physical characteristic which inevitably would lead to excessive symptomatic drinking" (1). There is, however, the equally reasonable position taken by Armstrong (5). After reviewing the literature on the "alcoholic personality," Armstrong concludes that "it would seem . . . premature to abandon the search because of failure to date to determine adequate methods or to discover the appropriate investigative tools. Thus we feel that the quest for an alcoholic personality or constellation of frequently predominant characteristics in alcoholism has barely begun."

BARRIERS TO PROGRESS

There are some basic issues in psychopathological research which need clarification before study of the psychodynamics of alcoholism can progress.

The primary question is one of definition and precision. This has two segments: a precision about whole and part in speaking of personality, and the fallacy of post hoc, ergo propter hoc reasoning in respect to psychopathology.

The concept of "alcoholic personality" has sometimes been discussed as if it must mean that all alcoholics have a total personality structure in common. This ignores all that is known and accepted about human variability, individual differences and the uniqueness of each personality (6). To speak of total personality structure in common may be setting up a straw man, yet to discuss "persons of one type" does imply that the whole personality is involved. The confusion here is, to some extent, a semantic one although it is a theoretical one as well. It is necessary to speak not of the "alcoholic personality" or "alcoholic types" but of a constellation or pattern of personality traits common to most alcoholics and characterizing the prealcoholic personality. One further assumption seems reasonable: that there is not a single pattern but several. This view, held also by Armstrong and others, rejects the idea that anyone may become an alcoholic or that there is nothing specifically predisposing toward alcoholism in the premorbid personality.

This position allows further speculation that the distinguishing feature of the prealcoholic patterns of personality traits may be the inclusion or exclusion of certain traits, or the degree to which certain traits are present, or both. That is, the characteristic pattern may be distinguished either by the coexistence of traits alpha, beta and gamma, or by the intensity with which alpha, beta and gamma, or a combination of them, exists in the personality structure.

Another question must be considered: Are these patterns of personality traits specific to alcoholism, or specific to the addictions, or do they occur also with significant frequency in other psychopathological populations?

Still another related question of precision is the almost omnipresent fallacy of post hoc, ergo propter hoc reasoning about the etiology of alcoholism. X behavior is observed in patients who have been drinking and getting into difficulties for the last 10 or 20 years and it is therefore assumed that X is a causative factor in their alcoholism. To know that X behavior exists may be of enormous value in treating the patient but it does not necessarily follow that it antedated and led to the alcoholism. Alcoholism has various social and personal consequences. Most alcoholics develop problem drinking over a period of time and through several well-defined phases (7), and the course of alcoholism involves a gradually far-reaching and intense involvement in keeping supplied with alcohol. The WHO report (1) points out that problems created by the problem drinking become the cause of more problem drinking. It would be within reason to assume that as the alcoholism begins and progresses, personality changes of some sort take place. It is a frequent clinical observation, for example, that the personality becomes more or less impoverished as the alcoholism plays itself out. That some reorganization in personality structure probably occurs when an alcoholic stops his drinking is also a reasonable hypothesis.

Obviously it would be an advantage to study alcoholic individuals before they become alcoholics. We can distinguish for this purpose three periods in the patient's past: first, infancy, childhood, adolescence and the early adult years; second, the onset period, varying considerably but for many the age between 25 and 35, the "purely symptomatic" phases described by Jellinek (7); third, the alcoholism period.

No one has studied alcoholic individuals at the point of entering the onset period,[3] i.e., before problem drinking began. We most frequently see alcoholics when they are well advanced in their alcoholism. There are evident difficulties in reaching the patient before he becomes a patient and it is a questionable solution to study the ex-alcoholic after he has been "dry" a given period of time.

The conclusion is inevitable that the most meaningful research into the psychological etiology of alcoholism will be longitudinal studies in which groups of adolescents and young adults are studied periodically and followed up for years. In such studies, however, it is not possible to investigate everything and the decision on what to study must be based on a choice of hypotheses concerning alcoholic individuals.

Another problem which has plagued the quest for the "alcoholic personality" has been the necessity under which investigators have labored to choose between a theoretical conceptualization of alcoholism by orthodox psychoanalytic thinkers or no conceptualization at all.[4]

Psychological research in alcoholism has foundered on this choice. Studies, frequently the analysis of case histories, often psychological test research, conducted within the framework of psychoanalytic theory, have seemed to justify the conclusion that "psychiatrically, it is possible to find just about what is sought in a group of alcoholics" (11). The case is chosen, the test data interpreted, to demonstrate a point of theory; but while the demonstration may benefit definition, it is not a test of the point of theory.

---

[3] Seeley (2, p. 354) in his critique of the WHO definition of alcoholism calls this "a critical question: What is to be regarded as the point of onset. . .?"

[4] It is true that there have been recent attempts to theorize in behavioristic or learning theory terms (8–10), but this approach has had little influence on clinical research thus far.

On the other side, psychological test studies which follow the summary or "let's analyze this group of records and see what comes out" method have usually led nowhere. Such test analysis has yielded statistical results, frequently not corroborated, as often as not contradicted by the next such test analysis (3, 4). The summary method can be useful at this stage of knowledge about alcoholism only if viewed as a source of ideas and hypotheses.

Those students of alcoholism who choose to take theory as a point of departure must face the challenge that psychoanalytic theory on alcoholism (12) needs revision and modification to take into account increasing information about the physiology and sociology of alcoholism and changing ideas within psychoanalysis. Several recent papers have moved in this direction (13–15).

To the more empirically minded researcher, clinical observations or test results might suggest generalizations which would lend themselves to study and verification. Using interview data, psychological test results, measures derived from the laboratory, methods of experimental psychology, or whatever acceptable and appropriate method of study is available, alcoholics may be compared with other equated groups of normal and pathological individuals, and with other groups of alcoholics. Such empirical research yields facts, and just as theory sets up hypotheses for empirical verification, facts feed back into theory and produce modifications and extensions therein.

THE COMPLEX ETIOLOGY OF ALCOHOLISM

Historically, the attempts to formulate theory about the origins of psychopathology have been weakened by a professional ethnocentricism in which neurologists see mental illness in neurological terms, biochemists in biochemical terms, psychiatrists and psychologists in psychodynamic terms, and the sociologically oriented behavioral scientists in societal terms. Both psychosomatic medicine and social psychiatry are relatively new disciplines; both represent the merger of approaches moving toward the recognition of man, healthy or ill, as a biological and psychological organism functioning in a social field. While each profession labors in the vineyard of its own research interests, each contributes a partial explanation, a piece of the puzzle which will eventually have to be integrated with the other pieces if understanding, explanation and prediction are to emerge. Duhl (16) presents an ecological viewpoint in which alcoholism is perceived as one of many "avenues of discharge" when the "normal adaptive mechanisms of coping with life" break down; such mechanisms and their breakdowns are to be understood only in terms of a "multifactored interplay of man and his environment."

Just as there have been attempts to define the causes of alcoholism exclusively in physiological terms,[5] there have been explanations of alcoholism by psychoanalysts, psychiatrists and psychologists in exclusively psychological terms. A broader conception of etiology, now held by many, assumes the interaction of physiochemical, psychological and sociological predisposing factors to be the basis for the development of such a disorder as alcoholism.

If now the question of the "alcoholic personality" is attacked at some given point of time, say at the beginning, the first drinking experience, the following must be taken into account:

X = certain aspects of the physiochemical state of the individual;
Y = certain aspects of the psychological state of the individual;
Z = certain aspects of the sociological state of the individual.

Y may equal the particular pattern of personality traits which characterizes the individual predisposed toward alcoholism. Z will include not only exposure to alcohol, but the attitudes and customs relating to alcoholic beverages practiced by the groups in which the person holds membership. Nor has the individual's psychological state at the moment in question developed independently of physiological and sociological conditions; at all stages of development they are intertwined. This complex interaction has resulted in an individual who, at this point in his life, represents a combination of X, Y and Z which allows prediction with reasonable certainty that he will develop a usage of alcohol characterized by problem drinking.

Once again the question of the specificity of the prealcoholic psychological state must be raised. There are a number of alternatives: that X, Y or Z alone is sufficient to account for the development of an alcohol problem, that the particular combination of X, Y and Z is specific to alcoholism, or that there is no pattern or combination of events which is specific to alcoholism. Presumably what will permit prediction of the development of alcoholism in a given individual will be the knowledge of X, Y and Z in combination. It may be assumed that while the predisposing prealcoholic psychological state may be limited to several patterns of personality traits, such pat-

---

[5] There is, for example, Williams (17), whose position has been that the "basic cause" of alcoholism is a nutritional deficiency.

terns are not necessarily unique to alcoholism. This view, that the prealcoholic patterns of personality traits are specific but not necessarily unique to alcoholism, does not seem to be a major obstacle to research on what the component parts of the pattern are.

The methodological problems in studying physiochemical, psychological and sociological variables in interaction seem formidable. In practice, it means that a long-term, longitudinal study, beginning perhaps with children or adolescents, must embrace measures of physiological, psychological and sociological variables. On the reasonable assumption that some individuals in the sample would in time develop an alcohol problem, there is then the possibility of defining out of the mass of data those variables that correlate significantly with the eventual onset of alcoholism. The critical problem is the preselection of some measures of variables which may be of significance.

HOMOGENEITY VERSUS HETEROGENEITY

The WHO Technical Report (1) states: "By and large . . . reactions to excessive drinking . . . give the impression of an 'alcoholic personality,' although they are secondary behaviors superimposed over a large variety of personality types which have a few traits in common, in particular a low capacity for coping with tensions." This suggests the following schema:

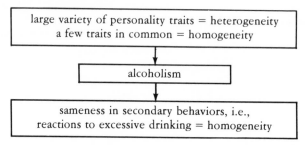

It is the so-called secondary behaviors, the consequences, which so often lead the clinician to see the homogeneity which he is likely to call "the alcoholic personality."

What confuses the issue here is the involvement of time and change. The particular concern of the present paper is with the personality patterns which exist prealcoholically and at the time of onset. There is no question but that behavioral changes occur as alcoholism progresses. The intense preoccupation with the obtaining of alcohol, the narrowing of interests, and the increasing disregard for the realities of economic necessity, marriage, interpersonal relationships and social status produce the impoverishment and the "secondary behaviors" frequently observed in alcoholics of some years' standing.

Perhaps related to this is the observation of tremendous variability in Rorschach test responses by alcoholics (3, 4) and the repeated observation that the Minnesota Multiphasic Personality Inventory (MMPI) consistently gives a picture of psychopathic deviation and depression (18–20). It is possible that the Rorschach test is reflecting more of the premorbid personality structure and that the MMPI is getting at the more overt, more conscious, more observable "secondary behaviors." There are, of course, many other possible reasons for the disparity of Rorschach results.

Putting aside the issue of changes with time, there is no reason to assume that predisposed individuals have more in common than the pattern of traits which has been hypothesized. There is both homogeneity and heterogeneity and this point of view is stated well by Zwerling (15): "A constellation of traits may well be basic to the etiology of addictive drinking, and yet be embedded in such a diversity of character structures as to be obscured to eyes focused only upon the most dominant integration of the total personality as it is manifested in the clinical diagnosis."

THE ALCOHOLISMS

It is apparent that the approximately 4 million individuals in the United States who are alcoholics or problem drinkers do indeed present wide variability in behavior, in emotional reactions, and in the manifestation of other symptoms. It is also reasonable to assume, with such a large sample, that there may be sensible ways of subgrouping these problem drinkers by some significant common features.

Many classifications have been suggested in terms of personality variables and symptomatology. Bowman and Jellinek (21) listed no less than 24 such suggested classifications. One of these, for example, is Knight's (22, 23) and K. A. Menninger's (24) classification: (a) "essential type," those with a long history of maladjustment, (b) "reactive type," those for whom alcoholism is precipitated by an "overtaxing situation," (c) "neurotic characters," or those alcoholics with other maladjustments, and (d) psychotic personalities, for whom alcoholism is only one symptom in a psychotic complex.

A more recent and different classification is that contained in the WHO report (1) in which "habitual symptomatic excessive drinkers" are differentiated from addictive drinkers. Work reported by Straus (25) suggests that Skid Row habitués, homeless men and chronic drunkenness offenders are more likely to fit into the first group, alcoholics seen at outpatient clinics into the second. From a study of two groups of women alcoholics, one in outpatient clinics and one in a state penal farm (26), it is clear that although both groups may be defined as alcoholics, the drinking problem of the state farm inmates is a concomitant of many severe social and psychological problems while for the outpatients it tends to be the focal and primary problem.

Still another approach to systematization has been made by Levy (14), who first differentiates the toxic effect of alcohol on the central nervous system as one of "discharge" or "narcotizing," and then adds "the effects of alcohol due to its various symbolic meanings." He concludes that "these elementary functions of alcohol are combined in various field patterns to produce various types of alcoholism."

What is sorely needed, for research purposes, is a meaningful and usable classification of the alcoholisms which takes into account psychodiagnostic differences related to the individual's life history, behavioral differences relating to where, when and how the individual drinks, and the functions which alcohol serves for him.

PSYCHODYNAMIC THEORIES

It is a good idea to keep in mind that those who theorize about the psychodynamics of alcoholism[6] have seen, as a rule, only very limited segments of the alcoholic population. A general, all-embracing psychodynamic theory which seeks to account for all problem drinkers everywhere is probably doomed from the start. Alcoholism is a social-psychological problem among American Indians and it is an observed phenomenon among primitive peoples, and in Mexico, France, Poland and other countries. The theorizing about alcoholism here presented concerns white male alcoholics in the United States.

It is also a reasonable assumption that theorizing about the psychodynamics of alcoholism has come from people whose contacts with alcoholics were limited to hospitals and private practice.[7] Such limitations are not fatal to theorizing but some of the proffered ideas make better sense when these limitations are kept in mind.

---

[6] This includes the present writer.

[7] The present writer's experience has been primarily in outpatient clinics, secondarily in mental hospitals.

The basic psychoanalytic viewpoint has been expressed concisely by Fenichel (27): "The reasons for reverting to alcohol are either the existence of external frustration, that is, states of misery one would like to forget and to replace by pleasurable fantasies, or internal inhibitions, that is, states in which one dare not act against the superego without such artificial help." Alcoholism is described as an impulse neurosis based on "difficult family constellations [which] created specific oral frustrations in childhood." Predisposition is summed up in "oral and narcissistic premorbid personalities," characteristic of all the addictions. Two consequences of the early frustrations are significant in alcoholism: the development of oral fixations and homosexual tendencies. The unconscious oral and homosexual impulses are, in a sense, acted out in the drinking bout in which the external frustrations imposed by reality are dimmed and the internal inhibitions are removed from consciousness.

In addition to the methodological problems of studying unconscious impulses, a major barrier to research has been the lack of definition of terms widely used. Thus, concepts like "orality" or "homosexuality" have many different meanings. "Orality" is used to refer to specific character traits, e.g., being dependent on others; it is used as synonymous with a generally immature personality arrested at very early levels of development; and it is also used in a more commonsense, descriptive way to characterize habits like smoking, thumb sucking, nail biting and the like. Theorizing about alcoholism has been confounded by the fact that alcoholic beverages are ingested through the mouth so that, at times, "orality" takes on a very specific, literal meaning, i.e., the drinking bout is an oral acting out and a symbolic substitution for breast feeding. It may be great wisdom and true insight to link these various meanings or levels of "orality" under a single, unifying conception, but it does not further the cause of clarification to use the different meanings almost interchangeably.

The same problems are involved with "homosexuality" in the male which, at different times, seems to mean difficulties in adjusting to a stable heterosexual relationship, feminine identification and interests, strong mother attachment, an adolescent-like seeking out of male companionship, passivity, overt homosexual experience, misogynism, or a desire to form one's closest interpersonal ties with men. Again, the concept of "homosexuality" as used by psychoanalysts may bring together related behaviors, but it makes for great confusion when one author uses one referent and another author a second referent while both refer to "homosexuality."

However these terms are defined, Lorand (28), surveying the psychoanalytic literature on alcoholism up to 1945, summarizes thus: "The common feature in the structure of the whole personality of alcoholics . . . is strong homosexual tendencies and oral cravings. . . . It is also commonly thought that the use of alcohol has as its aim a running away from problems which one cannot or does not want to face—i.e., regression toward infantile fixations."

Radó (29) and Knight (22, 23) formulated the dynamics in some detail. It is Radó's view that certain early life experiences leave the individual uncertain that he can solve life's problems satisfactorily through his own initiative; his childhood experiences have not permitted the kinds of achievements and satisfactions out of which healthy self-esteem develops. He therefore longs to return to the passively obtained, given-from-without satisfaction of infancy. When adult frustrations inevitably arise, he discovers in alcohol the double magic: the pain and tensions of reality are banished and the original narcissistic pleasure state of infancy is temporarily reinstated.

Knight, who viewed alcoholism as a symptomatic attempt to resolve emotional conflict, stated: "There is no special or typical kind of emotional conflict common to all cases. Any type of neurotic conflict may be present." He traced the "neurotic vicious circle" in which the alcoholic becomes involved, presumably the significant dynamic process which leads into and becomes more complicated by the alcoholism. Childhood experiences produce a demanding individual, constantly seeking indulgence. Excessive demands must, in the nature of the real adult world, be frustrated. Such frustrations evoke disappointment and rage, which motivate hostile acts and wishes, which in turn evoke guilt. The final link is described thus: "As reassurance against guilt feelings and fears of dangerously destructive masochism and reality consequences of his behavior, he feels excessive need for affection and indulgence as proof of affection. . . . Thus we are brought full circle back to the excessive demands for indulgence." Knight perceived the multiple role of alcohol for the alcoholic thus: "The use of alcohol as a pacifier for disappointment and rage, as a potent means of carrying out hostile impulses to spite his parents and friends, as a method of securing masochistic debasement, and as a symbolic gratification of the need for affection, is now interweaving itself in the neurotic vicious circle."

It is of interest and significance that two astute observers, studying their alcoholic patients, emerge with major emphases which seem to be contradictory. K. A. Menninger (24) summarized his point of view thus: "Alcohol addiction . . . can be considered a form of self-destruction used to avert a greater self-destruction, deriving from elements of aggressiveness, excited by thwarting, ungratified eroticism, and the feeling of a need for punishment from a sense of guilt related to the aggressiveness." Schilder (30) countered with an emphasis not on the need for punishment but rather on the need for love: "To stress the self-destructive tendencies of alcoholism, as Menninger does, overlooks the deep striving of the alcoholic to be loved and appreciated by society." The characteristic of the alcoholic, Schilder thought, is social tension.[8]

In a paper which expressed a modified view within the framework of psychoanalytic theory, Higgins (13) suggested this revision: "A predisposed person (and the predisposition may represent fixations at various levels of personality development) is confronted with a difficult life situation; the 'difficult situation' may or may not be one which has as its primary component an 'oral threat'." Succinctly, Higgins' view is that "pathological drinking may arise out of a variety of psychological conflicts," and that as the predisposed person's alcoholism progressively develops, the original psychodynamic conflict which was the etiological base becomes less obvious and the "oral narcissistic elements" become more obvious.[9] In addition to his view that the etiology of alcoholism is more general than the very specific "oral and narcissistic premorbid personality," Higgins differentiated between earlier and later stages of alcoholism within the same patients. The inference is that traditional psychoanalytic theorizing about alcoholism was based on contact with the later stages of alcoholism in which the "oral narcissistic elements" were most prominent. Concerning this view, that alcoholism may arise from a variety of psychological conflicts, Zwerling (15) has commented that "the existence of an underlying personality disorder common to alcoholics is . . . not at all precluded by the observation that alcohol may be pressed into the service of the personal-

[8] It is interesting to note that the emphasis on guilt emerges from a private sanitarium setting and the emphasis on social isolation from a city hospital. It would seem that Menninger and Knight on the one hand, and Schilder on the other, are referring to different groups of alcoholics.

[9] This view of shift with time brings to mind Allport's concept of the functional autonomy of motives (6). To put it in Allportian terms, the original, etiological conflict which acted as motive in the early formation of the habit, here problem drinking, becomes less significant with time. The habit becomes, in a sense, self-perpetuating. Higgins adds to this: certain aspects of the habitual behavior, problem drinking, become more significant with time.

ity at all levels of conflict and in association with all varieties of defenses."

A recent contribution by Levy (14) shows a fresh viewpoint developing within modern psychoanalytic theory. His major thesis is presumably a methodological one, i.e., that the problem of the "alcoholic personality" may be approached by studying and classifying "some of the major psychological functions served by the use of alcohol." Alcohol, he points out, may perform many psychodynamic functions at one and the same time. "Some [functions] it will perform for almost everyone, some require an idiosyncratic personality structure," and addiction is more likely when alcohol "solves" many problems or performs many functions simultaneously for the individual. His view of psychological predisposition is summarized thus: "Alcohol is a relatively specific solution to certain needs. If these needs are of great intensity, and if the remainder of the personality constellation permits it, then they may act as relatively specific determinants. It would seem that the two major sets of needs which can act in this way are the passive–infantile needs and the masochistic needs."

These oversimplified descriptions of psychoanalytic writings summarize where psychoanalytic theorizing stands at present; much of the reasoning and many of the details have been omitted. All of the writers presented case material to demonstrate and to support their ideas, and some of the psychological test studies in the clinical literature have reported results which seem to offer some supporting evidence.[10]

LEARNING THEORY

Although the interest of experimental psychologists has been confined to a few laboratory studies of the effects of alcohol on animals, and the effects of moderate quantities of alcohol on some aspects of human behavior, some recent behavioristic theorizing has dealt with the problem of alcoholism. Dollard and Miller (8) have presented the following hypothesis: In life situations, individuals are frequently faced with the necessity to act in approach–avoidance conflicts. Avoidance is based on fear. Alcohol reduces fear, therefore it reduces avoidance, therefore it reduces conflict. In a typical experiment, conflict is created by feeding and giving electric shock to laboratory animals at the same site in the experimental apparatus.

---

[10] For example, Singer (31).

Feeding results in approach behavior whereas fear of shock results in avoidance behavior. Alcohol apparently produces a temporary reduction in fear and in avoidance; thus it relieves the tension of conflict. Since fear is an undesirable, unpleasant emotion, a fear-reducer has reward value. In Dollard and Miller's (8) words, "alcohol seems to produce a temporary, direct reduction in fear and conflict and hence in misery. For people who are suffering from fear and conflict, this reduction will be expected to reinforce the responses involved in drinking."

Conger (9) elaborated this basic idea: The drinking response is learned because it leads to reinforcement, defined as a reduction in drive ("a state of tension resulting from an unsatisfied need"). Drinking is learned, then, because it is rewarding, and the problem is to discover the rewards involved and the tensions or unsatisfied needs being reduced. Conger (9) writes, "such an approach does not in any way reduce the necessity of finding out what need or drive patterns are particularly important among various kinds of alcoholics."

What the learning theorists offer, then, is some explanation of the process by which the habit of behaving like an alcoholic may be acquired: alcohol and the rewarding reduction of tension become associated. Essentially Levy (14), although he uses psychiatric rather than behavioristic language, discusses the same dynamic process. In Levy's terms, alcoholism develops when alcohol "solves" many problems for the individual, that is to say, because it is (in learning theory terms) reinforcing or rewarding. Levy, of course, goes further than the behaviorists in speculating about the nature of the reinforcement, i.e., the needs which are gratified through the ingestion of alcohol.

The behavioristic position does not spell out what the individual needs to carry with him from his past life to his experiences with alcohol in order to become an alcoholic; one may or may not combine this position with a psychoanalytic viewpoint (although such a combination seems more like coexistence than a truly integrated union of theoretical approaches). The antecedent circumstances which make alcoholism more or less likely are not defined except in the most general terms of more fear, more avoidance, more conflict.

Ullman (32), in what may be called a sociobehavioristic approach, believes that addictive drinking is "a tension-reducing activity with the source of tension lying in the ordinary problems of human beings." Minimizing the etiological significance of predisposing personality variables, Ullman believes that alcohol addiction may be acquired when three sets of circumstances are present. First, there must be "some motivation to drink which would include a certain amount of emotional arousal with regard to drinking"; second, there must be "the juxtaposition of a stress situation with drinking experiences"; and third, "enough alcohol must be taken in on such occasions so that tension-reduction, which is the result of the pharmacological action of alcohol, can occur." In essence, the three conditions are drive, contiguity, reinforcement.

To sum up in the briefest possible terms, the learning theorists emphasize the importance of conflict per se, the tension which the conflicts produce, and the fear-reducing role of alcohol; psychoanalytic theory has been concerned with the nature and developmental origin of the conflicts and tensions involved.

ROLE OF AMBIVALENCE

In summary of the descriptive observations of those who have concerned themselves with the psychodynamics of alcoholism, the following list, admittedly crude in its redundancies, overlap and unevenness, may be made:

> Orality, oral personality, fixation at an oral level
> Homosexuality
> Regression toward infantile fixations
> Dependence and passivity, passive–infantile needs
> Narcissism
> Low self-esteem, deep striving to be loved
> Excessive demands for indulgence
> Aggressiveness and hostility
> Guilt
> Masochistic needs
> Self-destructive tendencies
> Impulsiveness
> Tense depression
> Conflict, fear, anxiety.

A striking feature of this list is the number of apparent contradictions. Assuming that those who contributed to this list are equally good observers and that these descriptive terms are based on equally valid observations, how can self-love and self-hate, the intense need for love and affection from others and the simultaneous aggressiveness and hostility directed toward others be reconciled? If these are all valid observations, the contradictory aspects of the behavior of alcoholics may be brought together with a unifying conception, i.e., ambivalence.

Bleuler, who originated the term, distinguished three kinds of ambivalence: (1) emotional, i.e., oscillation between love and hate; (2) voluntary, i.e., inability to decide on an action; and (3) intellectual, i.e., belief in contradictory propositions. Freud generally used the term in the first of these senses (33).

Psychoanalytic theory proposes that an important characteristic of early object relations is a high degree of ambivalence: "That is to say, feelings of love may alternate with equally intense feelings of hate, depending on the circumstances" (34). Or, "Since it is particularly common to find both of these [love and hate] directed simultaneously toward the same object, their coexistence furnishes the most important example of ambivalence of feeling" (33). This high degree of ambivalence reaches its height, in normal development, from ages 2 to 5 and persists to some extent throughout life. A high degree of ambivalence may survive into adult life, although not overtly displayed, and, "Such persistent ambivalence is often associated with severe neurotic conflicts and symptoms" (34). Intense ambivalence in adults is linked to obsessional neuroses (35, 36) and to compulsion neuroses (27, 37) by psychoanalytic writers. If alcoholism is considered a variation of compulsive behavior, manifesting the individual's inability to stop this behavior or even keep it within bounds, and if ambivalence "plays so large a role . . . in compulsion neurosis" (37), then it seems reasonable to assume that ambivalence is an important component in alcoholism.

ROLE OF EARLY LIFE EXPERIENCE

The speculation has been offered that there are probably several different predisposing constellations of personality traits which, in combination with appropriate physiological and sociocultural conditions, make it likely that the individual in question will become an alcoholic. The following is an attempt to trace the hypothetical origin of one such constellation.

The starting point is the assumption that etiological conditions in very early life experience are not highly specific among individuals who later become alcoholics. For example, the view that "specific oral frustrations" in early childhood are of primary significance etiologically is not supported by the relevant studies available. Child (38), in a review of research on oral behavior and its relationship to child rearing and socialization processes, observed in summary that "There is little doubt that variations in treatment of the infant's oral behavior have important immediate effects on his oral behavior. With respect to more lasting or more general effects of oral socialization either before or at the time of weaning, no such definite conclusion is possible as yet from systematic research."

The etiological significance of the frequently cited family pattern of domineering–possessive mother and passive–dependent father is also not established. This may be one family constellation which encourages in children the development of traits predisposing to alcoholism, but there appear to be many others as well. The families of alcoholics of high socioeconomic status frequently include an achieving, demanding father and a docile, passive mother. The overindulgent, overprotective mother and the authoritarian but inconsistent father are described by Knight (22) as "absolutely typical" among his patients in a private sanitarium. Wahl (39), in a population of 109 alcoholics in a state hospital, found almost as high an incidence of "rejecting" mothers (26 per cent) as "overprotective" mothers (33 per cent). These are, of course, different socioeconomic populations, and different research methods are involved (psychoanalytic sessions and case record abstracts). There is some evidence that a loveless, emotionally deprived childhood is characteristic of some groups of alcoholics (40–42). There is reason to doubt that all alcoholics, in all social classes, men and women alike, have experienced the same kind of early family life.

It is assumed that the personality traits hypothesized here as predisposing toward alcoholism are rooted in early life experiences. It is further assumed that there is an optimal amount of experience with both love and frustration, with both pleasure and pain, in early life. What is optimal for future sound adjustment varies, within limits, from one individual to another. There are individual differences in the earliest needs for fondling and for rapid surcease of hunger pangs, and in ability to tolerate delay, stress, pain. This balance of pleasure and pain in early life is necessary to produce a sense of security, on the one hand, and a capacity to tolerate frustration, delay and limitation, on the other. The issue is that of love and frustration as experienced by the growing child; the easy, simple assumptions that, for example, one absent parent always means love deprivation, or that strict parental supervision equals frustration, need to be carefully thought through. The frustrations referred to here will have to be measured by studying individual experience and not by labeling certain conditions of the individual's social environment.

The individual predisposed toward alcoholism, it is here assumed, has experienced in early life too much "pain" or frustration. So much frustration has been imposed by his social environment in early life that he is wounded psychologically and remains stunted or arrested in various aspects of ego growth and function.[11] Frustration in early life appears in many different forms. A distinction between rejection and deprivation has been made by Goldfarb (43) and others. Deprivation, as the term implies, means an absence of affection and approval and, in fact, a minimal amount of interaction with other human beings. Rejection, "may or may not involve a factor of deprivation . . . and more generally implies severity and cruelty of early handling by parents" (43). Marked vacillation and inconsistency on the part of parents is still another pattern of early family life which seems related to psychopathology. It is conceivable that we shall be able eventually to relate class differences in child-rearing behavior, and differing patterns of love, attention, rejection, deprivation, inconsistency, etc., to different manifestations of psychopathology.

There are also predisposed individuals who have experienced too much "pleasure" in early life. This is usually spoken of as overindulgence and it takes the form of insufficient experience with frustrations and limitations imposed by the social environment.[12] The human condition being what it is, the excess of pain, rejection and frustration is most commonly found associated with alcoholic psychopathology and, presumably, other psychopathologies as well. But those who did experience overindulgence, aptly termed by Jellinek, "the pampered drinkers," should not be ignored.

In either instance, a constellation of personality traits is produced

[11] A relationship between insufficient pleasure or love in early childhood experience and ambivalence in later life was suggested by Abraham: "We should not forget that the Oedipal relationship which we rightly look upon as a source of serious and lasting conflict in the psychic life of the child and of the adult originally constitutes a source of pleasure, both in reality and in phantasy. If, however, the child is allowed a certain limited amount of pleasure, he gradually learns to renounce the greatest and most important of such wishes, namely those which are socially unacceptable. This seems to be, for the child, an indispensable aid to the successful overcoming of ambivalence toward the parents" (36).

[12] In the view of the psychoanalysts, overindulgence is a disguise; maternal overprotection may mask hostile, destructive feelings toward the child. Such a view may be completely valid, but it is still necessary to distinguish parental behavior which is overtly cold, hostile and rejecting from that which is overindulgent, overpermissive and "spoiling," and from that which is vacillating and inconsistent. Early life experience is not the same for children whose parents behave in these different ways.

and these traits are the crucial, necessary parts of the personality carried into the onset period in order to produce, in interaction with physiological and sociocultural conditions, an alcoholic. This is, of course, a vastly oversimplified exposition. The relationship between early life experience of frustration, early and later object relations, the problems of identification and related phenomena, and the subsequent development of alcoholism, need to be further explored.

A PREDISPOSING PERSONALITY CONSTELLATION

It is assumed that out of the experiences of infancy and childhood and adolescence, the imbalance of pleasure and pain, of satisfaction and frustration, the predisposed individual has developed the following traits with which he enters his adult years: (a) an intensely strong need, drive, impulse toward dependency; (b) weak and inadequate defense mechanisms against this excessive need, leading to, under certain conditions, (c) an intense dependence–independence conflict; there is also (d) a low degree of frustration or tension tolerance; and (e) unresolved love–hate ambivalences. All of these parts must be present to make up the predispositional whole, the core of personality which is necessary (although not sufficient) to account for the subsequent development of alcoholism.

The predisposed individual may, in the course of personality development, acquire any number of defensive mechanisms, e.g., repression, but they are not strong defenses. Because of his life experiences, this person has dependency needs stronger than other individuals. There is, then, a strong need and a weak defense.

Biologically and in terms of social role, this individual has now reached the adult years. It is at this time that trouble begins.[13] While dependency, the taken-care-of, passive state of freedom from responsibility, has its rewards, the state of male adult independence has rewards, too. Marriage and companionship, a reasonably satisfying job, a place in society, being a parent—these are not devoid of reward and satisfaction for this potentially alcoholic person. An in-

---

[13] When adolescent drinking behavior is systematically investigated, it is quite possible that in some American subcultures problem drinking will be observed in this earlier age group. This would not necessarily cancel out the significance of adult role demands. In some subgroups the adolescent years are not a transitional period from childhood to adulthood. Independence, financial and emotional, may be necessary in these subgroups at an earlier age than it usually is for most White middle-class adolescents.

tensely experienced conflict begins, a pull between two states, dependence and independence. This conflict exists for all human beings and it is handled in a wide variety of ways. And just as no adult achieves total dependence or infant status, so no adult achieves total independence. The child in man is manifest in many ways.

Clinicians observe the alcoholic patient years later, long after the onset of alcoholism. By then the acuity of the conflict is less apparent. The alcoholism is, in a sense, his surrender to dependency.

The male adult role and the demands placed on this hypothetical individual create this intense dependence–independence conflict. And unresolved conflict means a state of high tension. Such a state of high tension assumes critical significance when it is considered that this is an individual with a relatively limited capacity to tolerate frustration or tension or psychic pain. These tensions must, then, be experienced as unbearable stress. The implicit assumption here is that there is a "just enough" amount of experience with frustration and pain to produce an adequate capacity to tolerate frustration or stress, and that an excess (most usually) of frustration and pain produced the deficient capacity to tolerate the limitations and stresses of daily life.

Finally, this individual is one who has not overcome the ambivalences of early childhood. Young children may love and hate others at the same time, shifting rapidly back and forth from one feeling to the other. Most people, as Abraham pointed out, do overcome these childhood ambivalences; but for this hypothetical predisposed person, these ambivalent feelings still color his relationships with others and his attitude toward himself.[14] This is reinforced in adult life in his frustrated need for dependence and emotional nurturance. He wishes to be taken care of and loved, hence he must woo and charm others, and within his limits he loves those who serve his needs. His demands must inevitably be frustrated and his anger and hatred aroused toward those from whom he seeks love. The self-image, too, is colored by love–hate. This individual manifests, with his childish needs and demands, narcissistic and ego-

---

[14] There is a rapidly expanding literature in psychology and psychiatry dealing with the concept of the self. The place of such a concept in the psychodynamics of alcoholism is as yet unclear. Here the assumption is made that the individual perceives the self largely as he perceives others, that the attitudes and feelings manifested toward the self will not be essentially different from the attitudes and feelings manifested toward others. This may be true or untrue or partially true.

centric behavior; at the same time there is self-hate manifested in self-abasement and in masochistic behavior.

The emphasis on regression in the literature of alcoholism makes good sense if alcoholism is perceived as a progressive phenomenon. At the age of, say, 25, the dependence–independence conflict is more apparent and the ambivalence in interpersonal relationships less apparent. When the same person is seen at the age of 45 as an alcoholic patient, with a 15- or 20-year history of problem drinking, the conflict is less apparent; there has been a surrender to dependence. The ambivalences, the behavior of early childhood, are at this point more apparent.

At the period of onset there is, then, a built-in, self-perpetuating mechanism for trouble. Here are strong dependency needs and weak defenses; the adult role creates a dependence–independence conflict; the unresolved conflict produces discomfort and tension and the tolerance for such frustrating, painful tension is low. It may now become more readily apparent that alcohol does not serve a single need or function but that its tremendous value for this predisposed individual is that it serves him in a variety of ways, it provides a complex of gratification.

There is some evidence that alcohol reduces tensions. Alcohol also diminishes the perception of reality (time, space, person, object) and in this altered perception of reality, that which was conflictful and ambivalent becomes less so. In the dimming of reality, conflicts shrink in intensity so that irreconcilable feelings and acts do not appear quite antithetical. Alcohol diminishes the acutely felt sense of frustration created by the unsatiated needs for dependence and being-taken-care-of. At the very same time, alcohol evokes the conditions—in the state of intoxication—in which the individual does, in reality, need to be taken care of. It becomes evident, as one episode of intoxication follows another, that here is a way to be passive and to drift; and it is, at the very same time, a behavior which may serve as a more or less subtle means of revenge, of expressing anger. At one and the same moment the alcoholic is acting out "I need you, help me, take care of me," and "I'm getting even with you." It also becomes apparent that the drunken bout is a way of feeling, at least for the moment, both an illusion of loving and being loved, and a kind of degrading, punishing self-abasement. At one and the same moment the alcoholic is acting out "I am the center of the universe" and "I'm no good, I hate myself."

It is a question whether this personality core occurs only among individuals predisposed to alcoholism. Perhaps alcoholism is one psychopathology among others, e.g., obsessional neurosis, which have the same etiological core in the pre-onset personality.

There are two facts which suggest some answer to this question. First, alcoholism, unlike most neurotic and psychotic behaviors, does not occur among children. This indicates that the expectations and demands of the adult role are an essential ingredient of etiology. Second, alcoholism is more characteristic of some subgroups in the American culture than of others (44) and many sociologists believe that the subgroups which produce a relatively high proportion of alcoholics have a different perception of and attitude toward alcohol and its effects than do those subgroups which produce a low proportion of alcoholics.[15] Given, then, this personality core, the expectations of the adult role, and membership in high-alcoholism groups producing particular attitudes toward alcohol, the combination raises the probability that the individual will become an alcoholic. In effect, then, the predisposing personality core is not necessarily unique to alcoholism, but its interaction with other psychosocial conditions creates a unique set of predisposing variables.

Another question is whether this personality core is assumed to be common to all alcoholics: private patients of psychoanalysts, chronic drunkenness offenders, clinic patients, men, women, Whites, Nonwhites. The core itself being hypothetical, only a guess is possible. It is very unlikely. As stated earlier, it is more reasonable to assume not a single core or pattern of personality traits but several, perhaps similar but not identical.

THE PROBLEM OF EVIDENCE[16]

What has been delineated above as the psychological predisposition to alcoholism does not contain any elements which have not been noted and described as relevant to alcoholism in previous writings. All that is new is a systematic attempt to define the combination of elements which exist before the alcoholism and which are of vital significance in its subsequent development. It is, however, one thing to speculate about the psychodynamics of alcohol-

---

[15] For example, Snyder (45); see also his citations in support.

[16] Charles Darwin, after rereading his grandfather's "Zoönomia," commented, "I was much disappointed, the proportion of speculation being so large to the facts given." (From: BARLOW, N., ed. The autobiography of Charles Darwin. New York; Harcourt, Brace; 1959.) This well describes the state of affairs in psychopathology at the moment.

ism; it is quite another to demonstrate with acceptable scientific precision that the guesses are correct.

Yet the task seems far from hopeless. It is true that the techniques of the behavioral sciences are imperfect but there are applicable research techniques: life history material, laboratory methods of experimental psychology, interview data and psychological tests. The significance of the hypothetical predisposing personality core is testable. In a study of 18-year-old subjects (with college freshmen represented only in correct proportion) it is possible to establish ratings and evaluations of the relevant psychological variables: dependency crises, adequacy of defenses, handling of conflict, frustration tolerance, ambivalences. One advantage, of course, would lie in the fact that the raters would not know who would be the problem drinkers 10 and 20 years hence. Since sociological information about these subjects (for example, religious and ethnic and class background) could be gathered, it would be possible eventually to estimate the significance of the different psychological and sociological variables and their interaction in etiology.

Putting aside clinical writings and case history material as evidence (if a clinician says that dependency conflicts are of critical importance and cites three case histories as examples, it is hardly a rigorous scientific proof), what evidence, however slim or tangential, exists to support the significance of the hypothetical predispositional core and its elements? It must be kept in mind that most relevant information relates to the alcoholic, hardly any to the prealcoholic personality.

Dependency crises and the inadequate resolution of dependency needs. One route through which this may be approached is the comparative study of different ethnic, religious, racial and class subgroups in the United States. Such subgroups may differ in their alcoholism rates, and in family structure, parent–child relationships and acceptance or disapproval of different kinds of dependent behaviors. This terrain is not entirely unexplored (46).

The impact of the demands of the adult role on the predisposed person has been emphasized. There is a little evidence indicating that the early adult years may indeed contain premonitory signs of later alcoholism. In a recent sociological study of young adult "problem drinkers," Park (47) found the most significant behavior variable among them to be "role ambivalence," i.e., an "inability to play the adaptive role, or any other role for that matter, decisively." This conflictful behavior suggests the difficulties some of these young "problem drinkers" are having in coping with the adult role.

Another direct study of dependence, with perceptual techniques, has been reported by Witkin et al. (48), who found their alcoholic subjects "significantly more dependent, as reflected in perceptual performance, than a control group of nonalcoholic psychiatric patients."

Conflict states. There are laboratory studies, with animals, suggesting a relationship between conflict behavior and alcohol (49, 50), and descriptions of alcoholism in terms of conflict, fear reduction and reinforcement (8–10). It might compound the confusion, however, to assume that these laboratory studies of conflict and the "emotional conflict" or "neurotic conflict" (22, 23) or the "variety of psychological conflicts" (13) seen by psychiatrists in their alcoholic patients refer to identical phenomena. Clinical theorists speak of significant long-term motivational conflicts of needs and drives and wishes which are antithetical or blocked by anxieties, primarily unconscious, and manifested clinically in a wide variety of behaviors. A group manifestation of such conflict might be the following: The marital rates of most alcoholic samples resemble the marital rates of the population at large, but the rate of marital disruption is much higher in the alcoholic groups. Contained in these statistics is the conflict over the adult responsibilities of marriage. This question needs study but we do not appear as yet to have isolated in the laboratory the conflicts of which clinicians speak.

Low frustration tolerance. While there has been no study of stress or frustration tolerance in either prealcoholism or postalcoholism periods, this item appears very frequently in the clinical literature on alcoholism. The WHO Technical Report (1) singled out this particular trait as significant: Alcoholics present "a large variety of personality types which have a few traits in common, in particular a low capacity for coping with tensions." This statement, of course, does not prove its own validity; and it does not assert that a low capacity for coping with tensions predates the onset of alcoholism. The frequency of the observation does suggest that stress or frustration tolerance is a personality variable which merits research effort.

Ambivalences. Two recent studies of alcoholics (19, 51) which explored a number of personality variables presumably related to alcoholism both produced major emphasis on self-abasing, self-destructive behavior and on defiance and unconscious hostility toward others.

The study by Mathias (19) compared alcoholics drawn from a

state hospital population, members of Alcoholics Anonymous who had maintained sobriety for at least a year, general hospital patients diagnosed as "neurotics," and "normal" subjects. Differences between the alcoholics and others were hypothesized in the following variables: oral fixation, homosexual trends, paranoid trends, need for self-aggression, marked needs for submission and self-debasement, and marked needs for self-assertion and defiance. The data from a variety of psychological tests indicated differences in the predicted direction in the last three items. Interestingly enough, the alcoholics (state hospital) showed "strong self-aggressive trends" which seemed to alter their direction among members of Alcoholics Anonymous, whose aggression "is directed outward." Different sides of the love–hate dichotomy apparently become more or less visible under different conditions.

The study by Walton (51) compared two groups of cirrhotic alcoholics. One group adhered to a strict therapeutic regimen (relating to diet and abstinence from alcohol), the other did not. The death rate was understandably higher in the latter group. A number of psychological tests and ratings revealed that the nonadherents were more self-destructive and showed more "unconscious hostility" than the adherents. Alcoholics who behave differently in relation to a therapeutic regimen, be it dietary or Alcoholics Anonymous as in the first study, apparently do show variations in the direction and intensity of love and hate. Further, the adherents of this study were significantly more "emotionally mature" than the "suicidal" nonadherents, a difference which might be restated in terms of identification with and acceptance of the adult role.

A writer of genius may create, out of his sensitivity and perception, a portrait of the alcoholic which is more valid than any that the behavioral scientist can produce. While such observations do not meet the criteria of scientific evidence, they are worthy of attention. Eugene O'Neill, whose tragic background included alcoholism, dealt with this theme in all of his later plays. Alcoholism is a central theme, or at least characteristic of the central character, in *The Iceman Cometh*, in *Long Day's Journey into Night*, in *Moon for the Misbegotten*, and in *A Touch of the Poet*. Even in the gentle *Ah, Wilderness* the inadequate, pitiful alcoholic uncle is a major character and one of the most important incidents in the play is an adolescent's first experience with alcohol.

In *Long Day's Journey Into Night* (52), the four major characters shift back and forth with almost dizzying rapidity in overt expression of love and hate for one another. The father, once a prominent actor, is now a heavy drinker and an embittered, stingy man. The mother lives with perpetual longing for the budding days of her girlhood. She is a drug addict. Jamie, the older son, has had some success as an actor but is now hopelessly involved with alcohol. Edmund, the younger son, has been to sea and now, diagnosed as tubercular, is about to enter a sanitarium. Jamie and Edmund talk together, both having had a great deal to drink. Jamie speaks these drunken words of love:[17]

Maybe no one else gives a damn if you die, but I do. My kid brother. I love your guts, Kid. Everything else is gone. You're all I've got left. . . . We've been more than brothers. You're the only pal I've ever had. I love your guts. I'd do anything for you.

A moment later, Jamie expresses his hatred:

Want to warn you—against me. Mama and Papa are right. I've been rotten bad influence. And worst of it is, I did it on purpose. . . . Did it on purpose to make a bum of you. Or part of me did. A big part. That part that's been dead so long. That hates life. . . . Never wanted you succeed and make me look even worse by comparison. Wanted you to fail. Always jealous of you. Mama's baby, Papa's pet! And it was your being born that started Mama on dope. I know that's not your fault, but all the same, God damn you, I can't help hating your guts—!

In *The Iceman Cometh* (53), Hickey is a salesman who periodically goes on prolonged drinking bouts in Skid Row. For years he has professed great love and guilty feelings toward his wife, with long, flowery speeches, but he finally murders her. He describes it:[18]

And then I saw I'd always known that was the only possible way to give her peace and free her from the misery of loving me. . . . I remember I heard myself speaking to her, as if it was something I'd always wanted to say: "Well, you know what you can do with your pipe dream now, you damned bitch!" (He stops with a horrified start, as if shocked out of a nightmare, as if he couldn't believe he heard what he had just said. He stammers) No! I never—!

The major emphasis of this paper has been on the prealcoholic personality. That is not to deny the significance of the need for

[17] The lines from *Long Day's Journey Into Night* are quoted with the permission of the publisher, Yale University Press.
[18] The lines from *The Iceman Cometh* are quoted with the permission of the publisher, Random House, Incorporated.

help of hundreds of thousands of problem drinkers. For those trying to help, the question of predisposition may seem academic. Certainly there is need for research on the ways to help, the relative effectiveness of different kinds of help, and similar practical problems. The importance of research into the causes and etiological conditions of alcoholism is twofold: it may be useful in making the treatment process more effective; more significantly, it may suggest techniques of prevention. Prevention of psychopathology is the long-term social goal.

REFERENCES

1. World Health Organization. Expert Committee on Mental Health. Second report of the Alcoholism Subcommittee. (WHO Tech. Rep. Ser., No. 48.) Geneva; 1952.

2. Seeley, J. R. The WHO definition of alcoholism. Q. J. Stud. Alcohol 20: 352–356, 1959.

3. Sutherland, E. H., Schroeder, H. G. and Tordella, C. L. Personality traits and the alcoholic; a critique of existing studies. Q. J. Stud. Alcohol 11: 547–561, 1950.

4. Syme, L. Personality characteristics and the alcoholic; a critique of current studies. Q. J. Stud. Alcohol 18: 288–302, 1957.

5. Armstrong, J. D. The search for the alcoholic personality. Ann. Am. Acad. Polit. Soc. Sci. 315: 40–47, 1958.

6. Allport, G. W. Personality; a psychological interpretation. New York; Holt; 1937.

7. Jellinek, E. M. Phases of alcohol addiction. Q. J. Stud. Alcohol 13: 673–684, 1952.

8. Dollard, J. and Miller, N. E. Personality and psychotherapy. New York; McGraw-Hill; 1950.

9. Conger, J. J. Reinforcement theory and the dynamics of alcoholism. Q. J. Stud. Alcohol 17: 296–305, 1956.

10. Kingham, R. J. Alcoholism and the reinforcement theory of learning. Q. J. Stud. Alcohol 19: 320–330, 1958.

11. Smith, J. A. Psychiatric treatment of the alcoholic. J. Am. Med. Ass. 163: 734–738, 1957.

12. Abraham, K. The psychological relations between sexuality and alcoholism. Pp. 80–89. In: Jones, E., ed. Selected papers of Karl Abraham. 4th ed. London; Hogarth Press; 1927.

13. Higgins, J. W. Psychodynamics in the excessive drinking of alcohol. Archs Neurol. Psychiat., Chicago 69: 713–726, 1953.

14. Levy, R. I. The psychodynamic functions of alcohol. Q. J. Stud. Alcohol 19: 649–659, 1958.

15. Zwerling, I. Psychiatric findings in an interdisciplinary study of forty-six alcoholic patients. Q. J. Stud. Alcohol 20: 543–554, 1959.

16. DUHL, L. J. Alcoholism; the public health approach; a new look from the viewpoint of human ecology. Q. J. Stud. Alcohol 20: 112–125, 1959.

17. WILLIAMS, R. J. Nutrition and alcoholism. Norman; University of Oklahoma Press; 1951.

18. HEWITT, C. C. A personality study of alcohol addiction. Q. J. Stud. Alcohol 4: 368–386, 1943.

19. MATHIAS, R. An experimental investigation of the personality structure of chronic alcoholic, Alcoholics Anonymous, neurotic and normal groups. Ph.D. dissertation, University of Buffalo; 1955.

20. BUTTON, A. D. A study of alcoholics with the Minnesota Multiphasic Personality Inventory. Q. J. Stud. Alcohol 17: 263–281, 1956.

21. BOWMAN, K. M. and JELLINEK, E. M. Alcohol addiction and its treatment. Q. J. Stud. Alcohol 2: 98–176, 1941.

22. KNIGHT, R. P. The psychodynamics of chronic alcoholism. J. Nerv. Ment. Dis. 86: 538–548, 1937.

23. KNIGHT, R. P. The dynamics and treatment of chronic alcohol addiction. Bull. Menninger Clin. 1: 233–250, 1937.

24. MENNINGER, K. A. Man against himself. New York; Harcourt, Brace; 1938.

25. STRAUS, R. Alcoholism. Pp. 434–447. In: ROSE, A. M., ed. Mental health and mental disorder. New York; Norton; 1955.

26. LISANSKY, E. S. Alcoholism in women; social and psychological concomitants. I. Social history data. Q. J. Stud. Alcohol 18: 588–623, 1957.

27. FENICHEL, O. The psychoanalytic theory of neurosis. New York; Norton; 1945.

28. LORAND, S. A survey of psychoanalytical literature on problems of alcohol; bibliography. Yb. Psychoanal. 1: 359–370, 1945.

29. RADÓ, S. Psychoanalysis of pharmacothymia (drug addiction). Psychoanal. Q. 2: 1–23, 1933.

30. SCHILDER, P. Psychogenesis of alcoholism. Q. J. Stud. Alcohol 2: 277–292, 1941.

31. SINGER, E. Personality structure of chronic alcoholics. Ph.D dissertation, New York University; 1949.

32. ULLMAN, A. D. The psychological mechanism of alcohol addiction. Q. J. Stud. Alcohol 13: 602–608, 1952.

33. FREUD, S. Instincts and their vicissitudes. In: The complete psychological works of Sigmund Freud. Vol. 14 (1914–1916). London; Hogarth Press and Institute of Psycho-Analysis; 1937.

34. BRENNER, C. An elementary textbook of psychoanalysis. Garden City, N.Y.; Doubleday; 1957.

35. FREUD, S. Repression. In: The complete psychological works of Sigmund Freud. Vol. 14 (1914–1916). London; Hogarth Press and Institute of Psycho-Analysis; 1937.

36. ABRAHAM, K. Clinical papers and essays on psycho-analysis. Vol. 2. New York; Basic Books; 1955.

37. FREUD, S. The problem of anxiety. New York; Psychoanalytic Quarterly Press and Norton; 1936.

38. CHILD, I. L. Socialization. Ch. 18. In: LINDZEY, G., ed. Handbook of social psychology. Vol. 2. Cambridge, Mass.; Addison-Wesley; 1954.

39. WAHL, C. W. Some antecedent factors in the family histories of 109 alcoholics. Q. J. Stud. Alcohol 17: 643–654, 1956.

40. STRAUS, R. Alcohol and the homeless man. Q. J. Stud. Alcohol 7: 360–404, 1946.

41. MYERSON, D. J. Clinical observations on a group of alcoholic prisoners; with special reference to women. Q. J. Stud. Alcohol 20: 555–572, 1959.

42. PITTMAN, D. J. and GORDON, C. W. Revolving door; a study of the chronic police case inebriate. (Rutgers Center of Alcohol Studies, Monogr. No. 2.) New Brunswick, N.J.; 1958.

43. GOLDFARB, W. The effects of early institutional care on adolescent personality. J. Exp. Educ. 12: 106–129, 1943.

44. ROBERTS, B. H. and MYERS, J. K. Religion, national origin, immigration and mental illness. Am. J. Psychiat. 110: 759–764, 1954.

45. SNYDER, C. R. Alcohol and the Jews; a cultural study of drinking and sobriety. (Rutgers Center of Alcohol Studies, Monogr. No. 1.) Glencoe, Ill.; Free Press; 1958.

46. OPLER, M. K. and SINGER, J. L. Ethnic differences in behavior and psychopathology; Italian and Irish. Int. J. Soc. Psychiat. 2: 11–22, 1956.

47. PARK, P. Problem drinking and social organization. Ph.D. dissertation, Yale University; 1958.

48. WITKIN, H. A., KARP, S. A. and GOODENOUGH, D. R. Dependence in alcoholics. Q. J. Stud. Alcohol 20: 493–504, 1959.

49. CONGER, J. J. The effects of alcohol on conflict behavior in the albino rat. Q. J. Stud. Alcohol 12: 1–29, 1951.

50. WEISS, M. Alcohol as a depressant in psychological conflict in rats. Q. J. Stud. Alcohol 19: 226–237, 1958.

51. WALTON, D. A study of selected personality factors in chronic alcoholics with portal cirrhosis undergoing medical treatment. Ph.D. dissertation, Adelphi College; 1956.

52. O'NEILL, E. Long day's journey into night. New Haven; Yale University Press; 1956.

53. O'NEILL, E. The iceman cometh. New York; Random House; 1946.

Part IV

SOME PSYCHODYNAMIC ASPECTS
OF ALCOHOL USE AND MISUSE

Alcohol is an amazing drug. On paper, it would appear to be a panacea. Keller (1) wrote that "men found alcoholic beverages to be good—as food, as drink, as medicine, as euphoriant, and as intoxicant." Alcohol's interface with the behavioral sciences rests not on its sedative, anesthetic or caloric properties but on its pharmacodynamic utility. Its psychopharmacological effects seem so crucial to human alcohol consumption that ingestion of alcohol for its intoxicating effects is considered a sine qua non for an animal model of alcoholism (2).

The articles in this section explore some of the psychodynamic precursors and the consequences of drinking by both alcoholics and nonalcoholics. One aim is to try to discern whether there are differences between the two groups that would explain why or how an individual crosses the boundary between them. Another is to emphasize the notion that the behavior of drinking alcohol is somehow reinforced and maintained, if not by the consequences of drinking, then by some as yet unelucidated contingencies. Drinking is not spurious or fortuitous behavior.

A major focus in this area is felt internal state, mood or affect. Persons manifesting many different psychiatric disorders experience pain, suffering and dysphoria, and it has been suggested that they may use alcohol as a self-prescribed tranquilizer or mood-elevating drug. This applies even to those patients who, with a seeming plethora of energy and euphoria, misuse alcohol because being too driven, too "high," too active can be terribly disquieting (3, 4). The situation is much more complex than one of simply drinking alcohol to get a "lift" out of depression.

Alcohol use, then, has been perceived by some as an attempt to reestablish some kind of affective homeostasis. Since behavior is known to be neither chance nor random, the consumption of alcohol is thought to be related to some expected consequence, to some desired outcome by the user. From a systems theory point of view, pathological drinking has been viewed as behavior which preserves interactional homeostasis (5). This topic bears a relation to the treatment of alcoholism, for it points to the need for providing alternate modes of gratification for alcoholics.

Davis and his colleagues (Chapter 16) touched on such issues in their essay on the adaptive consequences of drinking. From early on, behavioral scientists have faced the necessity for theoretical formulations that encompass both adjustment and maladjustment. Explanations that deal with normal behaviors and then enumerate separate hypotheses for abnormal ones fail to accomplish this. The same holds for "typical" versus "atypical" and other equally euphemistic substitutes. Grinker (6) has called for a general systems theory, "a conceptual overarching global theory that embraces several limited theories." This is precisely what is needed if the interfaces between psychiatric disorders and alcoholisms are to be clarified. All represent, at least statistically, so-called deviant behaviors. But healthy emotional adjustment and normal, or nonproblem, drinking also have to be encompassed in such formulations. Reinert (7) suggested this, in a sense, when he asked, "Why is not everyone who drinks an alcoholic?" Similarly, Fouquet (8) asked, "Why are not all neurotic or psychotic patients alcoholics?" Would alcohol, in effect, have no utility for them?

Conflict resolution has long been regarded as a major psychodynamic function of alcohol. In the introduction to a paper on conflict resolution and alcoholism, I (9) wrote:

"In 1968, I submitted a manuscript, 'Alcoholism; the Role of Conflict,' for publication. It was, perhaps, a too convincing exposition of the psychodynamic function of conflict in the etiology of alcoholism, of the alcoholic's dependency conflicts, of the conflict-reducing properties of alcohol, and of the hospital as a refuge from conflicts. I documented the role of conflict by citing animal studies as well as clinical data. I unwittingly had made a stronger point for conflict in the etiology of alcoholism than I realized. When prepared for the printer, my manuscript was re-titled 'The Crucial Factor in Alcoholism' by the editor who wrote in the precis, 'This author suggests that the inability to resolve conflict . . . is an underlying force in the development of alcoholism.' Too late I wrote back with the galley proofs, 'My major corrections are in the title and precis where I do not wish to convey that conflict is *the* factor in alcoholism.' I feel even more that way almost seven years later. . . ."

Data and analyses to this effect have been impressive (10, 11). Whereas the initial work on conflict attenuation derived from animal studies purporting to be analogs of human conflict situations, assessment of the effects of alcohol in humans is beclouded and confounded by many interacting variables. Furthermore, the situation is not simply one where, confronted with a conflict, the alcoholic who does drink to deal with such dilemmas simply seeks alcohol. The very consumption of alcohol, the decision to drink or not to drink, is replete with conflict and often represents an emotionally debilitating inner struggle. Drinking may even increase conflict (11). Additionally, as Room (12) has pointed out, there are many normative or social conflicts over drinking.

In this context, alcohol's use—and then misuse—can be conceptualized as a defense mechanism for some individuals. Initially employed to alleviate other problems, it begins to produce problems of its own. The same can be said of compulsions, phobias, projections which attain paranoid proportions, or of analgesics (originally used to allay physical pain) to which some people become addicted. Interestingly, in this regard, Fouquet (8) placed alcoholopathies within the context of toxicopathy, asserting that they "do not officially belong to neurotic conditions or to perversions or to psychotic states. They are merely exogenous poisonings." Finally, a most unusual interface has been reported with regard to alcohol's pharmacodynamic properties—iatrogenic alcoholism, cases in which the physician originally prescribed alcohol as a hypnotic, for example, to a vulnerable person who then exceeded the prescription (13).

Of all the interfaces discussed in this book, the one concerning alcohol's psychodynamic properties probably is most derivative of animal research. Such studies have made major contributions to thought about alcohol as a tension reducer and conflict attenuator. Most of these experiments, however, were designed with alcohol as the independent variable and with the behavior exhibited by an animal in a conflict or stress situation as the dependent measure. Accordingly, they yielded data on the hypotheses they were designed to test, but, in so doing, they may have lent themselves to one-sided conclusions which unduly emphasized a specific interface. Although alcohol may reduce tension in some situations, it does not necessarily follow that this was the motivation for its use. Williams (14) acknowledged that psychogenic factors might be basic to alcohol misuse, but cautioned that this was "merely an educated surmise" lacking scientific documentation. In a similar vein, Sytinsky (15), exploring the etiology of alcoholism, wrote, "Psychologists have proposed that alcoholism is a disastrous attempt at the self-cure of an unidentified inner conflict, reflecting a failure of personality development. But it must be noted that the psychologists have made little progress in confirming these aspects of drunkenness and alcoholism. The psychological aspects of alcoholism and the psychological mechanism of 'alcohol craving' remain to be investigated and elucidated."

This section addresses a broad range of issues, including the psychologically reinforcing aspects of drinking, the social consequences, the consequences of labeling, the role of learning and the mediating role of nonpsychodynamic variables in alcohol consumption. The articles reprinted here examine what functions alcohol serves for individuals. My review (Chapter 15) considers evidence of alcohol's effects on affect and discusses the issue of whether alcohol is sometimes employed as a self-prescribed mood regulator. Davis et al. (Chapter 16) see excessive drinking as serving a number of possible adaptive functions, such as permitting interaction and communication. Chafetz's (Chapter 17) position is that alcohol use is a restitutive symptom. Roman and Trice (Chapter 18) discuss the sick role and alcoholism, and Rohan (Chapter 19) presents a view of drinking "as a functional behavior, an active response to environmental conditions." An attempt thus has been made to represent a number of theoretical orientations, both related and unrelated to mental health. The task is to try to identify factors which maintain or augment drinking behavior. While at first glance these would almost certainly appear to be individual in nature, strong points are made, too, for social and environmental parameters.

That the integration of the various etiological factors will not be easy to achieve is apparent when the vast number of multidisciplinary formulations of hypothesized determinants of drinking are reviewed. Kepner (16), for example, has described the etiology of alcoholism in terms of learning theory, drive reduction and the principles of reinforcement and has then convincingly detailed the implications of this for alcoholism treatment based on learning principles. On the other hand, Storm and Cutler (17) have hypothesized that "alcohol consumption is largely determined by the resources available for drinking, the activities competing for these resources, and the costs associated with drinking in the context of a particular social status." This view tends to de-emphasize individual motivational considerations, stressing instead the important role of the environment in drinking decisions. The two views are certainly not mutually exclusive and perhaps an integration can be achieved, despite the "failure to formulate a valid social–psychological theory that can demonstrate that selected sociocultural factors contribute to the molding of a mental illness observed in the phenotype" (18). The personal resources cited by Storm and Cutler are hardly psychodynamic in nature, and it is for this reason that I recommend them for consideration by mental health specialists. In a discussion of responsiveness in mental health care and the polarization over mental health models, Sussex and Weidman (19) noted that "the challenge beyond the therapeutic milieu is to begin to develop bridges between the in-house professional mental health culture, the patient's own community, and the broader social system within which we are all inextricably enmeshed." Building bridges, or at least finding narrow gaps where they can be built, is what interfaces are all about.

REFERENCES

1. KELLER, M. Alcohol in health and disease; some historical perspectives. Ann. N.Y. Acad. Sci. 133: 820–827, 1966.
2. LESTER, D. and FREED, E. X. Criteria for an animal model of alcoholism. Pharmacol. Biochem. & Behav. 1: 103–107, 1973.
3. FREED, E. X. Alcohol abuse by manic patients. Psychol. Rep. 25: 280, 1969.
4. REICH, L. H., DAVIES, R. K. and HIMMELHOCH, J. M. Excessive alcohol use in manic–depressive illness. Am. J. Psychiat. 131: 83–86, 1974.
5. WARD, R. F. and FAILLACE, L. A. The alcoholic and his helpers; a systems view. Q. J. Stud. Alcohol 31: 684–691, 1970.
6. GRINKER, R. R., SR. Psychiatry in broad perspective. New York; Behavioral Publications; 1975.
7. REINERT, R. E. The concept of alcoholism as a bad habit. Bull. Menninger Clin. 32: 35–46, 1968.
8. FOUQUET, P. Theoretical concepts of alcoholism and therapeutic management. Pp. 143–151. In: KESSEL, N., HAWKER, A. and CHALKE, H., eds. Alcoholism; a medical profile; proceedings of the first international medical conference on alcoholism, London, 10–14 September 1973. London; Edsall; 1974.
9. FREED, E. X. Conflict resolution and alcoholism revisited. J. Alcsm 10: 148–151, 1975.
10. CAPPELL, H. and HERMAN, C. P. Alcohol and tension reduction; a review. Q. J. Stud. Alcohol 33: 33–64, 1972.
11. BROWN, J. S. and CROWELL, C. R. Alcohol and conflict resolution; a theoretical analysis. Q. J. Stud. Alcohol 35: 66–85, 1974.
12. ROOM, R. Normative perspectives on alcohol use and problems. J. Drug Issues 5: 358–368, 1975.
13. BLUME, S. B. Iatrogenic alcoholism. Q. J. Stud. Alcohol 34: 1348–1352, 1973.
14. WILLIAMS, R. J. Alcoholism prevention and reality; comment on the article by M. E. Chafetz. Q. J. Stud. Alcohol 28: 350, 1967.
15. SYTINSKY, I. A. A schema of the etiology of alcoholism as a pathological motivation; a working hypothesis involving the interplay of sociological, psychologi-

cal and physiobiochemical factors on molecular, cellular and organosystemic levels. Q. J. Stud. Alcohol 34: 1140–1145, 1973.

16. KEPNER, E. Application of learning theory to the etiology and treatment of alcoholism. Q. J. Stud. Alcohol 25: 279–291, 1964.

17. STORM, T. and CUTLER, R. E. Alcohol consumption and personal resources; a general hypothesis and some implications. J. Stud. Alcohol 36: 917–924, 1975.

18. DUNHAM, H. W. Society, culture, and mental disorder. Archs Gen. Psychiat. 33: 147–156, 1976.

19. SUSSEX, J. N. and WEIDMAN, H. H. Toward responsiveness in mental health care. Psychiat. Ann. 5 (No. 8): 8–16, 1975.

15

Alcohol and Mood
An Updated Review[1]

Earl X. Freed, Ph.D.

IN 1970, I (22) published a review of the relationship between alcoholism and manic–depressive disorders in which speculation about
—and data on—alcohol and mood were summarized through early
1968. About that time, Mayfield and Allen (68) wrote, "A review
of the literature reveals little solid evidence for any answer to some
of the most fundamental questions about the nature of alcohol.
Some of these are: Does alcohol alter affect? If so, which ones, how
much, when, and in whom? Is the alteration euphoriant or palliative
or both?" My conclusions were not dissimilar:

Studies of alcohol effects upon mood have been an imaginative approach to
understanding the relationships between alcohol and disorders of affect. Investigations in this crucial area have been frustrated, however, by realistic
limitations in the ability and opportunity to (a) study alcohol effects in a
natural rather than a laboratory setting of (b) normal subjects, alcoholics
and manic-depressives during both phases of their illness, who (c) drink
varying amounts of alcohol with (d) physiological, self-report and clinical
evaluations of mood parameters. Still unclarified is whether alcohol ingestion results in affective improvement and attenuation of depression. However, there appears to be some agreement that excessive drinkers seek a
degree of tension relief in alcohol. Subjects' past learning experiences with
alcohol are probably important determinants of their expectations of the
drug's effects.

I also suggested that "a fruitful area for continued study is research on the measurement of mood states and the effects of varying dosages of alcohol on mood states in normals and in a variety of

[1] Reprinted from *The International Journal of Addictions*, Vol. 13, pp. 173-200,
1978, by courtesy of Marcel Dekker, Inc. Copyright by Marcel Dekker, Inc.

psychiatric patients." Inasmuch as intoxication is a highly subjective experience, it is not inappropriate that self-report data, heretofore often considered "unscientific," be gathered. It is gratifying to report that the past 8 years have resulted in increased and innovative research in this area. This paper updates and reviews these accomplishments.

PROBLEMS IN DELINEATING THE RELATIONSHIP BETWEEN ALCOHOL AND MOOD

Measurement

Measurement of mood states poses a methodological barrier (1). Mood, vague though the concept may be, is at the very core of human existence, for affects give life its uniqueness. It is surprising, therefore, that the definitive text on mood and personality (119) states that "one wonders why a subject of such obvious and intimate significance has been so slighted in psychological research." Part of the answer undoubtedly lies in the essential subjectivity of mood states and the resultant difficulty in obtaining valid and reliable measurements. However, self-ratings of depression by alcoholic patients and staff ratings of the patients' depressions were positively correlated, even though there was distortion in the patients' estimate of their depression (82). Ketai (52) made a distinction between mood as a mental state sustained over time and affect which implies a more immediate emotional experience. Reisby and Theilgaard (88) administered alcohol to students who completed a subjective checklist of moods and who were also rated objectively by observers. There were differences between the two evaluations, especially on the dimension of alertness. While the observers rated the subjects as normally alert, the subjects rated themselves as tired. The investigators speculated that perhaps the subjects had succeeded in compensating for the felt effects of intoxication in the eyes of the observers. Brown (9) addressed himself to this sort of dilemma:

The traditional study of emotions has emphasized reactivity, the *phasic* side of the experience. Yet what the clinician seeks to modify in his therapy of the patient is not these transient states of arousal, but the more pervasive affective status termed "mood." Because of its persistence in time, "mood," in contrast with evoked response, "emotion," affects a significantly greater portion of behavior, provides the background for more varied types of learning, and cumulatively can produce disturbance of significantly greater magnitudes.

There are precedents from other than the alcoholism field for the use of self-rating or self-report scales. For example, in a review of the prediction of response in the pharmacotherapy of depression, Bennett (7) stated that patient ratings were often most sensitive to change and that the "subjective feeling of relief [was] more pertinent to the therapeutic response than tests measuring cognition, intelligence, learning ability, perceptual functioning, and psychomotor performance." Unpublished research[2] indicated that patients' responses to the single question, "Are you depressed?", were in agreement with their scores on the MMPI Pt Scale 8 out of 10 times. Mood changes have been demonstrated with progestational agents (48), with attempts to stop smoking (97), in depressive disorders (128), with antipsychotic medication in neurotic syndromes (98), with a dramamine–analgesic–caffeine combination (11), with other psychotropic drugs (41), with the use of oral contraceptives (27), etc. Mendels and Cochrane (72) agreed that "patients' self-ratings would be of value" in studies of depression, and Hall et al. (35) demonstrated that there was a diurnal variation in subjective depressive mood in half of their patients with endogenous depression. A recent report (105) documented that outpatient alcoholics gave reliable and valid self-reports of life history information.

The rationale for utilizing self-ratings, such as mood scales, has been presented by Wessman and Ricks (119) and Lazarus (55) who regarded self-reports not as traditional introspective data but as verbal behavior subject to methodological behaviorism. Mood, then, is seen as an intervening variable. As Wessman and Ricks (119) stated, mood "is assumed to supply information about the current functioning of the organism and to be involved in the self-monitoring and self-regulation of complex behavior." The latter half of this statement has direct relevance to the notion of alcohol as a self-administered mood regulator, especially when one considers Ditman's (18) report that alcoholics seemingly had more mood and symptom complaints than normals. There is evidence (81) that mood-changing drugs other than alcohol are not used habitually but are taken "as 'psychological aspirin,' to prevent or deal with a specific crisis. After that, the drug use stops until the next need for it arises." Perhaps this is also the case with alcohol. Perhaps its use—or abuse—is linked to some specific mood state.

[2] FREED, E. X. and LAYNE, E. A further evaluation of the Pt Scale in differentiating depression and morale loss. [Unpublished manuscript.]

Mood Scales

A plethora of instruments have been employed to gauge moods in alcoholics and in others, both in sober and intoxicated states. In large part, such scales derived from the original Mood Adjective Checklist of Nowlis and Green.[3] One might question the appropriateness of the scales in some studies because (*1*) some were intended neither for longer term study nor for evaluation of diurnal changes of mood states and (*2*) some were validated with college students and thus may require a high reading or educational level. Sometimes an instrument has been a modification of another scale or a variation on a theme. Chart 1 serves as an instrument resource guide for some of the more frequently used self-report mood scales. The references cited therein are largely to original publications. For each scale, there has been substantial subsequent study, and the instruments have been administered to larger samples of varying nosological compositions.

The Clyde Mood Scale (14) has been a popular measure. A modified version, to measure the efficacy of thioridazine (Mellaril) in alcoholism treatment, has been reported (46). The Zung Scale (128) has been used extensively to evaluate depressive symptomatology. Other alcohol–mood studies have employed the Janke list of adjectives (115), the Hofstatter polarity profile (92), "52 mood items, each a five-step scale" (40), the Adjective Checklist Mood Scale (42), subjective ratings of mood variables by the Method of Magnitude Estimation (50), the Guilford–Zimmerman Temperament Survey (75), the Multiple Affect Adjective Checklist (85), a subjective checklist of mood (88), a modified Q-sort of self-report feeling states (111), the SAM Affective Checklist (84), Smith and Beecher's mood questionnaire (87), the Depressive Adjective Checklist (102), the Lorr Mood Scale (53), a mood adjective checklist (103), a self-report inventory of Situational Discomfort (32), visual analog scales of mood and feelings (76), and the NIMH Mood Scale (110). The use of so many instruments and the lack of demonstrated correlation between them—even though many use the same labels for mood factors—pose a methodological problem.

---

[3] NOWLIS, W. and GREEN, R. F. The experimental analysis of mood. Presented at 15th International Congress of Psychology, Brussels, July 1957.

CHART 1.—*Frequently Used Self-Report Mood Instruments*

Instrument	Author	Year	Areas covered	Standardizing population	N	Validity	Reliability	Utility
Clyde Mood Scale	Clyde (14)	1963	Factors: friendly, aggressive, clear-thinking, sleepy, unhappy, dizzy	Normals and schizophrenics	1379	Approximately 75% of drug and placebo patients classified correctly	Rater correlations on factors range from 0.32–0.91	Designed to measure the effects of drugs on human emotions and behavior
Depression Adjective Checklist	Lubin (59)	1965	Depression	Normals Depressed patients (plus additional groups for cross validation)	279 95	Concurrent validity with MMPI and Beck Inventory of Depression	Split-half correlations range from 0.82–0.93	Measurement of transient depressive mood
Depression Inventory	Beck (4)	1967	21 symptom-attitude categories, manifestations of depression	Psychiatric in- and out-patients	409	Concurrent validity with clinical ratings and other tests	Split-half reliability is 0.93	Designed to measure depth of depression. Later validation with general medical patients
Minnesota Multiphasic Personality Inventory, Depression Scale	Dahlstrom et al. (16)	1972	60 items probing depression	See reference for a compendium of data on standardization issues				Designed to measure depth of depression

[continued—

CHART 1.—continued

Instrument	Author	Year	Areas covered	Standardizing population	N	Validity	Reliability	Utility
Multiple Affect Adjective Checklist	Zuckerman et al. (126)	1964	Anxiety, depression, hostility	College students Neuropsychiatric patients	330+ 95	Validated in experimental stress and failure situations	Split-half coefficients range from 0.79–0.92	Designed to measure day to day changes in 3 affects
Profile of Mood States	McNair et al. (70)	1971	Tension-anxiety, depression-dejection, anger-hostility, vigor-activity, fatigue-inertia, confusion-bewilderment total mood disturbance score	Psychiatric outpatients College students	1000 856	6 factor analytic replications plus evidence of construct validity	Test-retest correlations range from 0.65–0.75. Internal consistency reliability approximately 0.90	"One-week" and "Right-now" versions. Recommended as a measure of mood states in psychiatric outpatients and as a method for assessing mood changes
Self-rating Depression Scale	Zung (127)	1965	20 depression items	Depressed patients Normal controls	56 100	High correlation with clinical evaluations and treatment course and EEG responses to auditory stimulation during sleep		Attempt to quantitate depression symptoms

Other Barriers

Alcohol is at the least a biphasic drug. Not only is there need for parametric studies of the effects of varying dosages of alcohol on mood in order to yield dose-response data, but there also is need to study moods during the course of ascending and then descending blood alcohol curves (29). For example, in a study of acute experimental alcoholic intoxication in 16 moderate social drinkers, it was found that their subjective ratings of the moods—elated, talkative, tired and working capacity—tended to peak an hour after alcohol consumption and then to fall rectilinearily, thus paralleling their blood alcohol curves (50). Subjects reported that they felt more elated and talkative than usual, less tired, but less able in terms of working capacity. These effects were more pronounced during the initial 2 hr after they consumed alcohol; then they waned. The implication is that multiple "longitudinal" measures are needed or, again, parametric time or duration of intoxication investigations. In another study where 2- and 4-hr mood ratings were separately summated to yield factors, one of which was "activity," ethanol decreased activity, "especially later on" (42). Intoxication and the subjective experience of moods occur along a temporal dimension. Furthermore, depressive phenomena are altered in the temporal course of an alcoholic's hospitalization (26), and this therapeutic result may be a confounding factor in research on moods. Tested 1 week after treatment and 6 weeks after hospital discharge, alcoholics showed improvement in anxiety, increased vigor, and decreased depression and neurotic symptomatology (103). Sims (101) reported on treated neurotic women, some of whom, on follow-up, had become alcohol or drug dependent. A small group of 8 drug addicts and alcoholics showed greater anger and hostility at discharge from a hospital trauma unit, although psychopathology generically had decreased since admission (94).

Depression

The relationships of depressive phenomena to alcoholism are unclarified and impair research efficiency in mood studies. For example, Holloway (43) found that alcoholics felt depressed when they drank and also that they said they drank when they felt depressed (among other reasons). Alcoholics drink to relieve anxiety (111) and prolonged drinking produces anxiety (49). It is no surprise, therefore, to find alcoholic wives of alcoholic husbands significantly more anxious and depressed than nonalcoholic wives of alcoholic husbands (6), nor to learn that alcoholic outpatients evidenced more symptoms of depression and anxiety than did controls (34). When we (24) compared symptom patterns of 325 male alcoholic psychiatric hospital admissions with 325 nonalcoholic psychiatric admissions, the alcoholics were significantly more anxious ($p = .0006$) and depressed ($p = .003$) while the nonalcoholics' affect was significantly more inappropriate ($p = .0002$) and flattened ($p = .02$).

In a follow-up study of felons who drank, it was stated that "alcohol will depress mood," "depressions sometimes may be associated with a drinking problem," "depression is commonly found in the families of alcoholics," and "heavy drinkers often have a family history of depression" (30). Possible cause and effect relationships between drinking and affect are certainly suggested. One interpretation has been that depression is symptomatic of alcoholism because 70% of 73 alcoholic admissions to a treatment program evidenced mild to high depression on the Zung Scale (118). However, Goss and Morosko (31) later criticized this study because the Zung Scale was not multidimensional and thus did not permit "completeness of symptomatic expression." Accordingly, they administered the MMPI to 200 outpatient alcoholics, reporting the following scales elevated: Psychopathic deviate, Depression, and Psychasthenia. Thus depressive symptomatology still appeared characteristic of alcoholics but it was part of a picture of multiple symptomatology. Elsewhere, the correlation between scores on the Zung Scale and the MMPI D Scale was reported as 0.72 in a group of psychiatric patients (74), and, among 38 hospitalized alcoholics, those with the highest ALCADD Test alcoholism scores had MMPI profiles consistent with a clinical picture of anxiety and depression (90). Thioridazine has been used in the treatment of alcoholics, some of whom had primary or secondary depression, to prevent emergence of depressive symptomatology (46). Also, recurrent depression reactive to losses and to social isolation has been cited in alcoholics (89). It is even possible that the depression, rather than the alcoholism, brings the patient to treatment. For example, when 28 alcoholic patients treated in a psychiatric clinic were compared with 25 untreated alcoholic relatives, they were similar on most variables but were significantly different ($p < .001$) in that the alcoholics showed more depressed mood (124). One speculation might be that (1) alcohol is employed to attenuate depressive mood and (2) should it fail to do so, the patient might then seek help for the depression. However,

Woodruff et al. (125) found that in all but 3 of 39 alcoholics with depression, the affective disorder developed after the alcoholism. Studying nonalcoholic depressives and alcoholics with—and without—depression, they concluded that "patients with alcoholism plus depression more closely resembled those with alcoholism than those with depression." On the other hand, Gibson and Becker (25), factor analyzing responses in self-reported depression, found major similarity between the factor structure of alcoholic depressions and that of primarily depressive patients.

Curlee (15), directing herself to depression among alcoholics, identified reactive depression, depressive masochistic personality, anaclitic depression and anhedonia associated with schizoid personality. She concluded that there is need to scrutinize individualized sources of depression in each patient because of the "tremendous diversity which can exist among patients showing what ostensibly are the same symptoms." This is akin to what Winokur (123) has called "depressive spectrum disease." However, Hayman (36) emphasized qualitative and quantitative differences between alcoholics and depressives, and he felt that "relatively few patients will drink during a deep depression." Sometimes the symptoms are not shown but are masked. Lesse (56) has addressed himself to masked depression, depressive equivalents and affective equivalents which often hide behind alcoholism (24, 36). Alcoholism in women occurs very often together with depression and suicide attempts (95). In male and female alcoholics, a metabolic disorder may be underlying (93). Another report (99) found depressive signs in 98% of 58 alcoholics on at least 1 of 3 self-report depression scales administered but also emphasized the "need to use multiple instruments in the measurement of depression."

Perhaps there has been too great an emphasis on the depression–dysphoria aspects of mood states. In this regard, Russell and Mehrabian (91) have proposed three basic dimensions of emotional state: pleasure–displeasure, arousal–nonarousal and dominance–submission.

Summary

While the relationship between alcohol and mood is very important from a pharmacodynamic point of view, there are barriers to its delineation. One derives from the essential subjectivity of moods and affects. Recognition of the subjectivity and attempts to measure it have resulted in many studies utilizing a multitude of self-report mood scales, mostly of the adjective checklist variety. Other methodological problems derive from the need for parametric studies of different doses of alcohol on mood and from the unclarified, possibly etiological, relationships of various depressive phenomena to alcohol.

SELF-REPORTED DEPRESSION IN ALCOHOLICS

Both clinically and anecdotally it is known that alcoholics and others report drinking to relieve depression, to "get a lift," to attenuate disquieting affect. However, it has been suggested that "alcoholics may interpret physical distress cognitively as depression analogous to the double meaning which can be given the expression, 'I feel bad.'" (26). This hypothesis resulted from data showing improvements in somatic complaints during a 6-week course of treatment for alcoholism during which depressive mood (measured by the Zung Scale) improved. Similarly, Morgan (74) suggested that an index of psychiatric patients' depression was their verbalization of physiological and psychomotor retardation. In an 8-year follow-up of alcoholic and nonalcoholic felons, 31% of the alcoholics and 9% of the nonalcoholics reported depressive symptomatology, "especially low mood and irritability" (30). Of 12 who had attempted suicide, 11 were alcoholics. Elsewhere it has been reported that interviewed alcoholics said that they became drunk when they felt depressed, among other reasons, and also that they felt depressed when they were intoxicated (43).

Using the Zung Scale, depressive phenomena have been seen in alcoholics in a day treatment program (118) as well as in alcoholics experiencing withdrawal (102). That such depression is other than situational was suggested by Clyde Mood Scale data showing that alcoholics in a state hospital were equally depressed on Friday and Sunday afternoons (38).

Treatment Effects

Depressive mood has been measured before and after treatment programs. It has been reported that alcoholics who completed a 90-day treatment program described themselves as less depressed and less dysphoric in mood than at the start of the program (121). Another group, tested with the Clyde Mood Scale 2 to 4 weeks after hospitalization, was still characterized as depressive (39). A study of dexoxadrol treatment used the Clyde Scale but gave no pretreatment data (100). After treatment, however, convalescing alcoholics felt significantly less unhappy.

These few investigations highlight some of the problems in research in this area. Alcoholic subjects may be characterized as acute, chronic, convalescing, outpatient, hospitalized, etc., ad infinitum. The nature of their treatments is heterogeneous. Finally, as Klett et al. (53) so well put it for subjects undergoing acute alcohol withdrawal, "A decline in symptoms in the first few days was expected as patients recovered, but the nature of mood changes was less predictable and in some instances it was not clear what direction of change would constitute improvement." Still, linear changes were seen with disquieting affect improving even when patients received placebos. Hoffmann and Abbott (40) found that a group of alcoholics tested after 3 weeks of treatment did not differ significantly from a group of undergraduates in hostile, depressive or tense moods. However, a group of alcoholics showed more anxiety than a nonalcoholic group on the Affect Adjective Checklist (13), and when the responses of 100 hospitalized alcoholics were compared with college student norms on the Guilford–Zimmerman Temperament Survey, one of the few significant differences found was the alcoholics' greater vulnerability to shifts in mood (75).

Another study (23) assessed the drinking behavior of 129 alcoholics 3 months after discharge from a hospital treatment program. Abstinent subjects had a very low degree of affective disturbance on a self-rating mood questionnaire, unimproved subjects had the highest level of dysphoria, and improved subjects were intermediate.

Tension Reduction

Regarding tension reduction, 93% of 2300 individuals admitted to an alcoholism treatment center reported that drinking helped them to relax (116). However, in an experimental drinking paradigm, 4 alcoholics demonstrated greater depression, anxiety and hostility while drinking, whereas 4 nonalcoholic controls did not evidence significant affective changes with drinking (77). Reviewing alcohol and tension reduction, Cappell and Herman (12) concluded that there was equivocal evidence for the tension-reduction hypothesis. Even if data supported the proposition, they pointed out that "one cannot infer the motivation for behavior from one of its consequences" and thus conclude cause and effect relationships. Their point was well taken. In mood studies investigators have, naturally, singled out mood as *the* reinforcer for drinking, and this approach tends to lead to a kind of circular reasoning. There are multiple motivations for drinking (20), and drinking to attenuate unpleasant affect is one of these. It has even been labeled "ataraxic motivation" (19). One of the minor criteria proposed for the diagnosis of alcoholism has been "drinking to relieve anger, insomnia, fatigue, depression, social discomfiture" but the Criteria Committee also noted that with large doses over long periods of time, alcohol produced anxiety (80). About 25% of a sample of physicians and controls reported that they drank more when they were under stress (112). Drinking to relieve tension emerged as a factor when the responses of problem and nonproblem drinkers to a Situations for Drinking Questionnaire were analyzed (17). Beckman (5) reviewed data on women alcoholics, reporting that there was conflicting evidence of a close relationship between drinking behavior and premenstrual tension. Higgins and Marlatt (37) concluded from their study of nonabstinent alcoholics and social drinkers that state anxiety was not a primary determinant of drinking. More recently, evidence in support of alcohol's tension-reducing properties has been presented but a "complex interaction between alcohol consumption, subjective distress, and muscular tension" was cited (108).

Expectancies

Clearly, the motivation to drink alcohol is related to expectancies concerning the consequences of drinking. Majczak (62) concluded that alcoholics' postdrinking moods were secondary to their predrinking moods. When he gave alcohol to alcoholic volunteers, he obtained heterogeneity in terms of reports of euphoria and dysphoria. Nonalcoholic social drinkers, however, anticipating a gay time, reported only euphoria after drinking. In another study, sober alcoholics predicted how they would feel during intoxication. After drinking, subjects observed significantly greater dysphoria in themselves than they had predicted (111). However, they "almost uniformly indicated that they drank in order to feel better and to become more sociable."

Lovibond and Caddy (58) tried to give alcoholics expectancies, and they used an anticipatory drinking methodology to train alcoholics to have discriminated aversive control of drinking. Subjects were informed that certain behavioral effects accompanied various blood alcohol concentrations (BACs). For example, they were informed that feelings of warmth and relaxation resulted at a BAC of .04 to .05%. Clearly, individual scales of BAC-accompanied symptoms have to be composed because of the great variability in alcohol-related behavior which has been documented.

Greenwald et al. (33) found no significant Lorr Scale mood differences between groups of alcoholics, heroin addicts, and orthopedic patients. However, while the alcoholic and drug patients believed that alcohol and heroin, respectively, helped them to be more alert, they did not differ significantly from the orthopedic patients in believing that these substances helped them to make friends or to relax. If alcoholics drank to obtain affective relief, as some studies of expectancies suggested, then, Hore (44) argued, there should be evidence of increased disquieting emotions preceding a relapse in a recovered alcoholic. When a discharge group of 22 patients, 18 of whom later relapsed and drank, kept daily mood self-ratings, there was no such evidence, nor did data suggest a relationship between mood level and drinking behavior.

A recent report (54) studied the effects of alcohol and tonic water on aggressive behavior in male social drinkers. Expectancies about the consequences of drinking alcohol were a significant factor. The authors concluded that "the most important finding . . . was that differences in the level of aggression observed were determined largely by subjects' expectations or belief about the content of the beverage they had consumed." Those who thought they drank alcohol, even if it really had been tonic water, behaved more aggressively.

Craving

These results, of course, relate to the issue of craving in alcoholics. One proposition has been that craving for alcohol might bear some relationship to affective state, that the urge to drink derived from affective need. However, Litman's (57) study of 2 alcoholics did not support such a relationship. Nor did a study of bender or periodic alcoholics reveal that they suffered more depressive symptomatology or that their bender drinking was a form of affective disturbance (96). On the other hand, Ludwig and Stark's (61) study did. It must be pointed out, though, that their data were garnered retrospectively with 78% of 60 alcoholics indicating on a questionnaire that they had experienced craving. The authors described craving which seemed to be reactive to affect: "In general, the craving occurs when an alcoholic is emotionally dysphoric or during stressful, unhappy situations." Another investigation sought data on drinking as related to responses to an inventory of situational discomfort (32). Twenty-five alcoholics were allowed to drink during a 6-week inpatient program and about a third either drank heavily, moderately, or were classified as nondrinkers. Initially, the 3 groups were not significantly different in terms of discomfort scores although the heavy drinkers did have the highest mean score, the moderate drinkers the next highest and the nondrinkers the lowest. At the end of the program, the heavy drinkers showed a slightly increased mean present discomfort score, the moderate drinkers' score was decreased somewhat and the nondrinkers' decreased significantly. These results might suggest a cause and effect relationship but it is difficult to identify whether drinking or discomfort was the causative variable. Heightened states of emotionality accompanying drinking could become explicable in terms of Hore's (44) suggestion that craving might be a state of hyperarousal.

Horn and Wanberg (45) found that drinking for psychological benefit emerged as a primary factor (and in a second-order analysis, too) when drinking questionnaire responses of 2300 alcoholics were studied. The second-order dimension dealt primarily with "controlled," binge drinkers. One conclusion might be that the motivation for binge drinking might be psychological benefit. Ludwig's (60) data ambivalently supported this. While follow-up of 161 alcoholics revealed that only 1% offered reasons for drinking related to craving, 25% did say that alcohol was used as a self-administered medication for symptoms of psychological distress. Among reasons given by former alcoholics for abstaining, 24% indicated no need or desire, but it must be pointed out that the need did not necessarily relate to needs created by discomforting affects. It is well known that retrospective reasons do not always adequately explain previous behaviors. Ludwig's (60) conclusions add provisos, too, regarding future behavior; namely, that reasons given for current behavior may have only limited impact on subsequent behavior. Vannicelli (114) tested the ability of alcoholics to make such predictions. Her results were interpreted as indicating that the alcoholic's knowledge about his drunken self is less than that about his sober self. Hence, retrospective and prospective data have to be viewed conservatively.

Studying 59 patients with cyclic disorders of affect, Mayfield and Coleman (69) found that about half who drank had a change in drinking during an episode of affective disorder. Earlier, Mayfield and Allen (68) had reported that intravenous infusions of alcohol most influenced disordered affect. This might explain why two-thirds of a group of manic–depressive patients, manic type, were alcohol abusers (21), even though alcohol use is popularly thought to be associated with depressed mood.

Summary

The literature is replete with mixed findings about the motivation for drinking alcohol being psychological benefit, tension reduction or affective improvement. Self-reported depression by alcoholics is found frequently and seems to be other than situational, but there is equivocal evidence that alcoholics are more depressed than normative groups. The consequences of drinking are related to expectancies concerning consequences, and some studies point out that alcoholics drink to obtain affective relief. However, there is conflicting evidence concerning the hypothesis that craving for alcohol derives from a need to attenuate dysphoric states.

ALCOHOL EFFECTS ON MOODS OF SUBJECTS

Normals

Investigators have long sought to evaluate the effects of alcohol on the mood states of normal subjects as a kind of baseline or frame of reference. When these studies have taken place under laboratory conditions of experimental intoxication, it becomes difficult to factor out affective changes derivative from the whole, unnatural milieu. Some (71, 78) have therefore sought to simulate a more naturalistic, live-in laboratory setting. While quite imaginative, even such investigations fail to control fully for the factor of expectancy or learned anticipation of alcohol effects when subjects identify the beverages they consume. Infusion which attempts to mask drug identity confronts the alternate dilemma concerning unnatural mode of administration. With regard to alcoholics, McNamee et al. (71) wrote, "It is possible that change in affect induced during experimentally induced intoxication is significantly different from mood changes which occur in real life drinking situations." A recent study (73) reported positive effects of alcohol on morale, for example, in old people living in a nursing home and a residence for the elderly. These were more natural, albeit semi-institutional, settings.

Cameron (10) had 13 normal social drinkers consume 60 ml of absolute alcohol in orange juice in 40 min. During the second half-hour after onset of drinking, subjects reported pleasant, carefree feelings of relaxation. Observers saw elevated mood in drinkers, and it was concluded that this represented an excitation or arousal effect of biphasic alcohol, one which normal social drinkers seek via alcohol. This was the same kind of anticipation of euphoria by social drinkers reported by Majczak (62). However, only 7 out of 15 men reported euphoria with low BACs when they drank undetectable 4% alcohol in grapefruit juice in a double-blind study (107). After drinking, negative experiential reports were statistically significant. In a similar study (106), some of the same authors reported that low BACs resulted in euphoria in 7 student subjects and dysphoria in 9. Elsewhere, decreased sociability and reduced alertness have been reported associated with alcohol (84), while in another study, normal social drinkers reported postalcohol elation and relaxation (76). Finally, social drinkers who had a history of aggressive behavior showed interpersonal aggression after drinking heavily in experimental group "parties" (8).

In a naturalistic setting, "paid volunteer" normals drank alcohol during a "party" (85). The Multiple Affect Adjective Checklist and the Eysenck Personality Inventory were administered first, and then multiple administrations of the former followed during stages of intoxication. It was found that alcohol (mean BAC was 0.113 mg%) reduced anxious and depressed moods in subjects initially adjudged to have high anxiety and that it reduced hostility for those with high neuroticism scores. Hurst and Bagley (47) corroborated the first finding: ingestion of alcohol reduced the Nowlis depression scores of student volunteers. Elsewhere, normals who drank rated themselves as having "high spirits" and their subjective ratings tended to agree fairly well with those of objective raters (87), students given 1.1 g of alcohol per kg of body weight showed mood changes "almost exclusively in the form of exhilaration" (88), other students became less inhibited after 4 oz of alcohol (122), and an additional group of students became less tense and anxious with increased BAC (117). In this last study, however, all other mood effects were negative and the authors thus found it "difficult to believe that people drink to reduce anxiety at the expense of other negative effects."

Kastl (49) reported a linear dose-response curve in this regard. Volunteers who drank 0, 0.33, 0.67 and 1 ml of alcohol per kg of body weight showed increased happiness (as measured by the Nowlis Checklist) with increased doses. Not only dose but time, too, is a variable. Two studies by Kelly and associates (50, 51) showed that alcohol-induced mood ratings, such as feeling elated, followed the course of blood alcohol, tended to peak at about 2 hr after intake, and subsequently fell rectilinearly. Goldberg (28), too, reported that most subjective alcohol effects increased proportionately to dose, but he suggested that the disappearance of such effects at the higher BACs might indicate an adaptation process.

Using the Holtzman Inkblot color score, interpreted as an index of affect and lability, Mayfield (66, 67) found that mean color score increased after volunteers were infused with alcohol but that other Holtzman variables did not differ significantly between alcohol and placebo conditions. He also reported that alcohol-infused "alcoholics showed no significant change attributable to intoxication on any inkblot variable."

Group Drinking

A social factor has been isolated as a significant factor in the affective consequences of drinking. For example, in an experiment studying alcohol effects on affect during male–female couple interactions, familiarity between subjects was a factor influencing the positive effects of alcohol (104). Pliner and Cappell's (86) volunteers became intoxicated alone or in groups. Clyde Mood Scale data indicated that the group subjects tended to describe their intoxication in affective terms, the solitary subjects in terms of physical symptomatology. This apparently holds with alcoholics to some degree, too. Allman (2) studied alcoholics under stress during conditions of isolation and socialization. Stress during isolation resulted in increased physical complaints even though alcoholics drank least during this condition. Drinking resulted in increased depression and anxiety. Martorano (63) reported the latter for his alcoholic subjects, too, but they also perceived themselves as more friendly. Studying group drinking decisions by alcoholics, researchers have concluded that the group or social influence is a "powerful determinant" in the consumption of alcohol (29). While Martorano's (63) alcoholic subjects saw themselves as more friendly when drinking in a group situation, observers did not confirm this behavior. Earlier, Nathan et al. (78) found that their alcoholic subjects drinking experimentally felt more depressed or anxious or both when drinking during isolation conditions than during socialization conditions.

Williams (122) reported that students drinking in staged social settings became less social after alcohol consumption exceeding 4 oz. To demonstrate the points about social factors, artificial environments, etc., he cautioned that results were "not necessarily generalizable to other than stag fraternity cocktail party settings."

Warren and Raynes (117) conducted an interesting study in which college students became intoxicated under three conditions: intravenous injection, social drinking and isolated drinking. Mood changes did not differ between conditions but social drinking tended to produce a less favorable pattern of mood alternations than drinking alone. The authors speculated that perhaps this was related to hostile feelings which are more threatening in social encounters.

Alcoholics

The traditional and popular view that alcohol attenuates alcoholics' disquieting moods increasingly appears open to question as a result of recent findings. One would anticipate that withdrawal would produce affective discomfort due, if for no other reason, to the accompanying physical concomitants. Goldman et al. (29) reported this for alcoholics in an experimental group drinking situation but they also found that rising BACs resulted in increasing discomfort in mood. McNamee et al. (71) also observed the latter phenomenon but not the former. Their chronic alcoholics, drinking in an experimental setting, showed increasingly severe anxiety and depression with consumption of increasing amounts of alcohol, but not only was depression not prominent during a postdrinking phase, subjects were symptom-free at the time of discharge. Martorano's (63) alcoholics subjectively perceived themselves as more depressed and tense when drinking, and this agreed with experimenters' views that drinking increased negative affects among the subjects.

However, Mayfield (64, 65) found that alcohol infusion resulted in affective improvement, and that this was more so in abstainers than among intemperate users of alcohol. In alcoholics, the improvement was transitory. He extended this in an experiment in which alcohol was infused twice—first while patients were severely depressed and later when they had improved. During depression, alcohol produced multiple affective improvements. During remission, significant improvement was observed only in the depressive factor.

Alcoholics' drinking poses a paradox. While sober, Nathan et al.'s (78) alcoholic subjects said that they drank to decrease anxiety and depression. After they drank, however, their behavior appeared as though anxiety and depression had increased. The latter was documented in another study (79) in which congener level was not implicated as a determinant of mood level. Of Vannicelli's (114) 30 alcoholic subjects, 15 had higher anxiety scores on the POMS after drinking and 15 had lower scores. However, mean depression scores were higher after the last drink than before drinking.

Before they drank experimentally, alcoholics said that they expected to become more relaxed and less depressed (109). Initially, upon drinking, pleasurable effects were experienced and later painful affects were recorded. It was concluded that anticipation of tension reduction was a motivational factor in initiating alcoholics' drinking. The increase in tension and anxiety in alcoholics noted above was also found by van der Spuy (113) who called attention to the hypothesis that these painful effects call counteracting compensatory defense mechanisms to the fore which may in themselves suggest the experience of tension reduction to the alcoholic. Hayman (36), too, spoke of alcoholics' defenses but he emphasized that the nature of the alcoholic's acting out will not likely tolerate depression or anxiety for long.

While studies (24, 83) suggest that anxiety and depression are associated with diagnoses of alcoholism, it is not known whether prolonged alcohol ingestion produces this affective state or whether the kind of anxious, depressive personality type, revealed in a factor analytic MMPI study (83), "is more prone to alcohol involvement." The association between this personality type and alcohol abuse is well documented, however. For example, the anxious, depressive neurotic was found to be a more serious abuser of alcohol then the aggressive, psychopathic personality type (120).

If alcoholics are basically depressed, then one might expect this depression to surface with abstinence. Hayman (36), emphasizing that overt depression was not a sine qua non for alcoholism, reported that of his alcoholic patients, "not one . . . has developed a clinical depression after achieving abstinence." In terms of self-perceptions of mood, however, alcoholics have been noted to feel more depressed when intoxicated than when sober—"feelings of unhappiness and uselessness increased with intoxication" (109). New data have been presented by Alterman et al. (3) who compared the discomfort of hospitalized alcoholic patients who chose to drink with those who elected to be abstinent. They found that the discomfort of the former increased and of the latter, decreased. They suggested that the discomfort may be less related to ethanol consumption per se than to the psychological correlates of decision making in an alcoholism treatment program.

Clearly, the final words on alcohol and mood are yet to be written. Psychophysiological measures of affective states will surely supplement self-report data and undoubtedly there will be improvements in methodologies to observe the effects of alcohol consumption in natural milieus and to assess the consequences of such behaviors.

Summary

There have been imaginative attempts to devise experimental analogs of naturalistic settings in which to study alcohol effects on the moods of normal and alcoholic subjects. Generally, non-alcoholics anticipate elevated moods and relaxation as a result of drinking, and this does tend to occur. The evidence suggests that alcoholics show increasing anxiety and depression with increasing alcohol consumption although they expect the reverse. There appears to be a social factor which plays a role in determining the affective consequences of drinking.

SUGGESTIONS FOR FURTHER RESEARCH

The need for more research emphasis in the areas discussed is great. One important focus might be on a long-term longitudinal study of mood with adolescent and young adult subjects cooperating in maintaining mood self-rating diaries or autobiographical logs. One would seek possible interdigitation of—or correlation between—dysphoric states or abrupt mood changes and episodes of—or onset of—drinking. This is the sort of methodology which has been used in studies of alcoholics' craving, but it might fruitfully be applied before the development of drinking patterns. Such data might help to cull out possible cause and effect relationships between alcohol ingestion and mood, could contribute to knowledge about the relationship of general emotional adjustment to drinking, and might cast light on the relationship between social adaptation and drinking generically as contrasted with drinking in social situations versus solitary drinking.

Alcohol (dose)–mood (response) data are needed so that too broad generalizations about alcohol effects are precluded. This holds for both alcoholics and normal controls. Such projects lend themselves to the innovative experimental drinking methodologies which have been reported. Physiological correlates of emotions and other objective measures, in addition to self-report information, would be invaluable. Self-report data should not focus solely on depression. There are other important affective states. Self-report mood scales, relatively easy to administer, might be considered as adjunctive measures in many experimental or laboratory alcohol studies undertaken primarily to test other hypotheses.

In a more naturalistic manner, it would be illuminating to know more about the measured mood states of subjects entering a bar, for example, compared with their affective states during drinking and later. By the same token, further baseline mood data of alcoholic subjects entering treatment would be helpful in program evaluation and in assessing therapeutic progress. Additionally, coupled with follow-up mood data after termination of treatment, valuable clues might be garnered as to prognostic factors for successful treatment, predictive variables for completion versus noncompletion of therapy, and identification of individual treatment goals for individual alcoholic patients.

REFERENCES

1. AITKEN, R. C. B. and ZEALLEY, A. K. Measurement of moods. Br. J. Hosp. Med. 4: 215–224, 1970.
2. ALLMAN, L. R. Group drinking under stress; effects on alcohol intake, psychopathology, mood, and group process. Ph.D. dissertation, Rutgers University; 1971.
3. ALTERMAN, A. I., GOTTHEIL, E. and CRAWFORD, H. D. Mood changes in an alcoholism treatment program based on drinking decisions. Am. J. Psychiat. 132: 1032–1037, 1975.
4. BECK, A. T. Depression; clinical, experimental, and theoretical aspects. New York; Harper and Row; 1967.
5. BECKMAN, L. J. Women alcoholics; a review of social and psychological studies. J. Stud. Alcohol 36: 797–824, 1975.
6. BELFER, M. L., SHADER, R. I., CARROLL, M. and HARMATZ, J. S. Alcoholism in women. Archs Gen. Psychiat. 25: 540–544, 1971.
7. BENNETT, I. F. Prediction of response in the pharmacotherapy of depression. In: WITTENBORN, J. R. and MAY, P. R. A., eds. Prediction of response to pharmacotherapy. Springfield, Ill.; Thomas; 1966.
8. BOYATZIS, R. E. The predisposition toward alcohol-related interpersonal aggression in men. J. Stud. Alcohol 36: 1196–1207, 1975.
9. BROWN, C. C. Psychophysiology at an interface. Psychophysiology 3: 1–7, 1966.
10. CAMERON, D. The physiological and behavioral effects of moderate doses of alcohol; the psychopharmacology of social drinking. J. Alcsm, Lond. 9: 50–55, 1974.
11. CAMERON, J. S., SPECHT, P. G. and WENDT, G. R. Effects of a dramamine-analgesic-caffeine combination on moods, emotions and motivations. J. Psychol. 67: 263–270, 1967.

12. CAPPELL, H. and HERMAN, C. P. Alcohol and tension reduction; a review. Q. J. Stud. Alcohol 33: 33–64, 1972.

13. CHESS, S. B., NEURINGER, C. and GOLDSTEIN, G. Arousal and field dependency in alcoholics. J. Gen. Psychol. 85: 93–102, 1971.

14. CLYDE, D. J. Manual for the Clyde Mood Scale. Coral Gables, Fla.; University of Miami Biometric Laboratory; 1963.

15. CURLEE, J. Depression and alcoholism. Bull. Menninger Clin. 36: 451–455, 1972.

16. DAHLSTROM, W. G., WELSH, G. S. and DAHLSTROM, L. E. An MMPI handbook. Minneapolis; University of Minnesota Press; 1972.

17. DEARDORFF, C. M., MELGES, F. T., HOUT, C. N. and SAVAGE, D. J. Situations related to drinking alcohol; a factor analysis of questionnaire responses. J. Stud. Alcohol 36: 1184–1195, 1975.

18. DITMAN, K. S. Review and evaluation of current drug therapies in alcoholism. Psychosom. Med. 28: 667–677, 1966.

19. EDWARDS, G., CHANDLER, J., HENSMAN, C. and PETO, J. Drinking in a London suburb. II. Correlates of trouble with drinking among men. Q. J. Stud. Alcohol, Suppl. 6, pp. 94–119, 1972.

20. FREED, E. X. Some barriers to rehabilitation of alcoholic patients. Am. Archs Rehab. Ther. 14: 25–26, 1966.

21. FREED, E. X. Alcohol abuse by manic patients. Psychol. Rep. 25: 280, 1969.

22. FREED, E. X. Alcoholism and manic-depressive disorders; some perspectives. Q. J. Stud. Alcohol 31: 62–89, 1970.

23. FREED, E. X., RILEY, E. P. and ORNSTEIN, P. Self-reported mood and drinking patterns following hospital treatment for alcoholism. Br. J. Addict. 72: 231–233, 1977.

24. FREED, E. X., TRIPLETT, D. G. and FREEMAN, E. P. Characteristics of male alcoholics. J. Med. Soc. New Jers. 68: 1011–1013, 1971.

25. GIBSON, S. and BECKER, J. Alcoholism and depression; the factor structure of alcoholics' responses to depression inventories. Q. J. Stud. Alcohol 34: 400–408, 1973.

26. GIBSON, S. and BECKER, J. Changes in alcoholics' self-reported depression. Q. J. Stud. Alcohol 34: 829–836, 1973.

27. GLICK, I. D. Mood and behavioral changes associated with the use of the oral contraceptive agent; a review of the literature. Psychopharmacologia 10: 363–374, 1967.

28. GOLDBERG, L. Effects of ethanol in the central nervous system. Pp. 42–56. In: POPHAM, R., ed. Alcohol and alcoholism. Toronto; Addiction Research Foundation; 1970.

29. GOLDMAN, M. S., TAYLOR, H. A., CARRUTH, M. L. and NATHAN, P. E. Effects of group decision-making on group drinking by alcoholics. Q. J. Stud. Alcohol 34: 807–822, 1973.

30. GOODWIN, D. W., CRANE, J. B. and GUZE, S. B. Felons who drink; an 8-year follow-up. Q. J. Stud. Alcohol 32: 136–147, 1971.

31. GOSS, A. and MOROSKO, T. E. Alcoholism and clinical symptoms. J. Abnorm. Psychol. 74: 682–684, 1969.

32. GOTTHEIL, E., MURPHY, B. F. SKOLODA, T. E. and CORBETT, L. O. Fixed interval drinking decisions. II. Drinking and discomfort in 25 alcoholics. Q. J. Stud. Alcohol 33: 325–340, 1972.

33. GREENWALD, S. R., CARTER, J. S. and STEIN, E. M. Differences between the

background, attitude, functioning, and mood of drug addicts, alcoholics, and orthopedic patients. Int. J. Addict. **8:** 865–874, 1973.

34. HAGNELL, O. and TUNVING, K. Mental and physical complaints among alcoholics. Q. J. Stud. Alcohol **33:** 77–84, 1972.

35. HALL, P., SPEAR, F. G. and STIRLAND, D. Diurnal variation of subjective mood in depressive states. Psychiat. Q. **38:** 529–536, 1964.

36. HAYMAN, M. The relationship of depression to alcoholism. In: Lesse, S., ed. Masked depression. New York; Aronson; 1974.

37. HIGGINS, R. L. and MARLATT, G. A. Effects of anxiety arousal on the consumption of alcohol by alcoholics and social drinkers. J. Consult. Clin. Psychol. **41:** 426–433, 1973.

38. HOFFMAN, H. How do alcoholic patients feel on Sunday in a state hospital? Psychol. Rep. **25:** 764, 1969.

39. HOFFMANN, H. Depression and defensiveness in self-descriptive moods of alcoholics. Psychol. Rep. **26:** 23–26, 1970.

40. HOFFMANN, H. and ABBOTT, D. Emotional self-description of alcoholic patients after treatment. Psychol. Rep. **26:** 892, 1970.

41. HOLLISTER, L. E. Some human pharmacological studies of three psychotropic drugs; thiothixine, molindane, and W-1867. J. Clin. Pharmacol. **8:** 95–101, 1968.

42. HOLLISTER, L. E. and GILLESPIE, H. K. Marihuana, ethanol, and dextro-amphetamine; mood and mental function alterations. Archs Gen. Psychiat. **23:** 199–203, 1970.

43. HOLLOWAY, I. Some psychological concomitants of addiction. Ph.D. dissertation, University of Adelaide; 1969.

44. HORE, B. D. Factors in alcoholic relapse. Br. J. Addict. **66:** 89–96, 1971.

45. HORN, J. L. and WANBERG, K. W. Symptom patterns related to excessive use of alcohol. Q. J. Stud. Alcohol **30:** 35–58, 1969.

46. HUDOLIN, V. and GRUDEN, V. Melleril-retard u lijecenju alkoholizma. (Melleril-retard in the treatment of alcoholics.) Alkoholizam Beograd 9 (No. 2): 5–21, 1969.

47. HURST, P. M. and BAGLEY, S. K. Acute adaptation to the effects of alcohol. Q. J. Stud. Alcohol **33:** 358–378, 1972.

48. KANE, F. J., JR., DALY, R. T., EWING, J. A. and KEELER, M. H. Mood and behavioural changes with progestational agents. Br. J. Psychiat. **113:** 265–268, 1967.

49. KASTL, A. J. Changes in ego functioning under alcohol. Q. J. Stud. Alcohol **30:** 371–383, 1969.

50. KELLY, M., MYRSTEN, A.-L. and GOLDBERG, L. Intravenous vitamins in acute alcoholic intoxication; effects on physiological and psychological functions. Br. J. Addict. **66:** 19–30, 1971.

51. KELLY, M., MYRSTEN, A.-L., NERI, A. and RYDBERG, U. Effects and after-effects of alcohol on physiological and psychological functions in man; a controlled study. Blutalkohol 7: 422–436, 1970.

52. KETAI, R. Affect, mood, emotion, and feeling; semantic considerations. Am. J. Psychiat. **132:** 1215–1217, 1975.

53. KLETT, C. J., HOLLISTER, L. E., CAFFEY, E. M., JR. and KAIM, S. C. Evaluating changes in symptoms during acute alcohol withdrawal. Archs Gen. Psychiat. **24:** 174–178, 1971.

54. LANG, A. R., GOECKNER, D. J., ADESSO, V. J. and MARLATT, G. A. Effects of

alcohol on aggression in male social drinkers. J. Abnorm. Psychol. **84:** 508–518, 1975.

55. LAZARUS, R. S. Psychological stress and the coping process. New York; McGraw-Hill; 1966.

56. LESSE, S. Depressive equivalents and the multivariant masks of depression. In: LESSE, S., ed. Masked depression. New York; Aronson; 1974.

57. LITMAN, G. K. Stress, affect and craving in alcoholics; the single case as a research strategy. Q. J. Stud. Alcohol **35:** 131–146, 1974.

58. LOVIBOND, S. H. and CADDY, G. Discriminated aversive control in the moderation of alcoholics' drinking behavior. Behav. Ther., N.Y. **1:** 437–444, 1970.

59. LUBIN, B. Adjective checklists for measurement of depression. Archs Gen. Psychiat. **12:** 57–62, 1965.

60. LUDWIG, A. M. On and off the wagon; reasons for drinking and abstaining by alcoholics. Q. J. Stud. Alcohol **33:** 91–96, 1972.

61. LUDWIG, A. M. and STARK, L. H. Alcohol craving; subjective and situational aspects. Q. J. Stud. Alcohol **35:** 899–905, 1974.

62. MAJCZAK, A. O nastrojach w przebiegu alkoholizowania sie czlowieka. (On mood changes during alcoholization in humans.) Probl. Alkzmu, Warsaw **15:** 4–6, 1967.

63. MARTORANO, R. D. Mood and social perception in four alcoholics; effects of drinking and assertion training. Q. J. Stud. Alcohol **35:** 445–457, 1974.

64. MAYFIELD, D. G. Psychopharmacology of alcohol. I. Affective change with intoxication, drinking behavior and affective state. J. Nerv. Ment. Dis. **146:** 314–321, 1968.

65. MAYFIELD, D. G. Psychopharmacology of alcohol. II. Affective tolerance in alcohol intoxication. J. Nerv. Ment. Dis. **146:** 322–327, 1968.

66. MAYFIELD, D. G. Holtzman Inkblot Technique in acute experimental alcohol intoxication. J. Project. Tech. **32:** 491–494, 1968.

67. MAYFIELD, D. G. Inkblot technique in experimental intoxication; a comparison of psychodynamic functions of alcohol in alcoholics and nonalcoholics. Br. J. Addict. **68:** 197–199, 1973.

68. MAYFIELD, D. G. and ALLEN, D. Alcohol and affect; a psychopharmacological study. Am. J. Psychiat. **123:** 1346–1351, 1967.

69. MAYFIELD, D. G. and COLEMAN, L. L. Alcohol use and affective disorder. Dis. Nerv. Syst. **29:** 467–474, 1968.

70. MCNAIR, D. M., LORR, M. and DROPPLEMAN, L. F. Profile of mood states; manual. San Diego; Educational and Industrial Testing Service; 1971.

71. MCNAMEE, H. B., MELLO, N. K. and MENDELSON, J. H. Experimental analysis of drinking patterns of alcoholics; concurrent psychiatric observations. Am. J. Psychiat. **124:** 1063–1069, 1968.

72. MENDELS, J. and COCHRANE, C. The nosology of depression; the endogenous-reactive concept. Am. J. Psychiat., Suppl. No. 124, pp. 1–11, 1968.

73. MISHARA, B. L., KASTENBAUM, R., BAKER, F. and PATTERSON, R. D. Alcohol effects in old age; an experimental investigation. Soc. Sci. Med. **9:** 535–547, 1975.

74. MORGAN, W. P. Selected physiological and psychomotor correlates of depression in psychiatric patients. Ed.D. dissertation, University of Toledo; 1967.

75. MOZDZIERZ, G. J., MACCHITELLI, F. J., FLAHERTY, L. and DEVITO, R. Tem-

perament characteristics of chronic alcoholics as measured by the Guilford-Zimmerman Temperament Survey. J. Psychol. 79: 97–102, 1971.
76. MUIR, G., POLLITT, N. and ROONEY, J. Oral vitamins in alcohol intoxication. Q. J. Stud. Alcohol 34: 373–380, 1973.
77. NATHAN, P. E., and O'BRIEN, J. S. An experimental analysis of the behavior of alcoholics and nonalcoholics during prolonged experimental drinking; a necessary precursor of behavior therapy? Behav. Ther., N.Y. 2: 455–476, 1971.
78. NATHAN, P. E., TITLER, N. A., LOWENSTEIN, L. M., SOLOMON, P. and ROSSI, A. M. Behavioral analysis of chronic alcoholism; interaction of alcohol and human contact. Archs Gen. Psychiat. 22: 419–430, 1970.
79. NATHAN, P. E., ZARE, N. C., FERNEAU, E. W., JR. and LOWENSTEIN, L. M. Effects of congener differences in alcoholic beverages on the behavior of alcoholics. Q. J. Stud. Alcohol, Suppl. No. 5, pp. 87–100, 1970.
80. NATIONAL COUNCIL ON ALCOHOLISM, CRITERIA COMMITTEE. Criteria for the diagnosis of alcoholism. Am. J. Psychiat. 129: 127–135, 1972.
81. Studies seek pattern in lawful use of mood-changing drugs. New York Times, 20 May 1968.
82. O'LEARY, M. R. and DONOVAN, D. M. Perception of depression in self and others among male alcoholics. J. Clin. Psychol. 30: 142–146, 1974.
83. OVERALL, J. E. and PATRICK, J. H. Unitary alcoholism factor and its personality correlates. J. Abnorm. Psychol. 79: 303–309, 1972.
84. PEARSON, R. G. Alcohol-hypnoxia effects upon operator tracking, monitoring, and reaction time. Aerospace Med. 39: 303–307, 1968.
85. PERRINE, M. W., WALLER, J. A. and HARRIS, L. S. Alcohol and highway safety; behavioral and medical aspects. Springfield, Va.; U.S. National Technical Information Service; 1971.
86. PLINER, P. and CAPPELL, H. Modification of affective consequences of alcohol; a comparison of social and solitary drinking. J. Abnorm. Psychol. 83: 418–425, 1974.
87. RAFAELSEN, L., CHRISTRUP, H., BECH, P. and RAFAELSEN, O. J. Effects of cannabis and alcohol on psychological tests. Nature 242: 117–118, 1973.
88. REISBY, N. and THEILGAARD, A. The interaction of alcohol and meprobamate in man. Acta Psychiat. Scand., Suppl. No. 208, pp. 1–204, 1969.
89. ROSENBERG, C. M. and AMODEO, M. Long-term patients seen in an alcoholism clinic. Q. J. Stud. Alcohol 35: 660–666, 1974.
90. ROSS, S. M. Fear, reinforcing activities and degree of alcoholism; a correlational analysis. Q. J. Stud. Alcohol 34: 823–828, 1973.
91. RUSSELL, J. A. and MEHRABIAN, A. The mediating role of emotions in alcohol use. J. Stud. Alcohol 36: 1508–1536, 1975.
92. RUTENFRANZ, J. and SINGER, R. Untersuchungen zur Frage einer Abhängigkeit der Alkoholwirkung von der Tageszeit. Int. Z. Agnew. Physiol. 24: 1–17, 1967.
93. RUTTER, L. F. Metabolic disorders in alcoholics. J. Alcsm 5: 91–96, 1970.
94. SATHANANTHAN, G. L., GERSHON, S. and LENN, E. Psychological profiles and effects in acute trauma; a pilot study. Dis. Nerv. Syst. 36: 17–19, 1975.
95. SCHUCKIT, M., The alcoholic woman; a literature review. Psychiat. Med. Conn. 3: 37–43, 1972.

96. SCHUCKIT, M., RIMMER, J., REICH, T. and WINOKUR, G. The bender alcoholic. Br. J. Psychiat. 119: 183–184, 1971.

97. SCHWARTZ, J. L. and DUBITZKY, M. Changes in anxiety, mood and self-esteem resulting from an attempt to stop smoking. Am. J. Psychiat. 124: 1580–1584, 1968.

98. SCRIGNAT, C. B., HORNSBY, L., BISHOP, M. P. and GALLANT, D. M. A controlled evaluation of butaperazine in the neurotic anxiety syndrome. Curr. Ther. Res. 9: 492–495, 1967.

99. SHAW, J. A., DONLEY, P., MORGAN, D. W. and ROBINSON, J. A. Treatment of depression in alcoholics. Am. J. Psychiat. 132: 641–644, 1975.

100. SIMOPOULOS, A. M., PINTO, A., BABIKOW, P. W., KURLAND, A. and SAVAGE, C. Psychotomimetic properties and therapeutic potentials of Dexoxadrol on convalescing alcoholics. Dis. Nerv. Syst. 31: 203–207, 1970.

101. SIMS, A. Dependence on alcohol and drugs following treatment for neurosis. Br. J. Addict. 70: 33–40, 1975.

102. SMITH, J. W., JOHNSON, L. C. and BURDICK, J. A. Sleep, psychological and clinical changes during alcohol withdrawal in NAD-treated alcoholics. Q. J. Stud. Alcohol 32: 982–994, 1971.

103. SMITH, J. W. and LAYDEN, T. A. Changes in psychological performance and blood chemistry in alcoholics during and after hospital treatment. Q. J. Stud. Alcohol 33: 379–394, 1972.

104. SMITH, R. C., PARKER, E. S. and NOBLE, E. P. Alcohol and affect in dyadic social interaction. Psychosom. Med. 37: 25–40, 1975.

105. SOBELL, L. C. and SOBELL, M. B. Outpatient alcoholics give valid self-reports. J. Nerv. Ment. Dis. 161: 32–42, 1975.

106. SPRINGER, E., STAAK, M. and RAFF, G. Experimentelle Untersuchungen zur Resorption geringer Alkoholmengen und ihre Auswirkungen auf die Verkehrstrüchtigkeit. Beitr. Gerichtl. Med. 31: 253–258, 1973.

107. STAAK, M., SPRINGER, E. and SCHOOR, P. Experimentelle Untersuchungen über die subjectiv registrierbare Wirkung niedriger Blutalkoholkonzentrationen im Doppelblindersuch. Blutalkohol 10: 17–24, 1973.

108. STEFFEN, J. J., NATHAN, P. E. and TAYLOR, H. A. Tension-reducing effects of alcohol; further evidence and some methodological considerations. J. Abnorm. Psychol. 83: 542–547, 1974.

109. TAMERIN, J. S. and MENDELSON, J. H. The psychodynamics of chronic inebriation; observations of alcoholics during the process of drinking in an experimental group setting. Am. J. Psychiat. 125: 886–899, 1969.

110. TAMERIN, J. S. TOLOR, A., HOLSON, P. and NEUMANN, C. P. The alcoholic's perception of self; a retrospective comparison of mood and behavior during states of sobriety and intoxication. Ann. N.Y. Acad. Sci. 233: 48–60, 1974.

111. TAMERIN, J. S., WEINER, S. and MENDELSON, J. H. Alcoholics' expectancies and recall of experiences during intoxication. Am. J. Psychiat. 126: 1697–1704, 1970.

112. VAILLANT, G. E., BRIGHTON, J. R. and McARTHUR, C. Physicians' use of mood-alternating drugs; a 20-year follow-up report. N. Engl. J. Med. 282: 365–372, 1970.

113. VAN DER SPUY, H. I. J. The influence of alcohol on the mood of the alcoholic. Br. J. Addict. 67: 255–265, 1972.

114. VANNICELLI, M. L. Mood and self-perception of alcoholics when sober and intoxicated. Q. J. Stud. Alcohol 33: 341–357, 1972.
115. WAMBSGANSS, E. and BREDENKAMP, J. Eine experimentalpsychologische Untersuchung über die Wirkung von Haloperidol in niedriger Dosierung bei alleiniger Applikation und in Verbindung mit Alkohol. Arzneimittel-Forsch. 18: 238–243, 1968.
116. WANBERG, K. W. Prevalence of symptoms found among excessive drinkers. Int. J. Addict. 4: 169–185, 1969.
117. WARREN, G. H. and RAYNES, A. E. Mood changes during three conditions of alcohol intake. Q. J. Stud. Alcohol 33: 979–989, 1972.
118. WEINGOLD, H. P., LACHIN, J. M., BELL, A. H. and COXE, R. C. Depression as a symptom of alcoholism; search for a phenomenon. J. Abnorm. Psychol. 73: 195–197, 1968.
119. WESSMAN, A. E. and RICKS, D. F. Mood and personality. New York; Holt, Rinehart and Winston; 1966.
120. WHITELOCK, P. R., OVERALL, J. E. and PATRICK, J. H. Personality patterns and alcohol abuse in a state hospital population. J. Abnorm. Psychol. 78: 9–16, 1971.
121. WILKINSON, A. E., PRADO, W. M., WILLIAMS, W. O. and SCHNADT, F. W. Psychological test characteristics and length of stay in alcoholism treatment. Q. J. Stud. Alcohol 32: 60–65, 1971.
122. WILLIAMS, A. F. Psychological needs and social drinking among college students. Q. J. Stud. Alcohol 29: 355–363, 1968.
123. WINOKUR, G. Types of depressive illness. Br. J. Psychiat. 120: 265–266, 1972.
124. WOODRUFF, R. A., JR., GUZE, S. B. and CLAYTON, P. J. Alcoholics who see a psychiatrist compared with those who do not. Q. J. Stud. Alcohol 34: 1162–1171, 1973.
125. WOODRUFF, R. A., JR., GUZE, S. B., CLAYTON, P. J. and CARR, D. Alcoholism and depression. Archs Gen. Psychiat. 28: 97–100, 1973.
126. ZUCKERMAN, M., LUBIN, B., VOGEL, L. and VALERIUS, E. Measurement of experimentally induced affects. J. Consult. Psychol. 28: 418–425, 1964.
127. ZUNG, W. W. A self-rating depression scale. Archs Gen. Psychiat. 12: 63–70, 1965.
128. ZUNG, W. W. Evaluating treatment methods for depressive disorders. Am. J. Psychiat., Suppl. No. 124, pp. 40–48, 1968.

16

The Adaptive Consequences of Drinking[1]

Donald I. Davis, M.D., David Berenson, M.D.
Peter Steinglass, M.D. and Susan Davis, M.S.W.

OF ALL THE QUESTIONS that can and have been asked about chronic alcoholism, the most elusive question seems to be the one that is most basic for a psychiatric understanding of the condition—namely, "Why do people continue to drink when everyone knows it's so bad for you?" In other words, what are the factors that maintain or support the behavior of alcoholism? No previous theory has gained wide acceptance; and, more importantly, no hypothesis has led to a conclusion that has widespread therapeutic application (1, *pp. 61–70*). In this paper, we propose a theoretical model of the maintenance of drinking behavior, derived primarily from a synthesis of systems analysis and operant behavioral analysis. We hypothesize that maintenance of drinking behavior is under the control of its adaptive consequences, and offer clinical vignettes to illustrate how we have been led to this hypothesis. We believe that this theoretical framework offers opportunities for broadly applicable research and clinical work on alcoholism.

Historically, there have been two premises underlying much of the therapeutic approach to alcoholism. The first is that excessive drinking is maladaptive. The second is that there are ultimate causes that lead to alcoholism, be they essential personality or biological traits.

These premises have led to certain therapeutic approaches. The stress on the maladaptive, destructive nature of drinking has led to moral exhortations and scare tactics by physicians, punitive legal ap-

[1]Reprinted, by special permission of the William Alanson White Psychiatric Foundation, Inc., from *Psychiatry*, Vol. 37, pp. 209–215, 1974. Copyright © 1974 by The William Alanson White Psychiatric Foundation, Inc., Washington, D.C. 20009.

proaches, and generally aversive therapeutic approaches, such as the use of disulfiram (Antabuse), apomorphine injections or video-tape self-confrontation. Therapeutic approaches based on ultimate cause hypotheses rather than multidetermined hypotheses have led therapists to apply uniform techniques to all "alcoholics." These approaches, while sometimes leading to short-term improvement, usually lead to relapse and increased frustration for both patient and therapist.

The search for ultimate causes has led to concepts such as biochemical sensitivity, genetic predisposition and oral dependency, which are interesting and perhaps valid in some cases (2), but our clinical experience leads us to a conclusion of a different order: That alcoholic behavior is more profitably thought of as a final common pathway and that excessive drinking can therefore be put to a wide variety of uses by a wide variety of types of people.

In addition to those who see ultimate causes in the nature of individuals who become alcoholic, there are those who attribute primary cause to drug effects themselves. For example, some researchers turn to the concepts of "addiction" (3, 4) or of "blackouts" (5) to explain persistence of the behavior of excessive drinking. These concepts derive from a medical-disease model of alcoholism in which research emphasis is placed on describing what seems maladaptive (pathological) about behavior and on finding the involuntary or addictive (disease) process that produces the disturbed behavior. Working with this model, some people treat an "addiction" as having qualities that remove control of behavior from behavioral contingencies.

In contrast, we have been studying alcoholism from the perspective of a behavioral-adaptive model in which emphasis is placed on finding what seems adaptive and reinforcing of drinking behavior. Using this model, it is not necessary to postulate that the addictive process serves as the mechanism for the persistence of largely aversive behavior. Rather, we take the view that a seemingly aversive dysphoria or other unpleasant conditions consequent to alcohol use will not necessarily make the over-all experience of drinking aversive.[2]

[2]By "over-all experience," we do not mean for each and every drinking experience. "Over-all" refers to the composite effect of many drinking episodes, the sum total of which is reinforcing. It is assumed that only occasional drinking experiences will be strongly rewarding. The well-established behavioral tenet that intermittent, rather than continuous, reinforcement leads to development of the most tenacious habits should certainly be expected to apply to alcoholic behavior.

HYPOTHESES

As an alternative to the two premises mentioned at the outset, we propose a model for conceptualizing alcoholism with the following characteristics: (1) The abuse of alcohol has adaptive consequences.[3] (2) These adaptive consequences are sufficiently reinforcing to serve as the primary factors maintaining a habit of drinking, regardless of what underlying causation there may be. (3) The primary factors for each individual differ and may be operating at an intrapsychic level, intracouple level or at the level of maintenance of homeostasis in a family or wider social system.

IMPLICATIONS FOR THERAPY AND RESEARCH

We feel that there are two main therapeutic implications that can be drawn from our central hypotheses.

(1) In each individual or family that presents with an alcohol problem, it is important to ascertain how the drinking behavior is serving an adaptive function. The maladaptive aspects are readily apparent and can usually be recited quite easily by doctor, patient and family members. Usually, in spite of the agreement by all of how terrible drinking is, the drinking pattern continues with a concomitant increase of feelings of frustration on everybody's part. Care must be taken to avoid this trap and to concentrate during the history-taking and clinical observation on what is adaptive about the drinking. We believe that in this way more useful information can be gathered, and a better therapeutic alliance can be established. In our experience, experimentally induced[4] intoxication has been helpful. Much information that might have been only secondarily inferred from observation of the patient while sober can be directly observed while he is intoxicated. We recognize that, at present, encouraging someone to drink, for whatever purpose, is highly controversial and must be evaluated further before it is generally recommended.

(2) Once the adaptive consequences of drinking have been ascertained, therapy may be structured around helping the patient to

---

[3] It must be emphasized that, by the word "adaptive," we are not implying good or any other moral value. There is certainly precedent within psychoanalytic explanations of symptom formation, learning theory descriptions of positive reinforcement, and systems theory assessments of levels of functioning to assert that behavior may be adaptive, yet not necessarily desirable.

[4] Experimentally induced intoxication here refers to intoxication occurring as a result of voluntary ingestion of alcohol in a hospital ward setting.

manifest the adaptive behavior while sober instead of only during drinking, and to learn effective alternative behaviors. We have found video-tape self-confrontation very helpful in this regard, although care must be taken to ensure that the confrontation focuses on the adaptive consequences of drinking rather than becoming another aversive experience which contributes to frustration of self-help efforts.

Similar considerations must be kept in mind in designing a research strategy. An awareness of the variety of systems operating will be essential. We have begun to develop a naturalistic research design to allow us to evaluate behavior both sober and intoxicated and at the individual, family and small group level. The presence or absence of adaptive consequences and therapeutic outcome will be measured.

CLINICAL ILLUSTRATIONS

In each of the clinical vignettes that will be presented in this paper, the use of alcohol has an ongoing, adaptive function. Originally, there may have been psychological or pharmacological reasons for the drinking behavior; yet the behavior persists because it is currently being reinforced at least intermittently.

Case 1—A Marital Couple

In the case of a couple in psychotherapy with one of the authors of this paper, the wife was labeled by herself, by her spouse and by her neighbors as the alcoholic in the family. She was frequently drunk, and when drunk, was quite outspoken and verbally aggressive. When sober, she was typically quiet and demure. Both drunken and sober behavior were observed numerous times in therapy. After some weeks of weekly family therapy, a pattern emerged in which it appeared that in a session following a stressful therapy hour, the wife predictably arrived acting drunk and argued with the therapist, while her spouse sat quietly, as was his custom. Upon careful inquiry, it was discovered that the woman drank no more than 2 oz of alcohol before these sessions (while her husband had been drinking at least twice as much).

That this pattern of behavior within the therapy setting was typical was supported by historical evidence that a similar pattern had been used by the couple in handling conflictual situations between the family and the outside community. For example, in an episode occurring 15 years prior to therapy, their daughter developed an acute fever and abdominal symptoms late one evening. The pediatrician was called and advised antipyretics and an office visit in the morning. However, the child appeared to her mother to be seriously ill, and after several hours with no change in symptomatology, the wife wanted to call the pediatrician back. Her husband urged her not to call, saying that doctors know best and that it wasn't right to be bothering the doctor at 2 AM. But his wife persisted, an argument ensued, she started drinking, and, when behaviorally drunk, called the doctor back, insisting that he see the child that night. He acquiesced, the child was taken to the local emergency room, was found to have an intestinal intussusception and was operated on that night, with a positive outcome.

Using the medical model, the wife's "drunken behavior" would probably be seen as obstreperous and obnoxious, and treatment would likely consist of something aversive, whether disulfiram, aversive conditioning or admonitions.

From our perspective, the wife's "drunken behavior" served an adaptive role in allowing the couple to respond to a perceived threat from the outside world. It would appear, in this case, that the alcohol has served as a prop in the presence of which assertive behavior becomes expressible by the wife and, perhaps, tolerable for the husband. The consequences of drinking for the wife appear to involve both assertiveness in the face of a perceived threat and tacit approval from her spouse, both of which reinforce her drinking behavior. Treatment, then, is focused on bringing to the attention of the couple the role alcohol has been seen to serve and on teaching more successful means of interacting without alcohol.

In this case, therapy never progressed to the point of learning more successful modes of interacting. The therapist found himself accepting the family belief system that drinking is the problem and drinking is intractable. Before adequately helping the couple to see the reinforcing systems aspects of their drinking for their family, he prematurely fell back on his familiar methods of therapy and began making observations on how the couple related to one another and to him. Soon the couple panicked. They informed him, with some wisdom, that they appreciated his interest in them, that they "knew" their way of doing things made no sense, but that it was their way, they had no other, and it would be best not to tamper with it anymore.

Case 2—Two Brothers

Another case in which alcohol serves an adaptive function within a family has been previously reported by Steinglass et al. (6). Two brothers, both chronic alcoholics, who were admitted together to a research program which involved experimentally induced intoxication, gave the following history of their drinking relationship to each other. The older brother had led a life characterized by frequent changes in job and geographic location and a peripheral relationship to the family. The younger brother's life, by contrast, seemed externally stable. He had been married for 15 years and had maintained close ties to the extended family. However, whereas his external life suggested relatively greater strength and stability, his reaction to alcohol was one of increasing violence. After a particularly violent drunken episode, during which he severely beat his mother, his older brother was called home in the hope that he would act as a stabilizing and controlling element for his brother.

Although both men were heavy drinkers, they would rarely be drunk simultaneously. The typical drinking bout would be initiated by the older brother after considerable encouragement from his sibling. The younger brother would then follow suit, but the older brother would simultaneously decrease his drinking, and, being relatively sober, function as a watchdog for his more provocative and aggressive brother. Exactly this sequence of behaviors occurred during the research study when these men were allowed to consume alcohol together on a voluntary basis.

From the perspective of a medical model, these two brothers would be of genetic interest as siblings now living apart, yet having the same addiction. In their treatment, the brothers would likely be seen separately and each be exposed to some aversive responses to his drinking condition.

Looked at from the point of view of the adaptive uses of alcohol, these brothers had established a drinking relationship that offered the opportunity for the controlled and manageable expression of aggressive and violent tendencies. It seemed likely, in addition, that this drinking relationship, at least on some occasions, allowed a perpetuation of a system in the family, the maintenance of which was reinforcing for each brother.

This formulation might lead to a very different treatment model. The two brothers would be seen together at times; their drinking situations would be analyzed retrospectively and as they occurred;

their uses of alcohol would be elucidated and clarified; and a more viable family system and means of reducing, coping with or expressing aggression would be sought.

Case 3—A Family

Another example of adaptive consequences maintaining the use of alcohol within a family is provided by the following observations. A family was seen twice: first when the husband, the identified alcoholic, was sober, and second, during a session of experimentally-induced intoxication for the husband. Most striking was the increased animation by all the family members during the intoxicated interview, even though only one of them was drinking. Although there were many verbal complaints about the husband's drinking, there was a great deal of laughing and joking by family members during the second session. Interestingly, while viewing the two tapes on a subsequent session, there was again a great deal of hilarity when watching the tape of the drunken interview. The complaints and other pointed comments made only in the drinking session seemed quite accurate expressions, yet they were spoken as if they would not be remembered because they were said in the presence of alcohol. Thus, the family has established a system in which affective communication is present during the husband's drinking and not while he is sober.

One might be tempted to use these observations to show the alcoholic how maladaptive his drinking is. After all, his drinking lays him open to criticism from his family. From an adaptive standpoint, however, we might see the greater intensity of relating and more open contact with the father when drinking as serving to reestablish bonds in the family and justify current roles in the family system.

In any case, what is most important about the comparison of this family in drinking and nondrinking conditions is not simply that the family behaved differently, but that their changed behavior probably is a reinforcing consequence of the drinking behavior for the alcoholic.

Case 4—Mr. A

The following clinical example will help illustrate the therapeutic implications of our hypotheses within the context of a preliminary, naturalistic research design. The authors have recently worked with psychotherapy groups of five or six alcoholics, when drinking as well as when not drinking, while they were hospitalized on the clinical research ward of the Laboratory of Alcohol Research, U.S. National Institute on Alcohol Abuse and Alcoholism. The experience of one man in one of these groups will help illustrate the formulation of, as well as the potential application of, the hypotheses in this paper.

Mr. A was one of five men who spent 4 consecutive weeks as inpatients on our hospital unit and who took part in 1½-hr group psychotherapy sessions every weekday throughout the 4 weeks. The first 10 days alcohol was not available. During the next 10 days alcohol was made freely available to each man, and group sessions continued. The last week, drinking was not permitted. Most sessions were video taped, and sessions during drinking as well as nondrinking periods were played back to the group during the final, sober week.

Mr. A took part in the group verbally from the start, but his voice was barely audible the first week. When disagreed with, he uniformly acquiesced to the other person. A tall man, he usually sat back deep into his seat, head low, with his back bent over. During the 10 days of drinking, Mr. A drank increasingly heavily, reaching a peak of 32 oz of 100-U.S. proof alcohol in 1 day. During the first few days of drinking, Mr. A's verbal participation in the group increased only moderately. His effectiveness in terms of audibility, being listened to without interruption and actively defending his position to the point that others listened to him increased greatly. At least when talking, he now sat upright or forward. As days of drinking progressed, Mr. A became so intoxicated that he had difficulty keeping his eyes open in the group or putting words together, though when he did participate, the qualities of increased assertiveness were still evident.

In viewing video tapes of drinking sessions during the subsequent, sober phase, Mr. A, like the other men, first looked at his drunken demeanor. As was typical of the group, he had expected to be shown, for shock value, evidence of lack of control and general sloppiness while drinking. Instead, the adaptive elements of his drinking, before level of consciousness was affected, were pointed out. He seemed genuinely surprised to see his own increased assertiveness and concomitant increased effectiveness in the group. Several times in the last week, Mr. A was encouraged to discuss again issues that he had discussed in the drinking session and to express opinions on current issues. Increasingly, he seemed to be reproducing the more effective elements of his drinking behavior without drinking, and this fact was repeatedly pointed out to Mr. A by therapists and by other group members. At termination, Mr. A elected to be referred to a new group psychotherapy program.

Discussion

The idea of alcoholism as a final common pathway (7), and of alcoholism as the expression of an intrinsic logic for the individual alcoholic (8), has been raised before. Steinglass et al. (6) have previously drawn attention to apparent systems maintenance aspects of drinking operating between familial pairs. MacAndrew and Edgerton (9) have illustrated how differing social expectations may have maintained a wide variety of drinking patterns, especially among different Indian tribes. Hunt and Azrin (10) reported quite successful outcomes with a small number of alcoholics using broad-scope manipulations of environment combined with some training in making use of these changed living and work conditions.

In an article by Sobell et al. (11), reference was made to a study by Sobell and Sobell (12) in which avoidance conditioning apparently had been combined with behavioral analysis of drinking situations and teaching of alternative, more appropriate responses to the situations. This type of broadened approach should shed more light on the importance of reinforcing contingencies in alcoholism.

There have been recent reports (13,14) of successful application of contingency management to the modification of drinking behavior, only one of these a case report from a therapy situation (15).

Thus, a small but increasing number of workers are treating the abuse of alcohol as if they assume it is an adaptive behavior, subject to the usual rules of reinforcement governing most other behaviors. To date, however, others have not dealt directly with the question of what had been maintaining the use of alcohol prior to use of modification procedures nor with the value in therapy of attempting to discover significant reinforcers of alcohol use. It is with the idea of generating a hypothesis, therefore, that we have presented our clinical observations, illustrating both what we believe to be examples of reinforcement of drinking and the broad range of situations that can be examined fruitfully in treatment and research with alcoholics.

REFERENCES

1. U.S. NATIONAL INSTITUTE ON ALCOHOL ABUSE AND ALCOHOLISM. Alcohol and health. First special report to the Congress. (DHEW Publ. No. HSM-72-9099.) Washington, D.C.; U.S. Govt Print. Off.; 1971.

2. GOODWIN, D. W., SCHULSINGER, F., HERMANSEN, L., GUZE, S. B. and WINOKUR, G. Alcohol problems in adoptees raised apart from alcoholic biological parents. Archs Gen. Psychiat. 28: 238–243, 1973.

3. MENDELSON, J. H., LA DOU, J. and SOLOMON, P. Experimentally induced intoxication and withdrawal in alcoholics. III. Psychiatric findings. Q. J. Stud. Alcohol, Suppl. No. 2, pp. 40–52, 1964.

4. TAMERIN, J. S. and MENDELSON, J. H. The psychodynamics of chronic inebriation; observations of alcoholics during the process of drinking in an experimental group setting. Am. J. Psychiat. 125: 886–899, 1969.

5. NATHAN, P. E., O'BRIEN, J. S. and NORTON, D. Comparative studies of the interpersonal and affective behavior of alcoholics and non-alcoholics during prolonged experimental drinking. Pp. 619–646. In: MELLO, N. K. and MENDELSON, J. H., eds. Recent advances in studies of alcoholism; an interdisciplinary symposium. Rockville, Md.; U.S. National Institute on Alcohol Abuse and Alcoholism; 1971.

6. STEINGLASS, P., WEINER, S. and MENDELSON, J. H. A systems approach to alcoholism. Archs Gen. Psychiat. 24: 401–408, 1971.

7. CHAFETZ, M. E. Fact and myth in alcoholism; a call for high-quality research. Ann. N.Y. Acad. Sci. 197: 8–10, 1972.

8. BATESON, G. The cybernetics of self; a theory of alcoholism. Psychiatry 34: 1–18, 1971.

9. MACANDREW, C. and EDGERTON, R. B. Drunken comportment; a social explanation. Chicago; Aldine; 1969.

10. HUNT, G. M. and AZRIN, N. H. A community-reinforcement approach to alcoholism. Behav. Res. Ther. 2: 91–104, 1973.

11. SOBELL, M. B., SCHAEFER, H. H. and MILLS, K. C. Differences in baseline drinking behavior between alcoholics and normal drinkers. Behav. Res. Ther. 10: 257–267, 1972.

12. SOBELL, M. B. and SOBELL, L. C. Individualized behavior therapy for alcoholics. Behav. Ther. 4: 49–72, 1973.

13. BIGELOW, G., COHEN, M., LIEBSON, I. A. and FAILLACE, L. A. Abstinence or moderation? Choice by alcoholics. Behav. Res. Ther. 10: 209–214, 1972.

14. COHEN, M., LIEBSON, I. A. and FAILLACE, L. A. The modification of drinking in chronic alcoholism. Pp. 745–766. In: MELLO, N. K. and MENDELSON, J. H., eds. Recent advances in studies of alcoholism; an interdisciplinary symposium. Rockville, Md.; U.S. National Institute on Alcohol Abuse and Alcoholism; 1971.

15. MILLER, P. M. The use of behavioral contracting in the treatment of alcoholism; a case report. Behav. Res. Ther. 3: 593–596, 1972.

17

The Alcoholic Symptom and its Therapeutic Relevance[1]

Morris E. Chafetz, M.D.

MANY OF US approach the alcoholic symptom, the drinking behavior labeled as alcoholism, as self-destructive behavior which must be eliminated. Implicitly and explicitly we therapists confront the patient with the "knowledge" that alcohol will destroy him and his immediate society. We then ask him to give up his destructive behavior if he expects to be helped. To stop drinking is good. To continue drinking is bad. *Our* morality is beyond question. This approach may tell us more about the caregiver than about the patient. The caregivers, who tend to cling to their stereotyped formulations and perceptions of what an "alcoholic" is, try to motivate the patient to accept treatment modalities that appeal to them.

My experience suggests that this negative approach to the patient's use of alcohol implies a lack of understanding of the role of alcohol in the total functioning of an alcoholic.

All symptom formation is restitutive in nature. The limp, for example, is a natural attempt to compensate and protect an injured limb. The paranoid's symptom of believing that everyone is talking about him, among other things, protects him from his feelings of being alone and isolated. Any compensatory or restitutive phenomenon must have a positive implication for the intrapersonal life of the individual. I do not wish to raise the question of whether alcoholism represents "disease" or "symptom." However, unless we regard alcoholism as willful behavior, we must accept the implication

[1]Reprinted by permission from the QUARTERLY JOURNAL OF STUDIES ON ALCOHOL, Vol. 31, pp. 444–445, 1970. Copyright by Journal of Studies on Alcohol, Inc., New Brunswick, New Jersey 08903.

that alcohol serves a positive intrapersonal function for the afflicted person. This holds true despite abundant external evidence of the destructive nature of certain kinds of alcohol use. It is clear that symptoms, although they serve compensatory and restitutive functions, may cause greater harm and injury than the original cause; e.g., the limp which protects a torn muscle may cause permanent fixation of a disused joint.

The position that the excessive use of alcohol is a restitutive symptom, and serves a positive function for the patient, requires us to adapt our therapeutic approach accordingly, regardless of specific treatment modalities. Most of us know that an alcohol problem is a symptom to be contended with; a negative approach, however, implies criticism and a lack of understanding of the individual in need of help. If the use of alcohol is serving a positive function in the patient's attempts to maintain his equilibrium and homeostasis, then it is unrealistic and even unfair to expect him to give up his alcoholic symptom unless meaningful substitutes can be found. The possible substitutes are endless; but what may serve for one person may be unsatisfactory for another. Therefore, attempts at removing the alcoholic symptom must be individualized. For one person, medication may suffice. Another may need a success, a relationship, a supportive group, an interest or a growth experience as in psychotherapy.

With my patients, I have explicitly discussed the positive nature of alcohol in their lives, as well as its destructive implications. I have also told them that if they could give it up, they would not need me. But I point out that alcohol is quicker and better for yielding immediate temporary relief to their hurt than any immediate therapeutic measures I can provide. I offer them a relationship with a caregiver who will see them whether or not the drinking is interrupted, and I enlist their alliance against the antitherapeutic implications of the use of alcohol. Often this is a most satisfactory clinical approach, but at times the needs of patients are such that other measures are necessary. The important point for the caregiver is that if the patient cannot lose his alcoholic symptom, the caregiver is not providing a substitute for the alcohol sufficient to enable the person to maintain his equilibrium without it. The caregiver together with the patient must then search for other substitutive means. With such an approach, both therapist and patient acknowledge the positive value of alcohol, minimize the moralistic, harsh, negating aspects of alcohol use, and together seek other positive balancing inputs which are ultimately less destructive to person and society alike.

Successful treatment of alcoholism may be defined, therefore, as the substitution for alcohol of some other form of response, hopefully less socially destructive, which allows the patient to maintain equilibrium and to begin to grow.

18

The Sick Role, Labeling Theory and the Deviant Drinker[1]

Paul M. Roman, Ph.D. and H. M. Trice, Ph.D.

MUCH EFFORT in recent years has been directed toward educating the public in the United States regarding the definition of alcoholism and deviant drinking as medical problems rather than as criminal offenses (1, 2). These efforts are reflected in the various publications of the Rutgers (formerly Yale) Center of Alcohol Studies, the U.S. Public Health Service and the National Council on Alcoholism. Likewise, as the therapeutic effectiveness of Alcoholics Anonymous has become increasingly visible, the public has become aware of the assumption that is held by this organization that a form of physiological allergy leads to alcoholism. The A.A. concept is somewhat different from the traditional medical model, but the two conceptions share a strong tendency to reduce individual responsibility for the genesis of alcoholism.

The effects of this redefinition have been regarded as positive by most, the most prominent impact being that alcoholics are committed to hospitals for treatment rather than being detained in prisons (3). Medical treatment is the natural corollary of the medical model and is aimed toward "recovery" rather than toward the "character reform" goal of incarceration. In any event, medical treatment is regarded as a more humane reaction to a form of behavior that may not be inherently antisocial or criminal.

However, the disease or medical model conception of alcoholism and deviant drinking is not without its adverse consequences. The concerns of this paper are (a) the possible social–psychological con-

[1]Reprinted by permission from the *International Journal of Social Psychiatry*, Vol. 14, pp. 245-251, 1968. Copyright by The Avenue Publishing Co., London NWII 7SJ.

sequences of the use of the medical model and (b) the development of a scheme of preventive intervention which is based on the knowledge of these consequences. Lest there be a misunderstanding about the position taken here, we emphasize at the outset that the disease concept of alcoholism is not being repudiated. Research has definitively shown that the chronic intake of large amounts of alcohol may have pathological effects on the human organism; likewise, the pattern of physiological addiction which develops at the later stages of the alcoholism syndrome may be viewed in itself as a major symptom of disease. Thus, chronic abuse of alcohol may have as one of its consequences organic illness. However, being sociopsychological in orientation, the primary concerns of this paper are the nature and consequences of the social labeling process rather than the nature and consequences of the alcohol ingestion processes.

The basic contention of this paper is that the medico-disease concept of alcoholism and deviant drinking has led to the assignment of the labeling function to medical authorities which in turn has led to the placement of alcoholics and deviant drinkers in "sick roles" (6; 7, *pp. 428–479*; 8). The expectations surrounding these sick roles serve to develop further, legitimize and in some cases even perpetuate the abnormal use of alcohol.

There are two basic mechanisms operating through the medical labeling process, which is based on the disease model of deviant drinking, that may serve to reinforce deviant drinking behavior. The first mechanism is assignment to the sick role, this being the consequence of being labeled by a physician as manifesting illness. The sick role assignment may legitimize deviant drinking patterns since these patterns have been labeled results of pathology rather than as inappropriate behavior. This is due to the fact that one of the main characteristics of the sick role is that the individual is not held responsible for his illness; thus, in this case the illness is abnormal drinking behavior and assignment to the sick role removes the individual's responsibility for engaging in this behavior. In his discussion of the relation between temperance movements and the different labels applied to drinking, Gusfield points out that the sick role "renders the behavior of the deviant indifferent to the status of norms enforcing abstinence" (3). This "indifference" likewise applies to the norms calling for "normal" drinking behavior.

There appears to be a significant parallel between the development of the disease model of deviant drinking and the disease model of hysteria, the latter having developed during the 19th century as an early step in a significant expansion of the aegis of psychiatry and medicine. Szasz (9) points out that, previous to the labeling of hysteria as a legitimate disease, such behavior was regarded as malingering and was met with social sanctions, the most prominent of which was the physician's refusal to pay any heed to such a patient (10). The "recognition" of hysteria as a "mental disease" changed this picture considerably; unfortunately we have no epidemiological data to indicate historical trends in the comparative incidence of malingering and hysteria, the implication being that the "legitimization" of malingering through labeling it a "real" disease may have led to more people "choosing" this behavioral alternative. The relativity of definitions of deviant and sick behavior to various sociocultural and historical conditions is borne out by the growing literature in transcultural psychiatry which focuses upon epidemiological variations (11). These data likewise augur against the location of explicit genetic or biochemical factors to explain the development of types of disordered behavior which are subject to discrete societal reactions and definitions.

The second mechanism operating through the disease model which may serve to reinforce deviant drinking behavior is that the labeling process may lead to secondary deviance through a change in an individual's self-concept as well as a change in the image or social definition of him by the significant others in his social life space (12–18). The individual with a medical diagnosis of alcoholic or deviant drinker occupies a social status which has accompanying role expectations, the principal expectation being engagement in deviant drinking practices. This is illustrated by the fact that we are not surprised to see a drunk alcoholic and we marvel when we see a sober one. Another sociological fact which helps explain the efficacy of the labeling process is that it is executed by the physician, who is a highly respected societal functionary whose authority is rarely questioned. The end result of the labeling process is a structure of role expectations and a set of self-concept changes that eventuate in the individual's performance of the deviant role. The behavior which is assigned is carried out.

A curious "double-bind" results from the dual operation of these mechanisms (5). Deviant drinking behavior is legitimized through the disease label in the sense that the individual is no longer held responsible for this behavior and this behavior is very rewarding to him. He is also assigned a social role which invidiously surrounds him with expectations for deviance as well as resulting in changes in his self-concept. Simultaneously he is expected by significant others in his life space to "shape up," seek treatment and, above all, stop drinking. Both this message and the message of his being "sick" appear legitimate but are contradictory. This double-bind may be an invidious cause of his mobility and differential association with those like himself, these behaviors representing the "escape from the field" that is postulated as a solution to a double-binding situation (5). This double-bind is very reflective of society's ambivalence toward the labeled alcoholic, a sort of half-acceptance of the sick role notion of problem drinking as well as half-acceptance of the criminal, immoral or "enemy" label of this behavior (3).

There are two other possible consequences of labeling which may occur and serve to further "lock in" deviant drinking patterns. First is the process of rejecting the individual from primary group associations that may result from the presence of the label as well as from intolerance of his deviant drinking. The developing alcoholic seeks out opportunities to affiliate with more tolerant drinking groups (2, 4, 11, 19, 20). The self-concept or personal identification changes that have resulted from labeling may also tend to lead the individual to primary groups composed of other deviant drinkers and alcoholics. This differential association serves to further legitimize, reinforce and perpetuate deviant drinking and leads further toward true addiction.

A second consequence of labeling may be the functional integration of the labeled individual into social groups which are composed primarily of nondeviants (21). There is a growing amount of research evidence which indicates that certain potentially unstable social groups, such as potentially unstable families or informal friendship groups, may be stabilized by the presence of a deviant member (10, 22–25). It is possible for the group to do its own labeling of a selected deviant, but labeling will be much more effective if executed by an outsider who has the institutionalized assignment to label and whose authority is not questioned. The presence of a formally and officially labeled deviant assures that it is not necessary to "pass the deviance around" among the members in order to hold the group together. The functions served by the deviant's presence include (1) the definition of other group members as "normal" because they do not share the deviant's symptoms or his label, (2) the presence of a submissive and relatively helpless target for scapegoating, which in turn allows for displacement of inter-member tensions onto the weak, deviant member and thereby reduces cross-cutting interpersonal conflicts which would weaken the organization of the group and (3) the presence of a rule breaker may offer the group a ready excuse for its shortcomings in goal attainment activities. These functions serve to lock the deviant member's role behavior into the group's patterns to the extent that his behavior is invidiously rewarded and attempts by outsiders to change his behavior are strongly resisted.

The basic point we are attempting to make is that the mere processes of labeling and sick role assignment may serve to aggravate and perpetuate a condition which is initially under the individual's control. In other words, the disease label has disease consequences. We are not arguing that chronic alcoholism is simply behavioral deviance; protracted heavy drinking with its physiological, psychological and sociological accompaniments has disease consequences in terms of physiological damage as well as in terms of physiological and psychological addiction. The point is that the use of the medical model conception of deviant drinking leads to processes of labeling and sick role assignment at a point previous to true addiction. In other words, something is called a disease or a disorder before it has actually become such. In most cases the behavior may still be under individual control at the time when labeling occurs. Labeling and the disease model do not allow for this fact, and may serve to "lock" the deviant drinker into a nexus of role expectations as well as changing his self-concept. The performance of this role coupled with the self-reaction to this self-image sets up a system of cybernetic action and reaction which may lead in many cases to true alcohol addiction.

Having developed the theoretical dimensions of the outcomes of labeling deviant drinking behavior, let us turn to an example of how these processes work. This example also sets the stage for applying knowledge of the impact of labeling to the development or revision of programs designed to identify and treat "alcoholics" in various stages of development.

We are acquainted with certain procedures of medical referral in work organizations which may serve to "lock in" the deviant role assignment (26). Early identification of the deviant drinker is stressed, and the immediate step following identification is referral to the medical department—in other words, labeling. We would argue that mere referral to a physician is a form of labeling, in terms of changing the individual's self-concept by telling him that he "needs professional help" and in terms of changing the role expectations held toward him by those who referred him. Thus, even if the physician does not formally label him as an alcoholic, he and those in his social milieu are "told" that his drinking has led him to require medical attention. In any event, it appears that in sociological terms the stage is set for progression toward true addiction in the sense of sick role occupancy and role expectations which may lead to secondary deviance.

Obviously the labeling of every early stage deviant drinker by a medical authority does not ultimately lead to alcohol addiction. Affiliation with A.A., various therapeutic interventions or simple response to the pressures to cease deviant drinking which are brought to bear by "significant others" may result in the termination of the progression. However, labeling and sick role assignment processes may create unnecessary risks for the individual whose drinking problem has not yet gone beyond his personal control. It is argued that the labeling and sick role assignment create actual pressures toward alcohol addiction rather than halting the progression.

In the light of this conceptual scheme, an attempt has been made to develop a model of intervention in which the risk-laden use of the alcoholic or deviant drinker label is avoided as much as possible. In light of knowledge that the early stage alcoholic or deviant drinker is unable or extremely reluctant to recognize his difficulties and do something about them, we have asked the question of what societal system possesses the institutionalized authority to bring effective pressure to bear upon him. The answer appears to be that this legitimate authority is possessed by the employer. The job is essentially an exchange relationship whereby rewards are given for a certain kind of performance. If the performance is inappropriate or inadequate, rewards may be legitimately withdrawn. This scheme of intervention is built on the assumption that the individual cannot perform a role in the work place adequately if he is impaired, and the consumption of alcohol or the presence of a hangover is defined as impairment. There is no evidence to indicate that alcohol consumption improves over-all job performance (with the possible exception of a few job roles in the arts). There is an impairment in performance brought about by alcohol consumption, whether the individual has a bottle of beer or a quart of whisky.

For the want of a better term, the intervention is labeled "constructive coercion." Constructive coercion is the confrontation of any employee who shows evidence of drinking on the job or who comes to work with a hangover. This is not only the early identification of alcoholics, but also covers much broader groups. It is the "early, early" identification of problem drinkers. It is total intolerance of drinking or hangovers when the individual is to be performing his work role. The early stage alcoholic is included under this umbrella, as well as those whose drinking may never eventuate into a problem.

The confrontation of the employee who allows alcohol to enter in any way into his work role involves a simple statement that repetition of this act will lead to termination. There is no referral to a medical department or introduction into therapy because such referrals are not necessary if confrontation occurs at this point. This approach is similar to the "no tolerance for drinking" policy employed in Czechoslovakian work organizations described by Chafetz (27).

It should be stressed that this is not a policy where an individual is confronted after alcohol interferes with his work performance; rather, the simple presence of alcohol in the form of drinking on the job or hangover is regarded inherently as impairment of performance. The hard-line norm against the interference of alcohol with job performance must be universalistic if it is to have potency. If it is universalistic, a company policy will encounter fewer difficulties and will be less often accused of inequity. The arbitrary decision of "how much" drinking actually interferes with job performance seems to offer many difficulties, particularly in training of first-line supervisors about when it is appropriate to "confront" an employee who is a problem drinker. Likewise the notion that certain jobs are more or less compatible with the effects of alcohol ingestion seems to lead in the same direction of arbitrary decisions, foggy policies and the risk of inequity.

It should also be pointed out that the "hard-line" approach, in which the individual is held responsible for his behavior rather than being allowed to enter the sick role and the nurturance of a doctor–patient relationship, does not tap into the psychic dependency of the deviant drinker. In other words, since psychological dependency has been found to be associated with the personalities of alcoholics, it may be argued that a tendency toward irresponsibility both precedes and accompanies alcoholic development (11). A focus on individual responsibility for deviant behavior runs contrary to this propensity, and constructive coercion may in this sense help to "break up" the progression toward addiction.

Several intervening factors which may temper the success of constructive coercion should be mentioned. First, it is assumed that the job role is the essential nexus of the individual's status set, particularly his status of breadwinner in the family. If he does not have such obligations or is not responsive to such obligations, the effectiveness of constructive coercion may be reduced. This factor may also reduce the potential effectiveness of constructive coercion with female problem drinkers who are not employed or whose employment role is not considered financially essential to the family.

Second, it is assumed that the individual has an investment in his job to the extent that quitting and obtaining other employment is too costly for him in terms of time, training, security and the personal benefits accompanying his present position. Employees who view quitting and obtaining a new job as a worthwhile investment in order to maintain their deviant drinking may well react in this way to the threat contained within the strategy of constructive coercion.

Third, the visibility of employee behavior to the supervisor is assumed in this scheme. Those who go unsupervised for long periods of time may move too far along the alcoholic progression before they come to supervisory attention to be effectively helped by constructive coercion. This is particularly true of occupations which require extensive traveling.

Fourth, it is assumed that there will be individuals in supervisory positions in the organizational hierarchy with adequate power and authority to carry out constructive coercion. The technique may not be effective for those in executive positions or for those in staff positions where lines of authority are unclear. This same problem may occur in small organizations which lack well-defined status hierarchies. Likewise, constructive coercion is not relevant for the self-employed.

Finally, it is assumed that the process will not be disrupted by the employee's total and effective denial of the existence of a deviant drinking pattern. This may present difficulties, particularly in light of anecdotal evidence of the manipulative skills of developing alcoholics.

A final word should be added regarding the relevance of this paper to current programs on the identification and treatment of problem drinking which are in operation or in the process of development in work organizations. These statements should not be interpreted as allegations that these programs are creating more problem drinkers than they are helping. Rather, the programs on the whole operate within a paradigm of problem drinking as a disorder or a disease, which is the rationale for certain characteristics of the programs (28). The purpose of this paper is to offer a supplemental paradigm for the disease model such that the disease label is not applied before the disease has developed.

It is recognized that there may be many instances in which the alcoholism progression moves beyond the point where medical assistance is unnecessary. However, in these cases the assumptions underlying the constructive coercion strategy are not irrelevant, for a policy of emphasizing individual responsibility for deviance will reduce the degree to which the individual is formally placed in the status of an "outsider" and thereby increase rehabilitation opportunities.

In summary, we have argued that the disease model of alcoholism and problem drinking has resulted in a labeling process that may in itself set the stage for the development of true alcohol addiction. We regard it as a risk factor possibly contributing to eventual addiction rather than as a sufficient condition for addiction. Through the examination of the social role dimensions of alcoholism and problem drinking, we have presented a tentative model of preventive intervention in which the label of disease or disorder is applied more cautiously.

REFERENCES

1. JELLINEK, E. M. The disease concept of alcoholism. Highland Park, N.J.; Hillhouse Press; 1960.
2. SUTHERLAND, E. Collected papers. Bloomington; Indiana University Press; 1956.
3. GUSFIELD, J. Moral passage; the symbolic process in public designations of deviance. Soc. Probl. 15: 175–188, 1967.
4. BACON, S. D. Alcoholics do not drink. Ann. Am. Acad. Pol. Soc. Sci. 315: 55–64, 1958.
5. BATESON, G., JACKSON, D. D., HALEY, J. and WEAKLAND, J. Toward a theory of schizophrenia. Behavl Sci. 1: 251–264, 1956.
6. GORDON, G. Role theory and illness. New Haven, Conn.; College & University Press; 1966.
7. PARSONS, T. The social system. Glencoe, Ill.; Free Press; 1951.
8. PARSONS, T. and FOX, R. Illness, therapy and the modern American family. J. Social Issues 8: 31–44, 1952.
9. SZASZ, T. S. The myth of mental illness; foundations of a theory of personal conduct. New York; Hoeber–Harper; 1961.
10. SONNE, J. C., SPECK, R. V. and JUNGREIS, J. E. The absent-member maneuver as a resistance in family therapy of schizophrenia. Fam. Process, Balt. 1: 44–62, 1962.
11. TRICE, H. M. Alcoholics Anonymous. Ann. Am. Acad. Pol. Soc. Sci. 315: 108–116, 1958.
12. BECKER, H. S. Outsiders; studies in the sociology of deviance. New York; Free Press; 1963.
13. ERIKSON, K. T. Notes on the sociology of deviance. Soc. Probl. 9: 307–314, 1962.
14. ERIKSON, K. T. Wayward puritans; a study in the sociology of deviance. New York; Wiley; 1966.
15. KITSUSE, J. Societal reaction to deviant behavior. Soc. Probl. 9: 247–256, 1962.

16. LEMERT, E. M. Social pathology; a systematic approach to the theory of sociopathic behavior. New York; McGraw–Hill; 1951.
17. LEMERT, E. M. The concept of secondary deviation. In: LEMERT, E. M., ed. Human deviance; social problems and social control. Englewood Cliffs, N.J.; Prentice–Hall; 1967.
18. SCHEFF, T. J. Being mentally ill. Chicago; Aldine; 1966.
19. CLINARD, M. B. The public drinking house and society. Pp. 270–292. In: PITTMAN, D. and SNYDER, C., eds. Society, culture and drinking patterns. New York; Wiley; 1962.
20. PHILLIPS, D. L. Rejection; a possible consequence of seeking help for mental disorders. Am. Sociol. Rev. 28: 963–972, 1963.
21. DENTLER, R. and ERIKSON, K. T. The functions of deviance in groups. Soc. Probl. 7: 98–107, 1959.
22. PAUL, N. L. and GROSSER, G. K. Family resistance to change in schizophrenia. Fam. Process, Balt. 3: 377–401, 1964.
23. RYCKOFF, I., DAY, J. and WYNNE, L. C. Maintenance of stereotyped roles in families of schizophrenics. Archs Gen. Psychiat. 1: 93–98, 1959.
24. VOGEL, E. F. and BELL, N. W. The emotionally disturbed child as family scapegoat. In: BELL, N. W. and VOGEL, E. F., eds. The family. Glencoe, Ill.; Free Press; 1960.
25. WYNNE, L. C., RYCKOFF, I. M., DAY, J. and HIRSCH, S. I. Pseudo-mutuality in the family relations of schizophrenics. Psychiatry 21: 205–220, 1958.
26. FRANCO, S. C. Problem drinking in industry; review of a company program. Ind. Med. Surg. 26: 221–228, 1957.
27. CHAFETZ, M. E. Alcoholism problems and programs in Czechoslovakia, Poland and the Soviet Union. N. Engl. J. Med. 265: 68–74, 1961.
28. KUHN, T. S. The structure of scientific revolutions. Chicago; University of Chicago Press; 1962.

19

Drinking Behavior and "Alcoholism"[1]

William P. Rohan, Ph.D.

"IT would therefore seem more realistic to think of drinking by alcoholics . . . as learned behavior rather than a medical illness" (1, *p. 508*). Regardless of which theoretical position is favored, this statement by Hershon emphasizes essential differences in current explanations of harmful drinking. Because of such differences, theories advanced so far can reasonably be considered only tentative, but it is useful to try to understand how such diverse explanations can exist for the same problem. A closer look at some of the current concepts relating to the harmful use of alcohol could clarify and perhaps resolve some explanatory conflicts.

One source of conceptual differences appears to be a failure to be·directly concerned with an obvious component of alcohol problems, namely the act of drinking itself. There is a tendency to dismiss the act of drinking as a superficial symptom or sign of an underlying condition. The observed behavior is thought to be caused by a more important internal disposition beyond what is seen. Consequently we fail to observe and measure drinking carefully while readily endorsing assumptions about internal regulatory mechanisms of a physiological or intrapsychic nature. Although the harmful use of alcohol may be related to these factors, overlooking drinking itself is ignoring the obvious. This oversight is a critical source of the confusion and ambiguity in the field of alcohol problems. Looking beyond the behavior for internal causes is related to a form of prescientific thinking which locates forces inside the observed moving objects without specifying what is actually observed.

[1] Reprinted by permission from the JOURNAL OF STUDIES ON ALCOHOL, Vol. 36, pp. 908–916, 1975. Copyright by Journal of Studies on Alcohol, Inc., New Brunswick, New Jersey 08903.

The semanticist Pemberton (2) has proposed that the idea of some internal thing causing drinking problems represents prescientific thinking. It would be beneficial to return to what should be considered a first step in a scientific account of problem drinking which is the careful assessment of a necessary antecedent, drinking behavior itself. The raison d'être of alcohol-related research, treatment and theory is ingestion behavior which eventuates in harm from alcohol.

The concern for underlying causes of drinking rather than for characteristics of drinking behavior is reflected in the language used to refer to alcohol problems. The term "alcoholism" connotes a special internal disposition to account for persistent drinking associated with physical and social harm. Although its exact nature is unspecified, it allegedly acts as a governing source of drinking behavior. When someone ingests the contents of a container of an alcoholic beverage frequently enough to generate severe problems, it is interpreted as a sign of this special inner process. The "alcoholism," or internal impetus to drinking, not the frequent and heavy drinking, is seen as the critical problem.

The frequent excessive drinker becomes more or less a victim of this internal force "alcoholism." In contemporary thinking this labeled disposition is embedded in a theoretical model which relates it to disease. Such an explanation minimizes the responsibility of the agent for the observed behavior by supposing it operates outside the control of the individual. An internal impairment suspends the agent's ordinary instigation of behavior or his freedom to perform or not to perform an act. Since there is interest in removing moralistic interpretations from harmful drinking, the concept of aberrant inner impetus is further reinforced by being consistent with the notion of disease, although this conclusion can be considered premature.

It is natural to search for basic causes to determine why a person would drink in a harmful way but this question directs attention away from *how* a person drinks. The "why" question inspires concern with underlying causes instead of fostering a careful study of drinking as it actually occurs. What is needed is a detailed analysis of the problematical behavior. Drinking is an observable act which, like any behavior, can be described and measured. This involves a description of drinking behavior in terms of frequency and magnitude over time, yielding information about specific characteristics of drinking patterns. Such a description would help clarify whether or not actual drinking patterns conform to preconceived notions concerning "alcoholism." The approach requires an appreciation of drinking as an act to be studied in its own right.

At the present time we have many explanations as to causes or whys of "alcoholism" but few clear descriptions of consumption patterns and how they change in individuals and groups.

The "why" of harmful drinking may become a less important question if ingestion patterns can be described and related to situations which increase or decrease consumption. A full description would not only include the frequency and magnitude of drinking over time, but also the circumstances in which drinking occurs. This should precede any theoretical formulations about causes, simply because it is easier to explain what has been clearly described.

It may seem simplistic to be concerned with rates of intake and perhaps that is why they have not been considered of critical importance. It seems more profound to be concerned with complex biochemical variables or intrapsychic events which allegedly have causal properties. It is obvious that some people drink a lot and to know exactly how much over time under what circumstances adds little to our explanations of a serious problem. But unless we understand drinking as a measurable act we will be forever enmeshed in the theoretical dead end of "alcoholism." "Alcoholism" is a fat and lazy term (3) which tries to be a substitute for accurate descriptions of varied drinking histories. Damaged drinkers are segregated into a single class even though their drinking histories and the effects of their drinking may differ considerably. Horn and Wanberg (4), for example, have found distinct drinking patterns among alcohol misusers. It is probable that the concept of "alcoholism" is an extreme simplification and that no common unitary element or elements can account for the various drinking patterns which develop. Verden and Shatterly (5) have stated that "the term 'alcoholism' is probably best described as *only* a term, one which describes behavior characterized by habitual uncontrolled drinking."

Recent evidence is beginning to question the usefulness and validity of the concept of "alcoholism." For example, many "alcoholics" can and do resume "normal drinking," but this has been difficult to accept because of a belief in some permanent internal impairment, which progresses irreversibly. As Knupfer (6) has indicated, there is a lot of evidence to substantiate Davies's assertion (7) that it is not only mild cases that can drink "normally," but that persons with histories of alcoholic psychoses have recovered and become "normal drinkers." Knupfer (6) points out that some problem drinkers abstain for a few years and then finally they can drink a little without losing control; others just cut down gradually as they get older or as their circumstances change.

Clark (8) and Fillmore (9) concluded from the results of follow-up studies that there is a large turnover in alcohol problems, both in terms of numbers and types of problems, occurring in respondents sampled over 4- to 20-year time spans. Many drinkers with numerous and severe problems are found to have gotten out of trouble when observed at a later time, or their problems have changed. Similar conclusions were made by Cahalan and Room (10) from their retrospective study of problem drinking.

Clark (8) suggests that "none of this fits with the disease model of alcoholism insofar as that model implies keeping 'early symptoms' and early problems and adding others as time passes." The progressiveness of the model is open to question. The apparent rapidity with which particular problems arise and subside suggests the possibility that situational factors may have a strong bearing on problem drinkers' behavior. "A more useful model of alcohol problems would place greater emphasis on the development and correlation of particular problems related to drinking, rather than assuming an underlying unitary phenomenon known as alcoholism" (8).

Ingestion rates and their changing patterns have not been studied thoroughly although Cahalan et al. (11) have reported some quantity relationships to personal and social variables. Rohan (12) reviewed the histories of problem drinkers and concluded that drinking patterns over time are relatively unpredictable, and rate of intake not only increases but often remains stable from year to year, and sometimes decreases. It is probable that many "alcoholics" periodically reduce their rate to a relatively harmless range. This is consistent with the idea that alcohol intake is more determined by life events and circumstances than by some internal factor.

The shift away from "alcoholism" to changing drinking patterns regulated by external circumstances is a refocus with many theoretical implications. This focus leads to the hypothesis that drinking is an active response to environmental conditions rather than the inexorable dictum of a progressive disease. Within this context, drinking would be understood as an aspect of the individual's effort to function or to deal actively with the contingencies of the environment. Increased ingestion rates signal a reduction of effective interaction between the individual and the environment. The persistence of inappropriate and harmful acts represents a breakdown in the organism's capacity to mediate selected effects within the provisions of the existing environment. This breakdown could be due to individual or environmental limitation. When an individual is unable to perform effective mediating behavior to reach preferred goals or resolve problems, a compromise behavior is performed. Drinking is a compromise behavior since it does not effectively alter the external environment in a favorable way, but it does alter the subjective relation of the individual to the environment. This compromise transaction can become a high proportion of total behavioral output, since it is usable for many types of problems, even the problems generated by drinking itself.

Horn and Wanberg (4) have proposed a functional explanation of problem drinking from data which appear to reflect "distinct patterns of development and reaction to ongoing events. That is, presumably excessive use of alcohol is part of a learned set of methods for dealing with the many problems of psychological and social adjustment and adaptation" (p. 634).

Although this emphasis on the importance of the behavior itself does not necessarily lead to the conclusion that drinking is a functional act, it is consistent with that possibility. The act of drinking warrants greater attention when the question of its functional aspects is considered. Treatment should be directed toward clarifying what drinking accomplishes for individuals within their life space. Pemberton (2) indicated "that only a small minority in the field are concerned with looking at drinking problems as failures in becoming effective, fully functioning humans" and that "a complete revolution in therapeutic and rehabilitative procedures would result, were this model basic to the thinking and behaving about these problems."

For a certain percentage of alcohol users, at various points in time and for different lengths of time, consumption rates can increase to a wide range of harmful levels. Like other acts, taking alcohol changes the relationship between the organism and the environment. Even though the act may be harmful or alien to the over-all welfare of the agent, it is not necessarily governed by a special disposition totally outside the usual origins of behavior. Excessive drinking is only one type of persistent maladaptive behavior that can be acquired in the course of development. The concept of "alcoholism" minimizes the role the agent plays and ignores the possibility that drinking, however faulty or harmful, is the agent's attempt to function within the circumstances of his environment. The view that ingestion rates are influenced by situational factors becomes more plausible in light of both experience and research.

which indicate that "alcoholics" manifest uncontrolled drinking in one environment and controlled in another. There are people who consume one or two quarts a day outside of a hospital but stop drinking when they enter a hospital setting even when it is possible to obtain alcohol.

Marlatt et al. (13) have shown that beverage consumption rates of "both normal drinkers and alcoholics" were largely determined by instructional set concerning the content of the beverage rather than the actual content. Gottheil et al. (14) found that some "alcoholics" drank in a controlled manner in a hospital experimental setting.

Information on drinking quantities seems particularly crucial in view of recent research which suggests that level of consumption is an important factor in determining the prevalence of alcohol problems (15).

The notion that harmful drinking reflects a disease process is already losing acceptance. Knox (16), for example, found in a survey of attitudes of U.S. Veterans Administration psychiatrists and psychologists that both groups rejected the disease concept in preference to characterizing alcohol misuse as a behavior problem. This emphasizes a shift from internal causes to the behavior itself. Davies (17), reporting to the first International Medical Conference on Alcoholism, recommended that reference to alcoholism as a disease should be dropped since it is misleading and often had the opposite to the desired effect. Jellinek (18) himself viewed alcohol dependence as a possible disease and he chose to say alcoholism is a disease for political reasons. Such politics prevent us from discarding preconceptions and from devising an alternative and more suitable frame of reference to account for drinking problems.

The thought processes involved in the formation of the concepts "alcoholism" and "alcoholic" are illogical and it is surprising that they have survived so well in our language. They involve transforming a descriptive label into an objective reality. By a process of circular reasoning, the term "alcoholism" is used to describe harmful drinking and then to explain it. Observed harmful drinking is labeled "alcoholism." Then harmful drinking is explained by saying a person drinks in a harmful way *because* he has "alcoholism."

The equivalent could be done to some other excessive behavior such as overeating. When the act becomes frequent enough to involve obvious negative consequence, the offending object, food, is changed into an abstract noun by adding -ism to it and the disease of foodism is invented for excessive eaters. When an explanation is sought for this negative behavior, excessive eating is said to be caused by "foodism." In this way we could also discover "cigarettism" and "moneyism."

Alcoholism has become an entity, a unitary force, an existing animism of some type which is classified as a condition or thing. Since this is now a part of our language–thought patterns, it is difficult to see that drinking is *what a person does* rather than *something a person has*. To describe drinking as an act which varies in frequency and magnitude depending on circumstances is a more subtle and less simplified concept.

All we know for sure is that some persons do harm to themselves and create problems for others by the way they drink. That drinking is a reflection of an internal regulating disease process is only one possible explanation, and I believe a misleading one. If drinking is viewed as an act, a different set of theoretical concepts will naturally evolve, which are less hypothetical and closer to observable events.

The positive effects of beginning to understand drinking as a measurable behavioral event are multiple. Not only is there less theoretical ambiguity, but research priorities are changing. The task will be to determine the antecedents of changes in consumption levels of alcohol and determine the social and physical consequences of various consumption levels. It is likely that alcohol users will not be classified into two categories of normal and abnormal drinkers but will be seen as located on a continuum of ingestion quantity, with negative effect being proportionate to patterns of ingestion levels (12, 19–21). Currently we select out some 5 to 10% of alcohol users who drink the most and do the most obvious harm, while not recognizing that many more people do harm by the way they drink, to a lesser degree. The essential differences between drinkers is quantitative rather than qualitative.

This conceptualization has implications for prevention. It is not necessary to wait until severe harm from alcohol use occurs so that it can be determined whether the person is "alcoholic" or not, since some degree of harm from drinking can occur at any point on the continuum beyond a minimum, safe limit. Corrective action can be taken when drinking begins to exceed the safe limit.

REFERENCES

1. HERSHON, H. I. Alcoholism, physical dependence and disease; comment on "The alcohologist's addiction." Q. J. Stud. Alcohol **34**: 506–508, 1973.
2. PEMBERTON, W. H. A semanticist looks at alcoholism programs. Pp. 30–32. In: U.S. CIVIL SERVICE COMMISSION. BUREAU OF RETIREMENT AND INSURANCE. The first step; a report of a conference on drinking problems. Washington, D.C.; U.S. Govt Print. Off.; 1967.
3. CHRISTIE, N. and BRUUN, K. Alcohol problems; the conceptual framework. Int. Congr. Alc. Alcsm, Proc. 28th, pp. 65–73, 1969.
4. HORN, J. L. and WANBERG, K. W. Dimensions of perception of background and current situation of alcoholic patients. Q. J. Stud. Alcohol **31**: 633–658, 1970.
5. VERDEN, P. and SHATTERLY, D. Alcoholism research and resistance to understanding the compulsive drinker. Ment. Hyg. **55**: 331–336, 1971.
6. KNUPFER, G. Ex-problem drinkers. Pp. 256–280. In: ROFF, M., ROBINS, L. and POLLACK, M., eds. Life history research in psychopathology. Vol. 2. Minneapolis; University of Minnesota Press; 1972.
7. DAVIES, D. L. Normal drinking in recovered alcohol addicts. Q. J. Stud. Alcohol **23**: 94–104, 1962.
8. CLARK, W. B. Distinction needed between alcoholism as disease and "problems." Fam. Practice News **4** (No. 2): 39, 1974.
9. FILLMORE, K. M. Drinking and problem drinking in early adulthood and middle age; an exploratory 20-year follow-up study. Q. J. Stud. Alcohol **35**: 819–840, 1974.
10. CAHALAN, D. and ROOM, R. Problem drinking among American men. (Rutgers Center of Alcohol Studies, Monogr. No. 7.) New Brunswick, N.J.; 1974.
11. CAHALAN, D., CISIN, I. H. and CROSSLEY, H. M. American drinking practices; a national study of drinking behavior and attitudes. (Rutgers Center of Alcohol Studies, Monogr. No. 6.) New Brunswick, N.J.; 1969.
12. ROHAN, W. P. Quantitative dimensions of alcohol use for hospitalized problem drinkers. Dis. Nerv. Syst. **37**: 154–159, 1976.
13. MARLATT, G. A., DEMMING, B. and REID, J. B. Loss of control drinking in alcoholics; an experimental analogue. J. Abnorm. Psychol. **81**: 233–241, 1973.
14. GOTTHEIL, E., CORBETT, L. O., GRASBERGER, J. C. and CORNELISON, F. S. Treating the alcoholic in the presence of alcohol. Am. J. Psychiat. **128**: 475–480, 1971.
15. DE LINT, J. and SCHMIDT, W. Consumption averages and alcoholism prevalence; a brief review of epidemiological investigations. Br. J. Addict. **66**: 97–107, 1971.
16. KNOX, W. J. Attitudes of psychiatrists and psychologists toward alcoholism. Am. J. Psychiat. **127**: 1675–1679, 1971.
17. DAVIES, D. L. "Alcoholism as disease" . . . should drop concept. The Journal, Toronto **2** (No. 11): 13, 1973.
18. JELLINEK, E. M. The disease concept of alcoholism. Highland Park, N.J.; Hillhouse; 1960.

19. DE LINT, J. and SCHMIDT, W. The distribution of alcohol consumption in Ontario. Q. J. Stud. Alcohol 29: 968–973, 1968.
20. HAYMAN, M. The myth of social drinking. Am. J. Psychiat. 124: 585–594, 1967.
21. HAYMAN, M. Warning! Social drinking may be hazardous to your health and welfare. Rep. Alc. 30 (No. 3): 3–22, 1972.

Part V

MENTAL HEALTH TREATMENT APPROACHES TO ALCOHOLISM

Psychotherapy for alcoholics and psychiatric patients has been an obvious interface between the two disorders, and psychotherapy for alcoholics, asserted Moore (1), is based on the assumption that alcoholism is a mental disorder. "Thus, we should expect psychological treatment to be effective," he added. "Unfortunately, we discover that the psychological approach is a difficult one, perhaps more difficult than with any other type of mental disturbance. Some cite this as proof that alcoholism is not a psychological disorder, and while this might be so, especially in some cases, it is a spurious reason for such a belief" (*p. 106*).

At any rate, many mental health specialists become involved in the treatment of alcoholics, and alcoholics have thus been accorded most of the treatment modalities which the mental health professions have to offer. These include—but are not limited to—individual and group psychotherapy, psychoanalysis, family therapy, chemotherapy, milieu therapy, case work, behavior modification, as well as hosts of more esoteric therapeutic approaches. Baekeland et al. (2) appraised alcoholism treatment methodologies, and Hamburg (3) reviewed broad-spectrum behavior therapies. Davidson's (4) finding of the lack of convincing theoretical underpinnings for aversive conditioning for alcoholics is, unfortunately, also applicable to a number of other therapeutic modalities. We need hypotheses for treatment; that a treatment "works" by itself is not enough. As new treatments come along for other, rather specific problems, they are quickly applied to alcoholism and they have varying degrees of success. A case in point is lithium therapy (5). Nevertheless, Moore (6) concluded that "psychotherapy remains the cornerstone of many programs" of alcoholism treatment.

While there may be so-called special treatment programs for alcoholics, these tend to be variations on a theme rather than special, in the sense of unique or innovative, therapies designed initially for persons with alcohol problems. This, it seems, is again a tacit classification of problem drinking as a variant of psychiatric disorder.

The situation is confused, however, with respect to hospital treatment of alcohol problems. Corrigan (7, *p. 3*) noted that "most general hospitals are unwilling to admit problem drinkers, even on an emergency basis, although they admit nonalcoholics with the same health or emotional problems." On the other hand, Seixas (8) applauded the fact that psychiatrists "have been the first to open the doors of their institutions to the alcoholic." However, the Cooperative Commission on the Study of Alcoholism (9) called attention to the fact that "relatively few problem drinkers receive treatment in special alcoholism hospitals or in private psychiatric hospitals," and recommended a more active role for community mental health programs in the provision of care and treatment for alcoholism problems. Of course, community-based programs are proliferating, taking the place of hospital treatment in all areas of mental health care.

Whether special alcoholism hospitals or treatment facilities are needed is a hotly debated issue. Opponents of such programs argue that alcoholism is an emotional problem meriting the same services as other similar problems. Hart (10) argued that separate treatment for alcoholics reinforced their resistance to treatment. Seixas (11) favored specialized rehabilitation units for alcoholics in hospitals rather than in nonmedical facilities. On the other hand, while acknowledging that there are many similarities between alcohol and drug addictions, Lief (12) advocated separate treatment for alcoholism. Huberty (13), too, recognized similarities between drug and alcohol addictions, but he also cited dissimilarities and implied that conjoint treatment approaches might be best.

Mental health workers are thus quite divided on whether there should be heterogeneous or homogeneous groups of patients in treatment. Homogeneous grouping is supported by the notion that patients with similar problems can understand, identify with and learn from each other. This understanding is seen as an asset in group therapy, in group living and in the "buddy system" employed in some hospitals and is basic to Alcoholics Anonymous. This argument is countered by those who say that alcoholics assembled together in a hospital ward might tend to reinforce each other's periodic inebriety. It has been argued that alcoholics, housed with other psychiatric patients, are threatened by the behavior disorders and the chronicity that they see and thus become pessimistic about their own futures. On the other hand, nonseparatists affirm that society is heterogeneous and that an alcoholic receives therapeutic benefit when he helps his less fortunate fellows. In some hospitals psychiatric patients are treated in the midst of medical patients because it is believed that such interpersonal exposure aids reentry to the community. Also, there has long been the proposition that segregation results in maladaptive elitist attitudes.

A key issue here is that patients should not be grouped on the basis of the diagnostic labels they carry but instead on the basis of what their needs are in the way of rehabilitation and treatment so that these therapies can be delivered to them more expeditiously by the institutional staff. At the heart of the matter, then, is whether we, in fact, have specific therapies for alcoholics, therapies which are different from those we deliver to other patients. Since there is such concern about segregation and integration of alcoholics, I am forced to the conclusion that milieu therapy (and the presence of other patients in the environment) probably is near the top of the list of available treatments, and this is hardly a treatment especially designed for alcoholics.

A survey by Ozarin and Taube (14) revealed that alcohol disorders were among the three leading diagnoses for inpatient admission to psychiatric facilities. That alcoholics have been welcomed in many psychiatric institutions may have proven a mixed blessing. On the one hand, hospitalization may have opened the sole therapeutic avenue for these patients. On the other, hospitalization has sometimes led to institutionalization in its most negative connotation. It is debatable whether a person with alcohol problems belongs in a mental hospital, and it is possible that, lacking a more appropriate environment, or a more appropriate one where such people are accepted, many mental hospitals have become a sort of repository for the unwanted. This represents an unfortunate interface; mental health professionals are made accountable for alcoholism treatment because most everyone else shuns the responsibility. Chafetz (15) has called this a "massive denial of responsibility." It becomes a sort of treatment by default, or bankruptcy. In this regard, while many have praised the decriminalization of alcoholism, Lew (16) questioned "the wisdom of destigmatizing a broad range of [alcoholismic] behaviors that frequently include abhorrent conduct only to impose the much more permanent and discouraging stigma of mental illness."

It is no wonder that the efficacy of mental health treatments for alcoholism often is questioned. To begin with, alcoholism tends to be chronic (17). Chafetz (18), advocating early diagnosis and treatment and criticizing the fact that alcoholism is treated mostly at advanced stages when symptomatology is fulminating, stated that the success rate for alcoholism treatment can be expected to be as poor as that for other chronic conditions. Evidence to contradict him has not been forthcoming, and the recidivism rate among alcoholics is notorious. If we had better biostatistical techniques for follow-up, we might see an even greater failure rate because it is difficult now to keep track of unsuccessfully treated alcoholics. Smart's (19) review found some evidence of spontaneous recovery in alcoholics who did not receive treatment, and in a 3-year study of untreated alcoholics, Imber et al. (20) failed to find "the commonly anticipated 'progressive' deterioration with alcoholism." Emrick (21) found that alcoholics treated by psychologically oriented approaches and untreated alcoholics did not differ in mean abstinence rates but that more of the former did improve. Improvement was defined in terms of reduction of drinking problems, not in terms of over-all emotional adjustment, a recommended criterion (22) with which I strongly concur. Finally, Bell (23) suggested that "one of the reasons that psychiatry has often failed is that the addiction did not originate in psychiatric illness."

There is also ambiguity about treatment goals, as, for instance, in the ongoing debate over abstinence versus controlled drinking. Increasingly, treatment planning is assuming importance in mental health care accreditation, in audits of services rendered and in utilization reviews. If the goals of treatment for alcoholism are uncertain, and they often are (24–26), then treatment management by objective is precluded. The *Second Special Report on Alcohol and Health* (27) noted that success in treatment of alcoholism is dependent on "recognizing suitable goals for special groups as well as for individual patients and applying the most appropriate modality to each." Kissin (28), too, made a distinction between core therapies and special therapies for alcoholics. A final word about treatment success is in order. To know anything about it, to be able to improve it, to say something worthwhile about it, all require program evaluation with suitable controls. Therefore, the model for alcoholism therapists should be that of the clinician–researcher.

The treatment interface is a crucial one. There has to be some clarification of what we are treating. Are we focusing on emitted behavior or on hypothesized personality structures? Are we treating the drinking or the person who does the drinking? In a broader view, are we treating the patient in the general context of his family and community? Such examples are simplistic but they illustrate the real schism between those who see alcoholism as a distinct and rather unitary disorder (which may or may not coexist with other psychiatric disorders) and those who view it as a symptom or manifestation of other problems. It is akin to the differences in philosophy and application between the behaviorally oriented therapist who treats a patient's phobias with systematic desensitization and the more dynamically oriented psychoanalyst who looks far beyond the presenting symptoms or complaints. That both represent mental health interfaces is beyond question. What is important is what underlies these mental health strategies—issues such as the notion of a basic personality structure, the appropriate goals of treatment, treatment attitudes toward recidivism and the revolving door, and criteria for determining significant therapeutic improvement.

An unusual treatment interface is the oft-mentioned proposition that recovered alcoholics are in the best position to understand and treat other alcoholics. This notion of "it takes one to know one," also prevalent in the field of drug addiction, is eschewed in the case of many other psychiatric disorders. It tends to implicate many of the negative treatment attitudes of mental health personnel which have confronted alcoholics for years. Thus, in contrast to interfaces which rest on the psychopathy presented by the alcoholic or on the pharmacodynamic aspects of the alcohol that he consumes, the treatment interface begins to focus on the therapist, his attitudes, his therapeutic armamentarium, etc. It also entails the whole area of evaluation of treatment efficacy and, in so doing, introduces issues about the goals of alcoholism treatment, controlled drinking and the need for follow-up data. The articles which follow present some of the thinking behind consideration of these topics. In their classic enumeration of some alcoholism treatment issues, Krystal and Moore (Chapter 20) debate the issue of who the therapist should be; the views of others involved in alcoholism treatment are also summarized. Kalb and Propper (Chapter 21) have updated some aspects of this question. Matkom (Chapter 22) and I (Chapter 23) have explored perspectives of hospital treatment for alcoholism, and Miller and Barlow (Chapter 24) have reviewed behavioral approaches, such as operant conditioning, in alcoholism treatment.

The treatment interface confronts a number of questions: Where should a person turn for assistance if he wants to do something about a drinking problem or what he thinks may become a drinking problem? Should he go to a hospital? Should he see his family doctor? Should he attend an A.A. meeting? Should he go to a mental hygiene clinic? Does he want to stop drinking, or does he want to be able to drink moderately without getting into trouble over his drinking? Does he complain about what alcohol is doing to him, physically, emotionally, socially, vocationally, or does he complain of other difficulties, depression and an anhedonic quality to his life from which he seeks escape via drinking? How much insight and self-awareness does he have?

That definitive answers to these queries are lacking should not be dismaying. The important goal now is to retain an open mind about alcoholism–mental health interfaces and to keep asking—and thinking about—the definitive questions. Woodruff et al. (29) did just this in comparing demographic, family history and other data on a group of patients who had sought psychiatric treatment for alcoholism with data on a group of alcoholic relatives who had not sought treatment. The two groups were similar except that the former presented more depressive symptomatology and were more likely to have a history of abnormal mental content. Questions which occur, then, are what the motivational properties of such syndromes might be and whether what the patients really sought help for was their alcoholism. One opinion has been expressed by Agrin (30): "We must recognize and reluctantly accept the fact that the alcoholic rarely wants help with anything except his drinking." If this is so, then what is the role of conjoint treatment for drinking and for emotional problems of adjustment?

The concept of motivation is important in the interplay between alcoholism and mental health. "Probably in no other illness is so much verbal concern manifested for the patient's motivation to recover as in alcoholism" (31). It is assumed that the patient has strong desires to alter his drinking behavior. If the patient does not, it is often said that it is the patient who has failed, not the treatment (32). This may be because alcoholics tend to be evaluated negatively, whether they are described as responsible for their behavior and recovery or as suffering from an illness (33).

Why does alcoholism so frequently appear to be chronic? Why do alcoholic patients often appear to undermine treatment efforts and sabotage therapy? One suggestion (34) was that the sick role might contain "an element of 'motivatedness' not merely in the etiology of the pathological condition [in this case, alcoholism], but also in the maintenance of it, a context which included resistance to therapeutic efforts on the part of various agencies." In this way, abstinence or remission might unconsciously threaten an alcoholic patient as antihomeostatic.

It is time to give more thought to the motivations of those who treat alcoholics—helpers, care givers and therapists, as they are variously referred to. Paradoxically, Clancy (35) began his essay on motivational conflicts of alcoholics with the statement: "The physician who tries to treat the alcoholic will at some time or other experience frustration and disappointment in his relationship with the patient." It seems that what was really being addressed was the therapist's motivation and negative reinforcement, an important consideration.

The fact that alcoholics are most often treated by mental health workers can be explained many ways. For instance, Washburn et al. (36), examining the biases and blind spots which determine decisions about psychiatric treatment settings, wrote that it had been "pointed out that a psychiatrist as a physician must act for the well-being of his patients, often in the face of ignorance about what the best course may be. . . . He may avoid awareness of that ignorance, as well as his sense of helplessness, by acting on a particular treatment hypothesis." Zwerling (37) wrote, "In response to the question of why I am in a community [mental health] program, I base my answer on an old prayer I used to chant on the eve of the Sabbath: 'If not I, then who; if not now, then when?' "

REFERENCES

1. MOORE, R. A. The problem of abstinence by the patient as a requisite for the psychotherapy of alcoholism. I. The need for abstinence by the alcoholic patient during treatment. Q. J. Stud. Alcohol 23: 105–111, 1962.
2. BAEKELAND, F., LUNDWALL, L. and KISSIN, B. Methods for the treatment of chronic alcoholism; a critical appraisal. Pp. 247–327. In: GIBBINS, R. J., ISRAEL, Y., KALANT, H., POPHAM, R. E., SCHMIDT, W. and SMART, R. G., eds. Recent advances in alcohol and drug problems. Vol. 2. New York; Wiley; 1975.
3. HAMBURG, S. Behavior therapy in alcoholism; a critical review of broad-spectrum approaches. J. Stud. Alcohol 36: 69–87, 1975.
4. DAVIDSON, W. S., 2d. Studies of aversive conditioning for alcoholics; a critical review of theory and research methodology. Psychol. Bull. 81: 571–581, 1974.
5. KLINE, N. S., WREN, J. C., COOPER, T. B., VARGA, E. and CANAL, O. Evaluation of lithium therapy in chronic and periodic alcoholism. Am. J. Med. Sci. 268: 15–22, 1974.
6. MOORE, R. A. Psychotherapeutics of alcoholism. Proc. 2d Annu. Alcsm Conf. NIAAA, pp. 222–233, 1973.
7. CORRIGAN, E. M. Problem drinkers seeking treatment. (Rutgers Center of Alcohol Studies Monogr. No. 8.) New Brunswick, N.J.; 1974.
8. SEIXAS, F. A. Preface. [Presented at the conference, "The person with alcoholism."] Ann. N.Y. Acad. Sci. 233: 5–12, 1974.

9. COOPERATIVE COMMISSION ON THE STUDY OF ALCOHOLISM. Alcohol problems; a report to the nation. (Prepared by PLAUT, T. F. A.) New York; Oxford University Press; 1967.

10. HART, W. T. The treatment of alcoholism in a comprehensive community mental health center. Am. J. Psychiat. 126: 1275–1281, 1970.

11. SEIXAS, F. A. Issues shared by alcoholism and other chronic diseases. J. Chron. Dis. 27: 503–505, 1974.

12. LIEF, V. F. Is alcoholism just another addiction? Drug Forum 4: 1–2, 1974.

13. HUBERTY, D. J. The addict and alcoholic in treatment; some comparisons. J. Drug Issues 3: 341–347, 1973.

14. OZARIN, L. D. and TAUBE, C. A. Psychiatric inpatients; who, where, and future. Am. J. Psychiat. 131: 98–101, 1974.

15. CHAFETZ, M. E. Alcoholism; alcoholism and health professionals. Psychiat. Ann. 6 (No. 3): 120–124, 1976.

16. LEW, D. Alcoholism as disease. J. Am. Med. Ass. 223: 800, 1973.

17. LEMERE, F. and SMITH, J. W. Medical models for understanding alcoholism. J. Am. Med. Ass. 226: 197–198, 1973.

18. CHAFETZ, M. E. Alcoholism prevention and reality. Q. J. Stud. Alcohol 28: 345–348, 1967.

19. SMART, R. G. Spontaneous recovery in alcoholics; a review and analysis of the available research. Drug. Alc. Depend. 1: 277–285, 1976.

20. IMBER, S., SCHULTZ, E., FUNDERBUNK, F., ALLEN, R. and FLAMER, R. The fate of the untreated alcoholic; toward a natural history of the disorder. J. Nerv. Ment. Dis. 162: 238–247, 1976.

21. EMRICK, C. D. A review of psychologically oriented treatment of alcoholism. II. The relative effectiveness of different treatment approaches and the effectiveness of treatment versus no treatment. J. Stud. Alcohol 36: 88–108, 1975.

22. HILL, M. J. and BLANE, H. T. Evaluation of psychotherapy with alcoholics; a critical review. Q. J. Stud. Alcohol 28: 76–104, 1967.

23. BELL, R. G. Who is qualified to treat the alcoholic? Comment on the Krystal–Moore discussion. Q. J. Stud. Alcohol 25: 562–568, 1964.

24. CRAWFORD, J. J. and CHALUPSKY, A. B. Evaluation strategies used in current alcoholism rehabilitation programs; problems and specifications for improvement. Proc. Am. Psychol. Ass. 81: 791–792, 1973.

25. FREED, E. X. Abstinence for alcoholics reconsidered. J. Alcsm 8: 106–110, 1973.

26. FREED, E. X. Treatment goals for alcoholics. J. Med. Soc. New Jers. 73: 611–613, 1976.

27. U.S. NATIONAL INSTITUTE ON ALCOHOL ABUSE AND ALCOHOLISM. Second Special Report to the U.S. Congress on Alcohol and Health. (DHEW Publ. No. ADM-75-212.) Washington, D.C.; U.S. Govt Print. Off.; 1975.

28. KISSIN, B. The use of psychoactive drugs in the long-term treatment of chronic alcoholics. Ann. N.Y. Acad. Sci. 252: 385–395, 1975.

29. WOODRUFF, R. A., JR., GUZE, S. B. and CLAYTON, P. J. Alcoholics who see a psychiatrist compared with those who do not. Q. J. Stud. Alcohol 34: 1162–1171, 1973.

30. AGRIN, A. Who is qualified to treat the alcoholic? Comment on the Krystal–Moore discussion. Q. J. Stud. Alcohol 25: 347–349, 1964.
31. STERNE, M. W. and PITTMAN, D. J. The concept of motivation; a source of institutional and professional blockage in the treatment of alcoholics. Q. J. Stud. Alcohol 26: 41–57, 1965.
32. MOORE, R. A. Alcoholism treatment in private psychiatric hospitals; a national survey. Q. J. Stud. Alcohol 32: 1083–1085, 1971.
33. RULE, B. G. and PHILLIPS, D. Responsibility versus illness models of alcoholism; effects on attitudes toward an alcoholic. Q. J. Stud. Alcohol 34: 489–495, 1973.
34. PARSONS, T. The sick role and the role of the physician reconsidered. Millbank Meml Fund Q. Bull. 53: 257–278, 1975.
35. CLANCY, J. Motivation conflicts of the alcohol addict. Q. J. Stud. Alcohol 25: 511–520, 1964.
36. WASHBURN, S. L., VANNICELLI, M. and SCHEFF, B. J. Irrational determinants of the place of psychiatric treatment. Hosp. Community Psychiat. 27: 179–182, 1976.
37. ZWERLING, I. The impact of the community mental health movement on psychiatric practice and training. Hosp. Community Psychiat. 27: 258–262, 1976.

20

Who is Qualified to Treat the Alcoholic?

A Discussion[1]

Henry Krystal, M.D. and Robert A. Moore, M.D.

I. INTRODUCTION

AMONG WORKERS in the field of the addictions, claims about "cures" mean different things, and treatment means many things to many people. It becomes important, though difficult, to question criteria of the qualifications required for the treatment of alcoholics. A variety of disciplines may have divergent views on this subject, and some workers in this field who are attracted to it by the need to handle their own addictive or religious problems complicate the situation. In order to highlight the problems involved, the authors of the following statements have tried to present two basic points of view which do not give all the answers but do pose a number of pertinent questions.

We feel that the problem of personnel is so basic that a failure to resolve it precludes effective action in the rehabilitation of alcoholics. Surprisingly, many state governments which sponsor alcoholism programs have failed to set up or even consider the minimum standards necessary for alcoholism clinic personnel. Neglecting to set up requirements for staff training would be unthinkable in the state's mental health programs. Paradoxically, many states have laws providing for the commitment and treatment of alcohol-addicted individuals in state hospitals for the mentally ill. Does this mean that alcoholism is or is not a mental illness? If the treatment of alcohol-

---

[1] Reprinted by permission from the QUARTERLY JOURNAL OF STUDIES ON ALCOHOL, Vol. 24, pp. 705–720, 1963. Copyright by Journal of Studies on Alcohol, Inc., New Brunswick, New Jersey 08903.

ism should be carried out by individuals trained differently from the staff operating the state's mental health programs, then the reasons for this should be studied, and the standards revised appropriately rather than left to chance. In order, then, to highlight these problems, the authors have tried to present a broad view of this question, hoping that this effort will be of help to those who have to ponder and decide who is able to treat the alcoholic with most help and least harm to himself and to his patient.

We should never assume that everything that is "treatment" is beneficial, even when it may produce abstinence. Not so long ago, parents, doctors and educators, following their own aversion to masturbation, managed to rationalize their need to punish the self-indulging child by imposing on him a variety of punishments—shackles, harnesses or other persecutions, or even circumcision. All these were successful in terminating masturbation but produced for those children a variety of problems from which they still suffer. Indeed, it may be true that the greatest evils are perpetrated in the name of goodness or help. Therefore, let us momentarily suspend our preconceived notions, and consider two opposing views on what it takes to provide help for alcoholic patients—safely and effectively.

II. ADVANTAGES OF THE PROFESSIONAL PSYCHOTHERAPIST

Henry Krystal

The problems of addictions are so complex that often a variety of disciplines become involved in the treatment of the patient. The physical and neurological complications of alcoholism, for instance, bring the patient to the physician's office. While the physician is qualified to care for these aspects of alcoholism, he may be totally unprepared and unable to deal with other aspects of it. Despite our current knowledge, however, some patients suffering from a variety of problems are cared for by particular disciplines mainly because they are linked traditionally to the problem at hand. For instance, tradition, rather than our best knowledge of the problem, determines that in the Armed Forces homosexuality may be handled by police and military courts as a crime. Thus history, rather than therapeutic indications, often decides who shall care for a given problem. For this reason it becomes imperative periodically to review our best and most up-to-date knowledge of as complex a syndrome as alcoholism and reconsider the question of the qualifications of the therapist which may be conducive to the best care of the patient.

In alcoholism, as in many other fields, medicine is slow to provide total care for the patient until a specific cure for the disease is available. In contrast, religion has a universal healing principle and a capability of giving comfort to believers, no matter what the nature of their problems. A clergyman is hard put to select the people to work with, either by the nature of their problems or his knowledge of them. Thus certain groups of professions or people with certain social activities will move in to fill the voids in the help available, providing solace where we cannot offer a cure.

The question of the qualification of the therapist must fall back on the nature of the problem of the patient to be treated. If alcoholism turns out to be an allergic disease, the allergist will become the best qualified person to treat the alcoholic. If it should be proven that nutritional deficiencies are really of importance in the etiology of alcoholism, then the specialist in internal medicine would be best qualified to handle these cases to the extent that he is proficient in the management of malnutrition.

At the present time, the consensus is that the basic problem underlying the addiction to alcohol or other drugs is an emotional one. The nature of it, however, is not a simple matter. Alcoholics do not share the same emotional problems—only the same way of dealing with their problems, namely, by self-medication with ethyl alcohol. Thus many of the symptoms of alcoholism represent either the failure of alcohol to provide relief, or the vicissitudes of its effect on the patient under the pressure of his problem. On the whole, we never see or deal with the "successful" alcoholic, that is, a member of the world's largest fraternity of people who manage their lives successfully with the regular or occasional use of alcohol for whatever ails them.

Experience over the years has shown that all types of problems and all combinations of nosological entities have been manifest and are of causal importance in the addictions (1). Glover (2), considering the rituals and obsessive–compulsive aspects of addiction, pointed out that their root lies in "both the neurotic and the psychotic system." He went on to describe how in the patient's relation to the drug, one observes paranoid anxieties, against which the compulsive use of the drug, as well as its ritual consumption, provides a protection. He stressed the orality of the underlying impulses, their cannibalistic nature, and finally the resulting anxiety and guilt, producing later a depressive state. He also described the almost manifest relation between the addiction and the homosexual impulse. Observations by Weijl (3) and others (4–7) demonstrate the variety and complexity of emotional problems found in alcohol-addicted people. Weijl contributed to our knowledge of the alcoholic by his emphasis on and explanation of the varieties of neurotic anxieties manifest in some alcoholic patients: those related to week-end drinking in response to the reinforcement of repressed impulses either to the indulgence of passivity and sexuality, or to aggression toward family members. Thus alcohol becomes the protector of family living, as it has been, perhaps, over the ages, the original tranquilizer, and a major force enabling mankind to harness its instincts constructively and live together in building a civilized society.

Clinical evidence accumulated over the last 70 years indicates that the emotional problems observed in patients addicted to self-medication with alcohol have ranged in degree of impairment of the ego function of reality testing from complete contact with reality to psychosis; in terms of object relations, from the genital (adult) type to the most infantile type, the anaclitic one fraught with fear of the ambivalent and destructive impulses. In every area of human function, alcoholics have spanned a wide spectrum. They have been known among the prudes and the libertines, the bravos and the cowards. They have come to the therapist with every possible type of libidinal arrest, regression or fixation, with every character problem imaginable, and have at times displayed the behavior pattern characteristic of every problem we see in the modern psychiatric clinic. Can anyone deny that alcoholics often show phobia-like or conversion symptoms? Do they not respond to offers of treatment much like sexual perverts? Do they not periodically develop a psychiatric picture mostly of a paranoid nature? If such a psychosis develops in a schizoid personality, which some alcoholics have often been described to have (5), does this history not fit the definition of chronic schizophrenia?

Thus, if we find that practically all emotional problems and psychological syndromes are observable in the problem drinker, we have to provide therapeutic personnel familiar with all of the deviations of mental health. The problem of the psychotherapeutic handling of the alcohol-addicted person, however, is made even more complex by the nature of the transference and countertransferences which develop in their treatment.

In the training of a person for psychotherapy, we must ascertain that he acquires certain skills, and can use them in a way that at the very least is not harmful to himself or to the patient. His ability to help the patient will consist not so much in his understanding of theory, or the capacity to understand the unconscious meaning of the patient's production, as in his ability to recognize and deal with the patient's resistances, transferences and his own countertransference.

The nature of the alcoholic patient's resistances is such that he behaves at times like an irresponsible child. This necessitates that the therapist or his aides take over the decision-making for a variable period of time, or directly interfere with the patient's relation with his spouse, employer or other significant figures. Necessary as this may be, it represents acting out on the part of patient and therapist. At least one of them should have an idea of the meaning of their joint actions. Powdermaker (8) pointed out that the alcoholic patient's need to establish an extremely dependent relation represents one of the pitfalls of therapy with him. She warned against allowing the patient to become overly dependent on the therapist, in which case the latter may experience much disappointment and this may increase the possibility of a negative response. He should, Powdermaker advised, "keep in mind the resistance of the patient to using his ability as long as his condition is endurable or his guilt unabated" (8). She further emphasized that in the dependent and regressed state, the patient is extremely sensitive to any expression of rejection or anger on the part of the therapist, even if these have nothing to do with the patient and are so slight or hidden as to be totally unknown to the therapist.

Thus the nature of the transference, and the susceptibility of the patient in this state, impose a grave responsibility on the therapist. Knowing this, and being able to recognize the manifestations of the various transference reactions, and their meaning, is difficult enough. This job is made more complex, however, by the fact that the recognition of the transferences is interfered with by the therapist's countertransferences. Frequently, the only way to discover the patient's transference reactions is by the therapist's ability to observe the nature of his own countertransferences and to understand the meaning of these.

The nature of the countertransferences in the management of problem drinkers is such that they are hard to handle. No wonder all the family and relatives of the alcoholic end up hating him and rejecting him. The alcoholic's oral hostility, combined with his self-destructive needs, cause him to "eat himself out of house and home." Contributions by Selzer (9) and Moore (10) show that the problems of countertransference represent the most important handicaps and difficulties militating against the successful treatment of the problem drinker.

Thus, a person qualified to treat the underlying emotional problems of the alcoholic is one who is trained to diagnose all emotional and physical problems, one who is able to treat the patient psychotherapeutically. He must be able to help the patient by the interpretation of his character problems, resistances and, when appropriate, transference resistances.

An indispensable part of the psychotherapeutic process is the therapist's ability to recognize and effectively deal with his own countertransferences. This ability is acquired in most people only after an adequate personal psychotherapeutic experience—ideally, psychoanalysis. Failing this, the therapist may need to have someone "looking over his shoulder" permanently lest he become involved in acting-out that would jeopardize the patient's progress, or raise havoc in the therapist's own life.

The idea that anyone who is not qualified to do "uncovering" psychotherapy is capable of giving "supportive treatment" is a spurious and dangerous one. Our current knowledge of psychoanalytic ego psychology forces us to revise the view that reassurance and guidance are uniformly ego-supportive. Neither is the making of unconscious impulses conscious always threatening to the ego. Many an interpretation of poorly warded off impulses can be immediately supportive and helpful to the ego, whereas the old "pat-on-the-back" may throw the patient into a homosexual panic, while that other "sovereign remedy," the "swift kick in the pants," may precipitate irreversible self-destructive behavior. The only difference of note between uncovering and supportive therapy is that the latter exploits the transference whereas the former also resolves it.

Of the disciplines now working with alcoholics, only some psychiatrists, social workers and psychologists seem to satisfy the criteria of adequate preparation for treating the emotional problems at hand. Physicians as a group are not prepared to practice psychotherapy. All too often, when his good will, enthusiasm or emotional involvement with a patient causes the physician to try to treat the alcoholic, he is likely to go at it with the enthusiasm of a boy scout, but lacking in the necessary skill. Such an approach crumbles with the patient's first relapse into drinking, and the physician joins the crowd of relatives, well-wishers and do-gooders the alcoholic leaves behind on his trail to self-destruction. It is better for the physician to avoid involvement with alcoholics than to undertake a single case while unprepared, for that one case is likely to make his attitude toward future alcoholic patients one fraught with disdain, disrespect, or overthreatening or punitive expressions.

Clergymen have only recently been receiving some training which might enable them to be of some help in this area (11). The most sophisticated teachers in pastoral counseling, however, such as Franzblau, who is both a clergyman and a psychiatrist, have cautioned (12) that "As long as the minister sticks to pastoral counseling and controls the temptation to venture into the forbidden precinct of psychotherapy, he will not get into trouble. . . . He must beware of a 'call' to psychotherapy based on pure inspiration, or a conviction that he has special talent for it which can be cultivated by a few psychology courses, a few months of clinical pastoral training and some bootleg 'supervision'."

A variety of laymen also tend to become involved in the treatment of alcoholism; Alcoholics Anonymous contributes the largest group in this activity. The former problem drinker, however, who controls his drinking on the basis of his A.A. activities, but who has not discovered and effectively worked through his own emotional problems, is in a worse position to function as an individual therapist to an alcoholic than a person without a history of alcoholism in the past but with experience. This statement seems to contradict the A.A. belief that only a former alcoholic can help a present alcoholic (13, *p. xvi*). The A.A. creed pertains, however, to A.A. activities. We must not equate A.A. work with psychotherapy. To ignore this difference is to fall prey to a tendency to minimize the importance, effectiveness or even "reality" of psychotherapy (14), an attitude undoubtedly motivated by fears of hypnotism, magic and, in the last analysis, the passive yearning that all people feel.

Acting within the well-circumscribed role of an A.A. sponsor, the ex-alcoholic derives considerable support from his role and from the group behind it. Though not invariably safe for him or for the person he sponsors, they both are fairly protected within the quasi-religious structure of A.A. Once the ex-alcoholic starts acting as a "counselor" or psychotherapist, the former protection is no longer available and the danger of personal involvement becomes much greater.

As long as the treatment of alcoholics is based on the assumption that the underlying problem is an emotional one, we should be consistent and provide for its treatment by personnel best trained to do psychiatric therapy, whether it is psychotherapy alone or in conjunction with other methods. The state authorities charged with the organization and supervision of treatment programs for alcoholics have the responsibility to set up minimum standards for personnel who may do psychotherapy. Failure to do so invariably results in the flooding of facilities with untrained men. The state officials concerned with alcoholism must be clearly aware that they are dealing with one aspect of the problems of mental health.

The criteria for qualification to work with alcoholics must be as high, or even more carefully considered, as those pertaining to other mental health personnel. Alcoholics are among the sickest and most difficult patients to treat, and none but the well-qualified person can be of help to them in a way that is safe for them or for himself. Others may obtain abstinence at times, but the price is even greater misery for the patient and his family, and a lessening of his industrial capacity as well.

Counseling with alcoholics must be carefully defined so as to protect the patients from injury and meddling. The definition of the function of a counselor cannot be left to the discretion of the non-professional person, to be coined in the heat of feelings that arise in intimate interpersonal relations.

Summary

A review of the nature of the problems found in alcoholics and arising in their treatment indicates that the therapist for the patients addicted to self-medication with alcohol must be able to do effective psychotherapy.

Psychotherapy is a technique of treatment in which the patient's unconscious problems are made conscious and the defects of his personality are corrected by working with the pathological manifestations. To be able to do this, a therapist must have the techniques and knowledge to deal with the problem at hand, as well as all possible complications which may arise. He must be able to understand the meaning of the patient's productions and actions, and their unconscious implications. He must be able to observe, understand and deal helpfully and effectively with the patient's resistances, including the transference resistances. Since the therapist is his own working tool, he must be freed from blind spots and inhibitions. Only in this way can he make constructive use of his counter-transferences, rather than have them disturb the treatment, his own life or both. Without a resolution of his own problems and continuing attention to them, a psychotherapist is best left functioning under the supervision of a person who has had such preparation.

REFERENCES

1. KRYSTAL, H. The management of alcoholism in the practice of medicine. J. Mich. St. Med. Soc. 60: 73–78, 1961.
2. GLOVER, E. Common problems in psychoanalysis and anthropology; drug ritual and addiction. Br. J. Med. Psychol. 12: 109–131, 1932.
3. WEIJL, S. Theoretical and practical aspects of psychoanalytic treatment of problem drinkers. Q. J. Stud. Alcohol 5: 200–215, 1944.
4. HALL, R. A. Obsessive–compulsive features in a case of alcoholism. Psychoanal. Rev. 37: 73–78, 1950.
5. BINSWANGER, K. Ueber schizoide Alkoholiker. Z. Ges. Neurol. Psychiat. 60: 127–159, 1920.
6. FERENCZI, S. Alkohol und Neurosen. Jb. Psychoanalyt. Psychopath. Forschungen. 3: 853–857, 1912.
7. FELIX, R. H. An appraisal of the personality types of the addict. Am. J. Psychiat. 100: 462–467, 1944.
8. POWDERMAKER, F. The relation between the alcoholic and the physician. Q. J. Stud. Alcohol 5: 245–249, 1944.
9. SELZER, M. L. Hostility as a barrier to therapy in alcoholism. Psychiat. Q. 31: 301–305, 1957.
10. MOORE, R. A. Reaction formation as a countertransference phenomenon in the treatment of alcoholism. Q. J. Stud. Alcohol 22: 481–486, 1961.
11. RICE, O. R. Contribution of the minister to the treatment of the alcoholic. Q. J. Stud. Alcohol 5: 250–256, 1944.
12. FRANZBLAU, A. M. Distinctive functions of psychotherapy and pastoral counseling. Archs Gen. Psychiat. 3: 583–589, 1960.
13. Alcoholics Anonymous; the story of how many thousands of men and women have recovered from alcoholism. 2d ed. New York; A.A. Pub.; 1955.
14. HOLLENDER, M. H. Is psychotherapy real? Am. Practnr Dig. Treat. 9: 369–370, 1958.

III. ADVANTAGES OF NONPSYCHOTHERAPISTS

Robert A. Moore

That alcoholism is one of our major public health problems is accepted by most professional health and social science personnel. The exact number is unknown and an exact definition escapes us. We are not in agreement as to the etiology, and there is considerable controversy as to the best treatment techniques. Still, we feel confident we are dealing with a tangible illness or pathological life reaction even if we may be reluctant to call alcoholism a specific disease.

Unfortunately, medicine has been reluctant to accept responsibility for the care of alcoholics, officially defining it as an illness only as recently as 1956. Perhaps, as Dr. Krystal suggests, this stems partly from the lack of a specific treatment. However, I suspect it is related more to the generally unsavory atmosphere pervading the subject of alcoholism from which the physician may recoil. Such unpopular illnesses characteristically attract the people in our midst who need an unpopular cause to champion for their own salvation, and such a need is not strong, I fear, among American physicians.

There is still considerable public reluctance to consider alcoholism as an illness, especially as a mental illness. A study by Lemkau and Crocetti (1) revealed that fewer people think a case history of an alcoholic represents mental illness than that of a paranoid or a simple schizophrenic, and fewer anticipated that treatment of alcoholism would be successful. The authors made reference to studies in two other communities where the difference was even more marked.

Physicians, too, are less certain in their view of alcoholism. A study of the similarities of treatment attitudes between general practitioners and psychiatrists (2) showed the greatest variance toward alcoholics of all the mentally ill; the psychiatrists recommended "counseling" and the general practitioners preferred to avoid it. Psychiatrists, too, are not without reluctance in this area. A study by Hayman (3) of attitudes toward alcoholism by psychiatrists in southern California revealed that half do not generally treat alcoholics, over half reported no recoveries whatever, and 80% of those with any success reported 10% or fewer recoveries. Most advocated some form of psychotherapy despite their pessimism about its value. On the other hand, 99% of them approved of Alcoholics Anonymous, 77% having referred patients to A.A. Of the patients they knew in A.A., 40% had been abstinent up to 1 year, 20% for 2 years, and 10% over 2 years, with about 50% "well adjusted"— certainly a much more positive statement than they made for their own work.

Dr. Krystal has addressed himself to the broad question of who is qualified to treat alcoholics but then limited his discussion to psychotherapy, individual at that, for alcoholics. This is not just a semantic issue but, rather, one of a hierarchical arrangement of psychiatric treatments. One-to-one treatment, especially psychoanalysis, gives the highest status to both therapist and patient. This has been well described by Redlich (4). Any other treatment is considered second best, even if there is no demonstrated superiority of psychotherapy for a particular condition. I do not agree that individual psychotherapy is the treatment of choice for the vast majority of alcoholics. In fact, I suspect it is generally a less effective technique.

Statistics are lacking to prove this, since there have been few long-term follow-ups of patients treated psychotherapeutically. A study by Moore and Ramseur (5) showed the effects of an intensive psychotherapy program for alcoholic inpatients. At discharge, after an average hospitalization of 105 days, 13% were improved and 33% slightly improved—improvement implying total adjustment, not just reduction in alcohol intake. A follow-up at an average of 42 months after discharge, when many had received extended outpatient treatment, revealed 14% improved and 21% slightly improved.

A similar follow-up study of alcoholics by Selzer and Holloway (6) at the Ypsilanti State Hospital (Michigan), of patients who had received no psychotherapy, revealed an over-all improvement rate of 41% compared to 35% in the psychotherapy group cited above. An interesting study by Hoff (7), reported from the Medical College of Virginia, also raises a question as to the ultimate effectiveness of psychotherapy. Patients were treated briefly in a hospital, then with psychotherapy in special clinics. In 1020 patients receiving disulfiram as an adjunct to psychotherapy, the improvement rate was 76% while in 484 controls receiving only psychotherapy it was 55%. A similar comparison of patients receiving psychotherapy alone or chlordiazepoxide and psychotherapy revealed rates of 52% and 72% respectively. Thus the mere addition of a pharmacologic agent, with all that it means psychologically, raised the results of months of tedious work in psychotherapy by about 40%.

For that small segment of alcoholic patients, perhaps 5 or 10%, whose drinking is "reactive," that is, in response to the acute precipitation of a neurotic illness, intensive psychotherapy is the treatment of choice. These patients have personality structures considerably more mature and resilient than the typical alcoholic. Where such treatment is indicated, without doubt it should be administered by a professional psychotherapist, preferably one who has had the advantage of a personal psychoanalysis. An A.A. sponsor or an Alcoholic Information Center director has no business attempting "therapy" with such a patient.

For an additional 5 or 10% of the alcoholic population who suffer from "symptomatic" alcoholism, that is, the alcohol is used as a desperate barrier against frank psychosis, a psychiatric evaluation is essential. The decision might be for psychotherapy, perhaps not, but if so, it should be conducted by a professional. The nonprofessional, perhaps not recognizing the underlying signs of an impending psychosis might too abruptly induce the patient to stop drinking, with resulting mental collapse. Some alcoholics can maintain relative control over their antisocial impulses and avoid obedience to hallucinatory commands only when sedated with alcohol. Occasional alcoholics, not so mentally disturbed as the above example, may frankly be better off drinking, and the professional evaluator is less likely to err in such a determination.

Perhaps 80 to 85% of the alcoholic population, in my experience, can be considered to be of the addictive type, people who have insidiously become increasingly powerless to control their drinking, who use alcohol to handle all stress, even the normal stress of daily life, and who become increasingly ill-at-ease when prevented from drinking. While efforts to define a typical personality profile have failed, clinical observation shows certain constant constellations of deep-seated pathological traits that may be hidden among the more obvious and variable personality traits. This has been well described by Zwerling (8), who has found as constant traits that alcoholics are dependent, hostile, schizoid, depressed and sexually immature. Typically, their omnipotent, clinging yet hostile one-way relatability makes them poor candidates for classic therapeutic approaches. As in a previously published discussion between Dr. Krystal and myself (9), basic to these disagreements, I think, is his tendency to think of alcoholism as if it were a neurosis in a higher percentage of cases than I do.

While fully agreeing with the opinion that alcoholism is a mental disturbance, I do not feel that efforts at resolution of unconscious conflicts in the large majority of alcoholics will be rewarded. The statement in the literature that makes this most clear is that by Shea (10): "Alcoholism must be tackled directly; it cannot be expected to perish by attrition when the fundamental neurotic roots are crushed. Such a technique, in my experience, always fails. The alcoholism flourishes protectively and the neurosis is never cornered. The easiest way to tackle the alcoholism directly is to make nonalcoholism an obsessive issue with the patient."

A study (11) of results of treatment in five outpatient clinics and an inpatient facility in Connecticut reveals a rather low success rate with their psychotherapeutic approach (11% abstinent and 14% better controlled); but more interestingly it suggested that the treatment itself seemed to have been of little importance in the successes achieved. The investigators were impressed with how often some other factor during the treatment or after seemed more vital, although it is difficult to know how much the treatment prepared the patients to react to these factors.

The question viewed more broadly, then, should be, Who is qualified to treat (not administer psychotherapy to) the alcoholic patient? We would feel more comfortable, I suspect, if treatment of any kind were carried out or at least supervised by adequately prepared professional therapists. As Hayman's study (3) demonstrates, most psychiatrists couldn't care less, and have little confidence that they are really "expert" on the subject. Since this group of patients is notoriously nonresponsive to psychotherapy (not necessarily to other approaches), and since there is a severe shortage of professional psychotherapists, it would seem poor manpower planning to limit the treatment of alcoholics to psychotherapists. Blain (12) has suggested four zones of human functioning, each requiring at times different types of professional assistance. He believes psychiatry should assume primary responsibility for the more advanced disorders, Zone IV, since our thin manpower precludes our assuming responsibility everywhere. He specifically suggests that such sufferers as alcoholic, overdependent personalities and delinquents should be included in Zone III. Psychiatrists would function in the Zone III problem areas by providing consultation, advice and training, but the bulk of the work would be done by other people. My criticism of his classification is the implied assumption that alcoholism is not a real or severe mental illness. Recommendations of the Joint Commission on Mental Illness and Health (13) include broadening our criteria for who will be allowed to treat the mentally ill, though specifying careful preparation as mandatory.

The fact is, however, that people not trained in psychotherapeutic techniques have stepped into the vacuum left by medicine and provide the bulk of care for alcoholics. Sometimes we are appalled by the manipulations and frank sadistic aggression visited on alcoholics by untrained personnel. One such "expert" finds considerable pleasure, and claimed success, in pushing wives to leave their husbands in order to bring them to their senses. Some of the "therapists" are religious fanatics, the gleam in whose eyes reveals not love of mankind but a nearly overt paranoid psychosis. Professional people tend to be critical of A.A. since it "doesn't do anything but trade one obsession for another."

Since we are partly responsible through our own neglect for much of the inadequate treatment of alcoholism, it hardly improves matters to draw up criteria, for those we would accept as fit to treat alcoholics, that are impossible to meet and unrealistic in concept. Rather, we should direct our efforts at training personnel who, though not having complete professional training, can do a reasonable job, with awareness of their limitations. We may provide this through postgraduate courses for physicians, social workers, clergymen and others, or by providing consultation or leadership to community committees or clinics working with alcoholics. Of course, I am in agreement that government bodies should be advised not to hire personnel, to work with alcoholics, who are without minimal training or who manifest gross character defects. I believe, too, that the professional psychotherapist should maintain a friendly if distant relationship with A.A. and with organizations that use former alcoholics as "therapists."

Dr. Krystal suggests that general physicians should avoid psychotherapy with alcoholics. Most family doctors treat a number of alcoholics with about as much success as psychiatrists. However, in my experience, they have a built-in protection against going too far; that is, they treat alcoholism as a physical problem, usually being unaware of the value of their kindness and concern for the alcoholic. The study on attitudes of general practitioners (2) revealed the same thing. This was made dramatically apparent recently at a meeting of the Michigan State Medical Society's Committee on Alcoholism and Drug Addiction, of which I am a member (and the only psychiatrist). The group is reluctant to accept the idea that psychiatry has any claim to expertise on the subject of alcoholism. In fact, their idea of what constitutes alcoholism is what we would call the complications of alcoholism, that is, malnutrition, withdrawal symptoms, liver damage, polyneuropathy, etc. I have found, however, that family physicians are responsive to training directed at helping them look at themselves as they work with their alcoholic patients so as to be able to tolerate them (and their own reactions to them). I believe this is much more useful in the long run than suggesting to them that they are not qualified to treat alcoholics and should refer them to psychiatrists or clinics that either don't exist in their community or are unwilling to accept alcoholics.

The argument is often made that abstinence is not enough—in fact, may do harm in some cases—and that untrained workers fail to realize this. No doubt exceptions occur, but generally the alcoholic and his family are better off when he stops drinking. The Connecticut study (11) demonstrated a clear connection between abstinence, or better control of drinking, and improved behavior in such areas as employment, physical health and marital adjustment. At the same time it also demonstrated that a large percentage of the abstinent alcoholics were still overtly disturbed people. Fear is expressed by some that impulses controlled by alcohol will break through during periods of abstinence. On the contrary, it is my experience that antisocial impulses such as sexual perversions, combativeness, aggression in the form of automobile accidents, or self-destruction, are more likely to find expression when the alcoholic is drinking.

Summary

Rather than establish criteria for therapeutic personnel which are impossible to meet, professionally trained people such as psychiatrists would best contribute to the treatment of alcoholism by (a) themselves accepting for treatment those alcoholics who would benefit from their particular skills; (b) participating in the postgraduate training of general physicians, social workers, clergymen, and others who are willing to work with alcoholics; (c) participating as supervisors and consultants of community committees or clinics treating alcoholics.

Psychotherapy is not the treatment of choice for most alcoholics. Where it is indicated, it should be done only by persons professionally trained and personally equipped to use it. Other techniques do not require such extensive training and may be equally or more effective for most alcoholics.

REFERENCES

1. LEMKAU, P. V. and CROCETTI, G. M. An urban population's opinion and knowledge about mental illness. Am. J. Psychiat. 118: 692–700, 1962.
2. TAYLOR, J. B. The psychiatrist and the general practitioner; reported treatment of the emotionally disturbed patient. Archs Gen. Psychiat. 5: 1–6, 1961.
3. HAYMAN, M. Current attitudes to alcoholism of psychiatrists in Southern California. Am. J. Psychiat. 112: 485–493, 1956.
4. REDLICH, F. C. Social aspects of psychotherapy. Am. J. Psychiat. 114: 800–804, 1958.
5. MOORE, R. A. and RAMSEUR, F. Effects of psychotherapy in an open-ward hospital on patients with alcoholism. Q. J. Stud. Alcohol 21: 233–252, 1960.
6. SELZER, M. L. and HOLLOWAY, H. A. A follow-up of alcoholics committed to a state hospital. Q. J. Stud. Alcohol 18: 98–120, 1957.
7. HOFF, E. C. The use of pharmacological adjuncts in the psychotherapy of alcoholics. Q. J. Stud. Alcohol, Suppl. No. 1, pp. 138–150, 1961.
8. ZWERLING, I. Psychiatric findings in an interdisciplinary study of forty-six alcoholic patients. Q. J. Stud. Alcohol 20: 543–554, 1959.
9. MOORE, R. A. and KRYSTAL, H. The problem of abstinence by the patient as a requisite for the psychotherapy of alcoholism. Q. J. Stud. Alcohol 23: 105–123, 1962.

10. SHEA, J. E. Psychoanalytic therapy in alcoholism. Q. J. Stud. Alcohol 15: 595–605, 1954.
11. GERARD, D. L., SAENGER, G. and WILE, R. The abstinent alcoholic. Archs Gen. Psychiat. 6: 83–95, 1962.
12. BLAIN, D. Zonal delimination of psychiatric service—an answer to personnel shortages. Am. J. Psychiat. 113: 176–177, 1956.
13. JOINT COMMISSION ON MENTAL ILLNESS AND HEALTH. Action for mental health. New York; Basic Books; 1961.

IV.   SUMMARY OF GENERAL DISCUSSION

Dr. H. KRYSTAL, in opening the discussion, noted that Dr. Moore had classified the patients suffering from alcohol addictions in a number of diagnostic categories, according to which he made predictions as to the treatment choice. The alcoholics who present themselves to clinics are those for whom alcohol has failed to support "normal" activities, and many of whom have tried A.A. as well. It is important to evaluate each new referral carefully and try to channel each patient to the type of treatment most likely to help him. It is essential to try to prevent mishandling in these chronically disappointed patients. In order to be able to do this, however, each clinic must have a team of psychologist and social worker, led by a psychiatrist who can make such an evaluation. Dr. Krystal agreed that it is a fact that psychiatrists are reluctant to treat alcoholics. He suggested that in alcoholism, as in acute schizophrenia, the therapist needs a number of "therapeutic assistants." This fact and the "dilution of the transference" are the reasons why alcoholics do better and are more welcomed in clinics. The psychiatrist who tries to treat the alcoholic "solo" is likely to get discouraged and become reluctant to try it again. Psychiatrists should be encouraged to treat alcoholics in clinics. Thus, the various state programs which set up inadequate clinics are really responsible for the failure to attract suitable professional personnel. In many cases, in areas where psychiatrists are plentiful, internists or other people are hired as clinic directors without any regard to the need for psychiatric supervision. As for the relative success of various approaches, the available statistics are highly unreliable. The skill of the observers, and the criteria used, are at wide variance at the present time. Most of the time we don't even know what we are trying to measure.

MR. RALPH DANIEL commented that, since alcoholism is a problem in which the drinking perpetuates the patient's problems, whatever is done to break up the pattern is beneficial. He felt that, although most of the people on the Michigan State Board of Alcoholism would desire to establish standards such as Dr. Krystal had recommended, a public agency, nevertheless, cannot do more than the people are prepared to pay for, and the public does not want to buy the expensive type of clinic care.

DR. ALVIN ROSENBLOOM emphasized the necessity for an empirical approach to the treatment of the alcoholic, since not all questions can be answered about the problems involved. He stressed the difficulty in the alcoholism programs resulting from the hostility of the community toward the alcoholic.

DR. EMANUEL TANAY distinguished between the approach to the individual alcoholic and the social, cultural and ethnic problems and differences. He pointed out that the former lies within the scope and training of the psychiatrist, psychologist and social worker, while the latter might be more suitably handled by the social scientist.

DR. THOMAS A. PETTY related that an approach being planned for narcotic addiction in Detroit envisions the utilization of a variety of community resources, along with a hospital to provide inpatient care and an outpatient clinic. Among the valuable community resources in this area is the family physician, with whom the clinic personnel can work to provide a pattern of family care and a favorable atmosphere at home. Unfortunately, the family physician is also a shrinking resource, being lost in the tendency toward specialization.

DR. LOUIS KOREN commented on the fact that with the variety of underlying problems observed in the alcoholic, the choice of the addiction in distinction to other patients with the same underlying characterological and nosological problem who do not choose addiction, still poses a riddle which cannot be explained. Perhaps involved here is a type of ego defect which also precludes the use of psychoanalysis in these patients.

DR. MARVIN MARGOLIS observed that at the Highland Park Alcoholism Clinic, which had a highly trained professional staff, the staff was able to modify techniques as experience indicated, with a significant improvement in treatment results. Not only was it necessary to have adequately trained personnel, but in view of the fact that we have not perfected the approaches to alcoholism as yet, we must provide a structure in which the management of each case is reviewed periodically in continuing case conferences. Exchange of observations enables the staff to learn from each case and modify procedures as necessary. He related experiences in which probation officers were involved in the management of clinic patients, with apparent benefit to all involved.

Dr. T. A. Petty, summarizing the discussion, emphasized that the greatest difficulty in the treatment of alcoholics is the nature of the therapist's countertransferences. Many alcoholics have the need to experience the therapist as the depriving, threatening mother of his past. Such patients so structure their treatment that they relate to the therapist in a demanding, unsatisfiable, "sucking" relation. The therapist has to be able to withstand such demands. The alcoholic forces the therapist to confront himself with the many little addictions which prevail in everyone's life, e.g., addiction to work, love, smoking, and many other things, thus mobilizing anxiety in the therapist. The countertransference reactions to the alcoholic patients often revive reactions one felt toward younger siblings who were thought to be overindulged at one's own expense and were hated for the deprivations imposed on the older child. In effect, the resentment and anger generated in the therapist is difficult to handle.

21

The Future of Alcohology
Craft or Science?[1]

Melvyn Kalb, Ph.D and Morton S. Propper, M.S.W.

A NEW TYPE of manpower, the professional alcohologist, has emerged on the alcoholism treatment scene as an outgrowth of the recent rich infusion of federal attention and funding through the establishment of the National Institute on Alcohol Abuse and Alcoholism.

While manifestly operating in harmony with the veteran nonprofessional, this influx of new professionals in the alcohol field has created unique problems and tensions. Unfortunately, the conflicts and frictions between the professional and paraprofessional have not been allowed to surface. Rather than attempting to resolve the problem, the approach has been to deny its existence.

The purpose of this paper is to illustrate and review the evidence of these conflicts, to trace their history and consequences, and to provide some explanatory hypotheses. Our intent is not only to provide a perspective on the problem but to stimulate dialogue in the belief that only with candid self-examination is there hope that the clinical alcoholism enterprise can meet the high expectations of the "new era" in alcoholism study and treatment.

"CRAFT" VERSUS "SCIENTIFIC" MODELS OF ORGANIZATION

The context in which the conflicts between the professionals and nonprofessionals in the alcoholism field can best be understood is the distinction between craft and scientific models of organization. A craft as opposed to a scientific organization can be defined by

[1] Reprinted by permission from the *American Journal of Psychiatry*, Vol. 133, pp. 641–645, 1976. Copyright 1976, the American Psychiatric Association, Washington, D.C. 20009.

differences in acquisition of knowledge, implementation of knowledge and the nature of loyalty among its members.

A craftsman gains his qualifying skill (knowledge) primarily through direct observation and experience under the tutelage of a master craftsman. The knowledge he acquires is a product of the experiences of his teacher. The test of the craftsman's learning is his demonstrated ability to replicate consistently the performance of his teacher. Acceptable deviations are limited largely to elaborations of style; critical analyses of the over-all traditions of the craft are actively discouraged. In fact, mutual agreement is the basis on which loyalty is established among the membership of a craftlike organization.

By contrast, the scientist–professional learns his skill not only experientially in a journeyman-apprentice relationship but also in a context relying on the cognitive teachings of many others. The scientist–professional in training is exposed to a broad variety of competing viewpoints and is encouraged to exercise autonomy in establishing his own conceptualization of the issues (1). Although there are craftlike aspects within the scientist–professional model (2), the demonstrated ability to engage in unique, independent thinking and to evaluate critically the work of one's teachers and peers is the sine qua non of the scientist–professional model.

It is this critical analysis and quest for new solutions using a body of mutually held methods (empiricism, rationality and freedom of investigation) that establish a bond of loyalty among scientists. The members of a scientific profession are not united by presenting a unified front against their critics but rather by a methodology that provides the tools for resolving disagreement.[2]

Paraprofessional preparation for service in the field of alcoholism has clearly followed the craft model outlined above. The indoctrination of new members in the philosophy and principles ("Twelve Steps") of Alcoholics Anonymous by teachers who are recovered alcoholics (and who followed the same course of learning and rehabilitation), the prescription to think and act as their teachers do, and the goal of one day being like their teachers and teaching others the same philosophy characterize the apprenticeship of para-

---

[2] Alfred North Whitehead (3) made the following distinction between a craft and a profession: "A craft is based upon customary activities and modified by the trial and error of individual practice. A profession [consists of activities] which are subject to theoretical analysis and are modified by theoretical conclusions derived from that analysis" (pp. 73–74).

professionals.[3] The strong devotion of most paraprofessionals in the field of alcoholism to traditional concepts, their general resistance to serious consideration of alternative views and studies on the nature, course and treatment of alcoholism, and their steadfast refusal to question their own premises in the light of conflicting evidence all serve to create an intense loyalty and unity.

As long as the alcoholism treatment enterprise was composed of an overwhelming preponderance of paraprofessionals, this craftlike organizational structure was appropriate and beneficial. It was only when professionals with their own scientific organizational model came on the scene that the perpetuation of the craft model became questionable.

It is our thesis that the future of alcohology will have to be established along either craft lines, exemplified by the paraprofessional alcoholism counselor, or scientific lines, embodied by the professional scientist. Because the defining properties and operational principles required for membership in a craft are different from those of a science, a détente would be difficult to achieve. The point is *not* that either approach is superior, but that the marriage of the two prevents growth and progress. The synergism that is created acts in a negative rather than a complementary way.

HISTORY OF THE PROBLEM

The clinical treatment of alcoholism has been governed largely by lay groups of recovered alcoholics. This group of dedicated individuals, acting in response to the benign neglect and abdication of the helping professions, banded together to fill the vacuum in the treatment of alcoholics. The predominant group has been the fellowship of Alcoholics Anonymous. Prior to the implementation of NIAAA in 1971, professionals in alcoholism treatment represented a scant fraction of the manpower in the field (5, 6).

While the number of professionals in the alcoholism field has increased dramatically, professionals are still a small percentage of the total manpower pool (5). This disproportionate distribution of professionals and paraprofessionals has continued to place the power, both political and clinical, in the hands of the nonprofessional.[4]

---

[3] It is interesting that the book *Alcoholics Anonymous* (4) is commonly referred to as "the Bible." The implications of this nickname are obvious.

[4] It is obvious that if nonprofessionals suddenly stopped working with alcoholics, alcohol treatment programs would be brought to a halt. This would not be the case were the professionals to pursue a similar course.

The distribution of power between professionals and para-professionals in the treatment of alcoholism is in marked contrast to that in the mental health field. Professionals have entered the field of alcoholism treatment after more than two decades of paraprofessional dominance, while the trend in the mental health field in the last decade has been in the opposite direction—the recruitment of paraprofessionals to join the ranks of the professional (7, 8). Moreover, while the paraprofessional in the mental health field has functioned adjunctly to and under the supervision of the professional, the paraprofessional in the alcoholism field has been a teacher or colleague rather than a student.

By virtue of this power, lay groups in the alcoholism treatment field have been and continue to be the gate-keepers of clinical knowledge and clinical operating style. Thus, despite a growing research literature that has pointed to new directions in the conceptualization of etiologic and therapeutic models, empirically unvalidated clinical notions regarding the nature of alcoholism persist. These clinical notions have firmly established themselves as traditional and inviolate wisdoms. Their survival is ensured by the protection provided by their disciples in the form of intense loyalty to them. Examples of this loyalty and the sometimes fierce attacks visited on the "heretic" are numerous (9–13).

Ravetz (2), in a book on the philosophy of science and its social problems, discussed the general problems of the relationship between the growth of an empirically based scientific establishment and the attendant conflict with the preexisting body of beliefs and doctrine (which Ravetz labels "folk science").

"Value [of the folk science] is determined by the degree to which a problem situation is central to the experience of the audience; and adequacy by the success in offering reassurance and the promise of understanding. . . . The conflicts between academic science and strongly based folk sciences provide many insights into the social situation of science, and into some insoluble problems inherent in that situation. [One such problem] occurs when the results of a disciplined scientific inquiry contradict the beliefs of a folk science, usually a popular one which is also adopted by the established cultural organs of society" (*pp. 388–389*).

As is the case in all craft organizations, this loyalty to traditional concepts is the "glue" that binds the nonprofessionals in alcoholism treatment (14). Toch (15) pointed out that all self-help groups have by definition an inherent antiprofessional bias. Pattison (14) noted that a self-help group also has "a self-fulfilling prophecy of success, and the validation of its theories is ideological rather than scientific. However, these elements of a self-help group are the 'social glue' that holds a self-help group together, promotes cohesion and integration, validates hope and commitment and in short makes it work!" (*p. 620*).

One of the most serious (and costly) by-products of this ideology is the lack of integration of research findings into the mainstream of the clinical treatment of alcoholism. Research in the treatment of alcoholism and the actual clinical treatment of alcoholics have been allowed to coexist, but rarely (if ever) to intersect.

Research findings (especially those not in keeping with the "party line") seem to have been simply ignored by the paraprofessionals. They have died not because of contradictory research studies or polemic discussions, but simply by being disregarded. In fact, vigorous and open scientific debate rarely occurs within the alcoholism treatment setting. What does occur is either personal invective directed against the speaker or writer who presents "heretical" findings (the data being ignored) or systematic attempts to smother debate, with the rationale that "We are all in the field to help the alcoholic so let's not argue."

Filstead and Rossi (16) have pointed out that a publication in the 1940s, *Alcohol, Science and Society* (17), dealt with issues and problems that predominated in the 40s and still persist in this decade. They asked why there had not been more progress.

Some answers to this question might be found by questioning directors of alcoholism treatment centers as to the amount of change in the last 10 years in the functioning style of their clinic or the treatment offered to alcoholics that originated not from political and community pressures but directly from published scientific findings. It might be more frightening and revealing to ask how different the psychotherapeutic clinical treatment of the alcoholic would be had there been no scientific research on the treatment of alcoholism published in the last 25 years. Ludwig,[5] discussing the assets and liabilities of the mental health system's approach to the alcoholic, noted that "there are not enough searching and probing questions or effort expended to accumulate more facts. . . . In fact the current service oriented professional mentality is such that re-

[5] LUDWIG, A. Assets and liabilities of the mental health system in its approach to the alcoholic and drug addict. Proc. 6th Annu. Eagleville Conf., Alcohol, Drug Abuse, and Mental Health Administration, Eagleville, Pa., 6–8 June 1973.

search is not only discouraged in many treatment settings but also regarded somehow as suspicious and even immoral."

An example of the blatant disregard of scientific findings in the alcoholism treatment field is the belief that one drink triggers an uncontrollable urge in an alcoholic to keep drinking. An article by Paredes et al. (18) reported that this hypothesis as it is commonly understood is not supported by empirical evidence. The authors underscored the results of their own research by citing similar findings in 20 previously published studies. Mendelson (19), the first chief of the National Center for the Prevention and Control of Alcoholism, reported that his own experimental work showed no evidence for such an automatic biochemical triggering effect. Despite the overwhelming weight of empirical evidence against this hypothesis and the absence of any substantiating scientific evidence, it continues to flourish in the ideology of alcoholism treatment and philosophy as if it had been confirmed time and time again.

The work of Cahalan (20) serves as a variation on the same theme. Cahalan found that many men with serious drinking problems are able to change their drinking habits and "mature out of" problem drinking without therapeutic intervention. He also found that the largest proportion of serious alcohol-related problems occur in men in their early twenties, who have apparently high rates of maturing out (spontaneous remission) in their early thirties.

Cahalan's findings raise serious questions about the validity of the "progressive illness" concept of alcoholism as it is commonly understood. Pattison (21) pointed out over 10 years ago that the well-known Jellinek chart illustrating the progressive and disastrous decline of physical and emotional health that accompanies alcoholism was based on a biased sample of Alcoholics Anonymous members who were physically and socially bankrupt. Ironically, in his original article, Jellinek (22) pointed out that many people remain "stuck" at a given level of alcoholism behavior. This point, generally unknown or ignored, is not reflected in the famous "progressive illness" chart.

It seems that scientific research in alcoholism occupies a unique position. Research is not used, as in other fields, as a springboard for developing and testing new hypotheses and abandoning old ones that are empirically disproved. Alcoholism treatment concepts in the overwhelming majority of clinic settings have developed and survive not with the aid of research but in spite of it. Clinical treatment is not the logical outgrowth of scientific discoveries but instead remains an encapsulated body of theories and shopworn slogans that are apparently immune to the outcome of scientific research.

The unencumbered flow between research and clinical treatment that Chafetz (23) has called for can occur only in an environment in which the practicing clinician is free from a personal investment in the perpetuation of a particular theory or construct. It is only in such an environment that clinicians can choose therapeutic concepts on the merits of scientific evidence. It is paradoxical that personal investment and the lack of openness to new findings and fresh conceptualizations are the hallmarks of the typical alcoholism treatment setting.

Ludwig,[5] writing about the role of innovation and the use of research findings in the alcoholism treatment system, noted,

"Despite the embarrassingly poor long-term results of most treatment and rehabilitation programs, enormous sums of money and staff time are being spent to perpetuate traditional approaches (and various mythologies) rather than being diverted to innovative demonstration projects. It is as though the underlying philosophy of these programs is based on the principle that if sufficient manpower can be deployed to employ ineffective procedures then this multiplication of ineptness will hit therapeutic paydirt."

A clinical field that claims to employ scientific principles and theories in the service of helping the alcoholic while creating a climate in which research findings are ignored and disregarded aligns itself to anachronisms, sloganeering and opinion rather than to science. Ullman and Krasner (24) posed the question that might eventually be put to the alcoholism treatment system: "If a particular theory does not utilize data based on scientific procedures, it may well be asked whether it is a reasonable basis for the treatment of human beings" (p. 36).

COGNITIVE STYLES AND COMMITMENTS OF PROFESSIONALS AND PARAPROFESSIONALS

There is an obvious divergence of learned cognitive styles between professional and paraprofessional workers. Most professionals have been trained to use an analytical-objective-inductive cognitive style. Their long years of schooling have not only emphasized a respect for inductive empirical reasoning but also equipped them with the skills to interpret and critically evaluate empirical research data. The paraprofessional usually lacks this training and uses an intuitive-subjective-deductive cognitive style. Empirical data are often perceived as obscure and irrelevant, especially when they conflict with intuitive, experiential understanding.

This contrast in cognitive style is reflected in the early literature on alcoholism treatment. Much of the early research was conducted without the experimental controls vital to sound experimentation, and the literature consisted mostly of anecdotal reporting (25). The popular view of alcoholism was created largely by laymen (5) and fashioned out of their personal experience.

The intensely personal commitment the recovered-alcoholic paraprofessional may feel to the traditional model of alcoholism is quite understandable. The traditional model defines alcoholics as victims of a disease, entitling them to many social services for the disabled. It also saves recovered alcoholics from the moralistic stigmata of "weak character" and "mental illness" (26). Thus, the recovered-alcoholic paraprofessional's self-esteem is often a very real part of his "stake" in sustaining the traditional views of alcoholism. The individual who, for example, has the deep conviction that his sobriety rests solely on his acceptance of the tenets of Alcoholics Anonymous or on some other traditional understanding of alcoholism is likely to feel deeply and personally threatened by any information that might call those understandings and interpretations into question.

For the professional, a challenge to traditional beliefs is often an academic issue for debate, but for the recovered alcoholic, it often becomes a threat to his sobriety, his stability, his job and his very existence. It is quite understandable that a recovered alcoholic whose sobriety is founded on abstinence may, for example, be deeply disturbed by the idea that some alcoholics can recover and drink socially. Selzer (10) maintains,

"Perhaps another important reason for the almost reflex rejection [of normal drinking in recovered alcoholics] is that many people working in this field are alcoholics themselves and are compelled to remain abstinent. It may be especially difficult for the alcoholic who must remain dry to accept the idea that others can recover and drink socially. To hear of the 'success' of others may be frustrating—and those workers prefer not to hear about it since it also upsets their treatment concepts. . . . Granted that experimentation will yield discouraging relapses in most instances, this is not sufficient excuse for prejudiced persons to vilify the truth" (p. 113).

IMPLICATIONS OF THE INFLUX OF PROFESSIONALS

The professional is rather in the position of a newcomer or, in some cases, a tentatively welcome visitor in the "house" of alcoholism treatment. He may very well feel that he must, like a visitor, be on his best behavior and be sensitive to the house rules. His "gifts" and talents (clinical skills, inductive and analytic reasoning) are viewed with suspicion or contempt. He must tread carefully because, on a practical day-to-day level, he is the most dispensable member of the treatment team. Under these circumstances, the professional has three options. (1) He can reduce his cognitive dissonance by subscribing to traditional views. If he does this, he will eventually be accepted and find his circumstances increasingly comfortable. (2) He can attempt to use his professional training and perspective. His success will often be a function of his charisma, diplomacy and the nature of the clinic. Often, he will find himself stymied by the passive—and sometimes active—resistance of the paraprofessional workers and those of his colleagues who have opted for tactic number 1. (3) He can flee to more comfortable and less divisive and frustrating clinical pastures (e.g., mental health). Those who choose to stay are likely to be the best and the worst (27).

PROBLEMS AND PARADOXES

Unfortunately, problems rooted in the very origin and structure of an institution are not likely to yield to simple or painless solutions. The problems and conflicts we have discussed are deeply rooted in the history, dogma and constituency of the alcoholism treatment enterprise. Each conceivable pragmatic revisionist strategy carries with it a paradox.

If through some administrative fiat empirical research findings were suddenly incorporated into clinical practice, a panoply of problems would result. First, it would be apparent that the vast majority of treatment personnel lack the training to apply innovative treatment methods. The paraprofessional's area of expertise would become obsolete: his credentials in the field (i.e., his personal experience) would no longer be marketable (28). The sudden shifts in power that would be produced by the application of treatment procedures and philosophies unfamiliar to the paraprofessional but within the area of expertise claimed by the professional could present an even greater problem.

We envision yet another Pandora's box of complications if the clinical field were somehow made more tolerant of healthy controversy, more responsive to empirical findings and more receptive to new methodologies.

It is not unlikely that a training and orientation program that would inevitably tend to "professionalize" the paraprofessional would produce massive resistance, conflict and upheaval. The process of professionalization, of increasing the paraprofessional's clinical sophistication and versatility, would produce a crisis of commitment by threatening the underlying antiprofessionalism that binds these workers to the organizational structure and validates their beliefs. Pattison (14) warns that "A self-help group should not be professionalized or scientificized, because that would undercut the very socio-psychological matrix that makes a self-help group effective" (p. 620).

The alcoholism treatment enterprise now finds itself in a Procrustean dilemma—to eschew the empirical, scientific orientation for the sake of intramural tranquility and therefore abandon alcohology as a scientifically oriented clinical enterprise, or to adopt the classical professional–scientific model and risk the alienation of a large segment of current treatment personnel. Ignoring this dilemma, as was done in the past, is no longer an option and would only cause further alienation and dissension within the field and even more confusion in the public about the nature of alcoholism. The alcoholism treatment field can no longer masquerade its craftlike organization under the banner of science.

Until this decision is made, no amount of funding, training, recruitment, or bureaucratic reorganization will materially alter the impact of the alcoholism treatment system. As Ludwig[5] notes, the promise of the alcohol system "will not be realized by having more money, more staff and more facilities but rather by qualitative changes in the nature of the activities conducted, a willingness to admit to relative scientific ignorance and a concerted effort to remedy these deficits" (p. 156).

REFERENCES

1. LYNN, K. The professions in America. Boston; Houghton Mifflin; 1965.
2. RAVETZ, J. Scientific knowledge and its social problems. New York; Oxford University Press; 1971.
3. WHITEHEAD, A. N. Adventures of ideas. Harmondsworth, England; Pelican Books; 1948.
4. ALCOHOLICS ANONYMOUS. Alcoholics Anonymous. New York; 1955.
5. ASHER, J. Alcohol agency wants to be #1. APA Monitor, pp. 12–14, October 1973.
6. Alcoholism constituency urged to join forces in united effort. Alc. & Health Notes, Rockville, Md., p. 1, April 1974.
7. GUERNEY, B. Psychotherapeutic agents; new roles for nonprofessionals, parents, and teachers. New York; Holt, Rinehart & Winston; 1969.

8. HOBBS, N. Mental health's third revolution. Am. J. Orthopsych. 34: 822–833, 1964.

9. DAVIES, D. L. Normal drinking in recovered alcohol addicts; comment on the article by D. L. Davies. Q. J. Stud. Alcohol 24: 330–332, 1963.

10. SELZER, M. L. Comment on D. L. Davies' "Normal drinking in recovered alcohol addicts." Q. J. Stud. Alcohol 24: 113–114, 1963.

11. SOBELL, M. B. and SOBELL, L. C. Individualized behavior therapy for alcoholics. (Calif. Ment. Hlth Res. Monogr. No. 13.) Sacramento; California Department of Mental Hygiene; 1972.

12. VERDEN, P. and SHATTERLY, D. Alcoholism research and resistance to understanding the compulsive drinker. Ment. Hyg. 55: 331–336, 1971.

13. ZIMMERMAN, D. Teaching alcoholics to drink. Today's Hlth 50(No. 4): 26–30, 1972.

14. PATTISON, E. M. Rehabilitation of the chronic alcoholic. Pp. 587–658. In: KISSIN, B. and BEGLEITER, H., eds. The biology of alcoholism. Vol. 3. Clinical pathology. New York; Plenum; 1974.

15. TOCH, H. The social psychology of social movements. Indianapolis; Bobbs–Merrill; 1965.

16. FILSTEAD, W. and ROSSI, J. Some suggested priorities in the alcohol-problems field. Q. J. Stud. Alcohol 34: 1360–1363, 1973.

17. HAGGARD, H. W. and JELLINEK, E. M. Alcohol, science and society. Westport, Conn.; Greenwood Press; 1972.

18. PAREDES, A., HOOD, W. R., SEYMOUR, H. and GOLLOB, M. Loss of control in alcoholism; an investigation of the hypothesis, with experimental findings. Q. J. Stud. Alcohol 34: 1146–1161, 1973.

19. MENDELSON, J. H., ed. Experimentally induced chronic intoxication and withdrawal in alcoholics. Q. J. Stud. Alcohol, Suppl. No. 2, 1964.

20. CAHALAN, D. Drinking practices and problems; research perspectives on remedial measures. Public Affairs Report 14 (No. 2): 1–6, 1973.

21. PATTISON, E. M. A critique of alcoholism treatment concepts, with special reference to abstinence. Q. J. Stud. Alcohol 27: 49–71, 1966.

22. JELLINEK, E. M. Phases of alcohol addiction. Q. J. Stud. Alcohol 13: 673–684, 1952.

23. Chafetz calls for greater usage of current knowledge. Alc. & Health Notes, Rockville, Md., p. 1, May 1973.

24. ULLMAN, L. and KRASNER, L. A psychological approach to abnormal behavior. Englewood Cliffs, N.J.; Prentice–Hall; 1969.

25. GIESBRECHT, N. Sociological trends in the treatment of alcoholics, 1940–1972. Presented at the North American Congress on Alcohol and Drug Problems, San Francisco, Calif., 12–18 December 1974.

26. ROOM, R. Governing images and the prevention of alcohol problems. Prev. Med. 3: 11–23, 1974.

27. CAHN, S. The treatment of alcoholics; an evaluation study. New York; Oxford University Press; 1970.

28. WISEMAN, J. P. Stations of the lost; the treatment of Skid Row alcoholics. Englewood Cliffs, N.J.; Prentice–Hall; 1970.

22

The Alcoholic in the State Mental Hospital[1]

Anthony J. Matkom, Ph.D.

WITH INCREASING RECOGNITION and acceptance of alcoholism as an illness, society's way of dealing with the alcoholic is changing. Treatment is replacing punishment. One result of the change is an increased placement of alcoholics in mental hospitals. Moon and Patton (1), for example, report that "the period 1951–1960 saw a fourfold increase in the proportion of nonpsychotic alcoholics among all first admissions to the civil state hospitals of New York." Currently in Wisconsin alcoholic patients constitute about 25% of all first admissions to the state hospitals. Recently, in California mental hospitals (2), one in five patients admitted for the first time was diagnosed as alcoholic, and one-quarter of readmissions each year were for alcoholism.

The purpose of this paper is to discuss some of the consequences of the placement of alcoholics in mental hospitals, and to suggest a rationale for effecting changes in the typical present-day approach of mental hospitals toward the problem of alcoholism.

The increasing preference for treatment as opposed to punishment is a positive change in the public attitude toward the alcoholic; however, it should not be mistakenly assumed that hospitalization always implies treatment or that imprisonment could not be effectively combined with treatment. In fact, despite the increasing number of admissions, relatively few mental hospitals in this country have acknowledged this fact by effecting necessary changes in their approach to the treatment of alcoholic patients, or have developed services to meet their specific needs. In most state hospitals there is no special program of treatment and follow-up care for al-

[1] Reprinted by permission from the QUARTERLY JOURNAL OF STUDIES ON ALCOHOL, Vol. 26, pp. 499–506, 1965. Copyright by Journal of Studies on Alcohol, Inc., New Brunswick, New Jersey 08903.

coholics; they are treated like all the other patients. Placing the alcoholic in such a mental institution instead of a prison could very possibly have undesirable consequences. For example:

(1) The patient's relatives are encouraged to anticipate an improvement because of the hospital setting. If the hospital is not in the position to provide an appropriate treatment program, however, the alcoholic patient is not likely to improve. Thus, his family is disappointed and has even less tolerance of his behavior than if he had been incarcerated.

(2) If the alcoholic comes to believe that what he experienced in the hospital was treatment for alcoholism, he himself may develop the attitude that he cannot be helped by treatment.

(3) Unless a dynamic treatment program is in operation, the physical environment of a hospital might become so comfortable that it may have the negative effect of supporting dependency needs and thus even delay recovery.

(4) Being put in jail suggests to the alcoholic that he may be a criminal; placement in a mental institution, mixed with other mental patients, suggests that he may be mentally ill. Both of these implications are potentially threatening to the alcoholic. However, the suggestion of being mentally ill might well be more threatening than that of being a criminal, because it is easier for him to be sure he is not a criminal than to rationalize that he is not mentally ill. Therefore, the alcoholic's defenses are likely to be tighter, and his resistance stronger against being identified with the mentally ill. Thus, if identical treatment programs were administered in both settings, the one in the prison framework might prove to be more effective than the one in the general ward of a mental hospital.

In summary, although the increasing tendency to send alcoholics to a mental institution instead of prison is undoubtedly a reflection of a positive change in the public attitude toward alcoholism, the alcoholic's stay in a mental hospital does not always result in better treatment of his alcoholism.

Rationale for Equal Treatment

The practice of treating alcoholics no differently from other mental patients has its justification in a well-accepted philosophy that underlying causes rather than symptoms should be treated. The application of this rationale to the treatment of alcoholism leads to the practice of equal treatment for alcoholics and mental patients in the following two logical steps:

(1) The heavy drinking is viewed as only a symptom of a basic

personality disorder. Thus, it might be best to disregard the drinking (the symptom) and to focus attention on the underlying dynamic forces responsible for this symptom.

(2) It is believed that the underlying causes of alcoholism are not essentially different from those of some other mental disorders. Thus, the alcoholic should be treated like most other mental patients.

Consequences of Equal Treatment

In practice the consequences of the equal treatment approach are predominantly negative (3).

The alcoholic patient, typically, believes that very little is wrong with him. He is frequently heard to say, "I must be sick if they put me here," but very rarely will he say, "I am in the hospital because I am sick." The alcoholic, in fact, can readily see that he is in much better mental health than the nonalcoholic patients, which encourages him to dispose of his problems by rationalizing that he is really not sick. He resents identification with other mental patients and refuses to assume the role of a mental-hospital patient. The fact that the staff does not differentiate between him and the "sick" makes him feel he is not understood; thus he does not expect to be helped.

Conversely, the staff members resent the alcoholic's unwillingness to "cooperate," and they respond with irritation toward him. They feel that alcoholic patients are not making use of professional skills and other resources offered by the hospital and are just taking a rest cure at public expense. The alcoholic patients easily sense that they are disliked by the staff and they react in the way anyone would in a hostile atmosphere.

This self-perpetuating situation cannot be improved until some significant changes are made in the treatment philosophy. As long as alcoholics are grouped with all types of mental patients, specialized ward management and treatment procedures cannot be instituted, and the establishment of a community in which members have the degree of self-determination of which alcoholic patients are capable is not feasible. When alcoholics are submitted to the same routine as other mental patients, they chafe under ward security and restrictions, are critical of the staff's attempts to help them, and avoid participation in community therapeutic endeavors.

Alcoholics Differ from Other Mental Patients

(1) Unlike patients in other diagnostic categories, alcoholics,

once they stop drinking, are capable of being proud of having been excessive drinkers in the past. This may be due to their tendency to perceive recovery as their own accomplishment or as an act of their own will power. This gives them a feeling of strength and self-respect, and a reason for pride. In addition, alcoholics often receive the admiration of others when sustaining abstinence. Thus, instead of hiding their past, they often boast about it in order to elicit approval and support. Other types of mental patients are rarely able to view their predicament in the same way.

(2) Unlike other types of mental patients, the alcoholic likes and needs the company of another alcoholic, not only while drinking but also when struggling for sobriety. Alcoholics, when drinking, encourage one another to drink; when striving for sobriety, they are able to encourage each other's sobriety. Alcoholics form groups easily because the alcoholic is able to respect another alcoholic. Other mental patients do not function well as groups, primarily because they lack respect for one another.

(3) The symptom of heavy drinking is different from other mental symptoms. Overindulgence in alcohol has, of course, some deep-seated unconscious reasons. So does an overindulgence in food. In fact, some students of human behavior believe that the underlying causes of excessive drinking are very similar to those of excessive eating (4–7). In view of this similarity, it is necessary to explain the fact that alcoholism is a grossly distressing social, moral and economic problem while obesity is not, despite the fact that the incidence of obesity is far greater than that of alcoholism. The difference is evidently due largely to the consequences of the symptom of heavy drinking. Unlike most other symptoms of mental disorder, heavy drinking ruins its victims personally, morally, economically and socially, at the same time that it inflicts injury on families and society. Moreover, the consequences of the alcoholic symptom tend to become reasons for further drinking, as if the symptom, apart from its underlying cause, were in itself dynamic. Thus, an alcoholic after losing his job, his family and his friends is likely to experience an even stronger urge to drink.

Heavy drinking is particularly destructive in the area of human relations. Yet, paradoxically, one reason why it is so difficult for the alcoholic to stop drinking is that drinking is his way of relating to others. This apparent paradox disappears when it is remembered that the alcoholic drinking behavior has had a long history of development, a long history of what may be considered "successful drinking," or even "happy drinking." During those many years of successful drinking, the drinking behavior was a focal point of all his social occasions; it developed into his way of relating to others, and it served that function well until it got out of hand. Now he must stop drinking, but he has no other way of relating to people. In this sense, "to stop drinking" for the alcoholic may carry the meaning "to stop living"—a frightening proposition. A great deal of conditioning to drinking takes place in the alcoholic's life, because for years he has continuously combined drinking with almost all life situations which become conditioned stimuli prompting him to reach for a drink. This aspect of alcoholism is a serious problem in itself, apart from the problem of the underlying cause of drinking. Thus, even if the underlying cause of drinking were removed, the alcoholic would still be left to cope with the countless number of powerful conditioned stimuli which constantly bombard him and push him toward drinking. This may explain why, to the dismay of the therapist, the alcoholic often starts drinking again, for no apparent reason, after what appeared to be a favorable response to psychotherapy.

If he is to recover, the alcoholic must either avoid exposure to the stimuli situations, which actually may mean changing his entire living pattern, or he must submit himself to a painful and risky process of deconditioning by exposing himself to these situations without drinking. In either case his major struggle will be with the symptom of alcoholism; and in either case he is likely to need much support. For a person in the low socioeconomic level who possesses few social skills and perhaps no hobbies, the task of changing his entire way of life may be of such tremendous magnitude that he cannot begin visualizing how it may be undertaken.

If the alcoholic chooses to eliminate alcohol from his life, without changing too many of his established ways, he is going to have an equally difficult time. The temptation to reach for a drink during the initial stages of recovery should not be underestimated. Very few alcoholics will have the strength to resist temptation during this period if left entirely to their own resources.

For these reasons, the symptom of heavy drinking presents a problem in its own right and must be treated as such (8). The symptom must not be neglected, also, because the underlying cause cannot be successfully treated unless the symptom has been first eliminated (8, 9).

Capitalizing on the Differences

The alcoholic's pride in his past excessive drinking and his need for support from other alcoholics are traits that should not be passed over lightly, because in the treatment of alcoholics these traits can be developed into powerful therapeutic and motivating agents. The utilization of these two characteristics of alcoholics plus the recognition of the importance of the symptom of heavy drinking is the structure on which the success of Alcoholics Anonymous largely rests. No treatment approach to alcoholism can afford to ignore that structure.

These potentially useful traits of alcoholics, however, are extremely difficult to capitalize on in the hospital treatment of alcoholics, if the alcoholic patients are mixed randomly with the patients from other diagnostic classifications. If alcoholics are to be treated in the mental hospital, it is essential that they be provided with separate living quarters and with a treatment program designed to meet their special needs. They must be treated separately and differently from other mental patients.

The group atmosphere is important in affecting the attitudes of alcoholics (10). Group living, combined with a program designed for alcoholics, tends to facilitate the alcoholic's acceptance of his condition as a serious illness and helps him to develop enthusiasm about his new prospect of sobriety (11). Both the acceptance of alcoholism and the enthusiasm to change serve to enhance the chance for recovery. The group tends to develop its own standards, aspirations and expectations which are readily transferred to the new members joining the group. The group culture that develops in such a setting is contagious and tends to maintain itself within the group. The communication coming from the group is often more effective than the communication coming from the therapist. Group therapy with hospitalized alcoholics living together is more effective than group therapy with participants who come together only for that occasion, because when patients know each other intimately they are less inhibited, and therapy tends to continue after the termination of the formal session (12).

Separate quarters for alcoholics would serve to demonstrate staff realization that the alcoholics are different from other mental patients and would indicate staff willingness to treat them differently. Hopefully, this would tend to enhance their feeling of being understood, and for that reason, their cooperation might be expected to increase considerably (3, 12).

Selection of Patients for an Alcoholic Ward

The full therapeutic potential of a separate alcoholism treatment unit within a mental hospital could not be achieved without some degree of selectivity. The principle of selection of alcoholic patients for the special treatment unit is indispensable in order to keep out those with adverse motivation who might have a demoralizing effect on other patients. This does not imply that motivation for sobriety should be considered a criterion of selection. On the contrary, to create motivation for sobriety should be considered the responsibility of the alcoholism program and one of the main goals of the treatment. Thus, while lack of positive motivation is not a contraindication for treatment, the presence of adverse motivation, expressed perhaps in the ridicule of those who are trying, should not be tolerated.

The principle of selection is furthermore desirable for at least two other reasons: (1) To make the treatment opportunity more desirable; the fact that admission to the program is limited to those alcoholics who meet certain requirements makes the opportunity for treatment more desirable to potential candidates, and more appreciated by those selected. (2) To provide conditions for the evaluation of the program's effectiveness and for research. Selection increases control over the characteristics of the patient population and thus creates favorable conditions for the evaluation and testing of specific hypotheses related to the treatment of alcoholism.

Follow-Up Program

Recognition of the importance of the symptom of alcoholism, i.e., of the drinking behavior, in the treatment of alcoholics, implies the development of a supportive follow-up program. The lack of such a program seems to be a weak spot even in well-designed hospital projects. While the alcoholic is still in the hospital, he has not yet even started to deal with that part of his problem which I have referred to as the drinking behavior. The habit of drinking must be broken, but it can be broken only after discharge, when the patient is again exposed to the powerful conditioned stimuli which prompt him to reach for a drink. For this reason, any hospital treatment of alcoholics which ends with discharge is incomplete and not likely to be effective.

The first few weeks after discharge may be considered the most critical period in a patient's struggle for sobriety. These are trying and often lonely days during which the patient is seeking employment, readjusting to his disrupted family life or finding a place to live. If the alcoholic is not helped during this period of his recovery the effort invested in his treatment is likely to be lost.

The organization of an ex-patients club at a convenient place in the community, where ex-patients and their wives can meet twice a week, is an economical way of providing the necessary support after discharge from the hospital (13, 14). The club can be viewed as an extension of the treatment initiated at the hospital, i.e., as reinforcement for the motivation acquired in the hospital setting.

SUMMARY

Treatment is replacing punishment as society's way of handling the alcoholic. But placing an alcoholic in a mental hospital that does not have a special alcoholism treatment program, rather than in a prison, does not necessarily result in better treatment of his alcoholism. In a mental hospital the alcoholic is commonly treated no differently from the other patients. The alcoholic resents the suggestion that he is mentally ill; and the hospital staff respond with irritation to his apparent refusal to cooperate.

The alcoholic, however, is different from patients with other types of mental disorders in at least three significant ways: (1) He is capable of being proud of the symptom of his illness, the heavy drinking, unlike other mental patients; (2) he likes and needs the company of other alcoholics, while other mental patients do not function well as groups; (3) the symptom of heavy drinking, unlike other mental symptoms, is a conditioned response and a serious problem in itself requiring treatment apart from its underlying causes.

In order to capitalize on these specific traits of alcoholics they should be housed in separate quarters in the mental hospital and be offered a special treatment program based on group therapy and planned aftercare.

REFERENCES

1. MOON, L. E. and PATTON, R. E. The alcoholic psychotic in the New York state mental hospitals, 1951–1960. Q. J. Stud. Alcohol 24: 664–681, 1963.
2. PASTERMACK, S. and WAHL, J. R. Do state mental hospitals also have a "revolving door?" (Report No. 8.) Washington, D.C.; North American Association of Alcoholism Programs; 1964.
3. BELDEN, E. A program for the treatment of alcoholics in a mental hospital. Q. J. Stud. Alcohol 23: 650–653, 1962.
4. LOLLI, G. Alcoholism and obesity both problems of hunger. Conn. Rev. Alcsm 5: 1, 3–4, 1953.

5. LOLLI, G. Centers for research on nutritional habits and for the prevention and correction of their deviations. Q. J. Stud. Alcohol 16: 393–396, 1955.
6. KAPLAN, H. I. and KAPLAN, H. S. Psychosomatic conception of obesity. J. Nerv. Ment. Dis. 125: 181–201, 1957.
7. BRUCH, H. Importance of overweight. New York; Norton; 1957.
8. TIEBOUT, H. M. Direct treatment of a symptom. Pp. 17–26. In: HOCH, P. H. and ZUBIN, J., eds. Problems of addiction and habituation. New York; Grune & Stratton; 1958.
9. KEPNER, E. Application of learning theory to the etiology and treatment of alcoholism. Q. J. Stud. Alcohol 25: 279–291, 1964.
10. MECHANIC, D. Relevance of group atmosphere and attitudes for the rehabilitation of alcoholics; a pilot study. Q. J. Stud. Alcohol 22: 634–645, 1961.
11. STRAYER, R. Social integration of alcoholics through prolonged group therapy. Q. J. Stud. Alcohol 22: 471–480, 1961.
12. VOTH, A. C. Group therapy with hospitalized alcoholics; a twelve-year study. Q. J. Stud. Alcohol 24: 289–303, 1963.
13. GLIEDMAN, L. H. Concurrent and combined group treatment of chronic alcoholics and their wives. Int. J. Grp Psychother. 7: 414–424, 1957.
14. EWING, T. A., LONG, V. and WENZEL, G. G. Concurrent group psychotherapy of alcoholic patients and their wives. Int. J. Grp Psychother. 11: 329–338, 1961.

23

The Dilemma of the Alcoholic Patient in a Psychiatric Hospital[1]

Earl X. Freed, Ph.D.

THAT alcohol is a drug which may be employed by many individuals to help reduce the discomfort engendered by emotional conflicts is fairly well established (1). Because the numbers and types of these basic, underlying conflicts are legion, the search for a unitary cause for alcohol abuse has continued in vain. However, I earlier noted a perhaps less well recognized, but probably universal, sequela of excessive drinking, i.e., that alcoholism produces its own conflict (2). The diametrically opposed poles of this conflict are: should one continue resorting to alcohol, or should one abstain? The present paper elaborates on this dilemma of alcoholics with special reference to the psychiatric hospital.

The alcoholic seems to "need" alcohol. True, he may not need it in the same sense that drug addicts need their drugs. The question of a physiological or a tissue need for alcohol is still under investigation. Related to this hypothesis is the theory that alcoholics may keep drinking to postpone withdrawal symptoms, symptoms that are quite real and certainly of a physical and physiological nature, in addition to being emotionally traumatic. Nevertheless, psychological needs perpetuating excessive drinking abound, too. These may be subsumed largely under the rubric of learning: The alcoholic has learned to use alcohol.

The very conflict, to drink or to abstain, often generates anxiety leading to further refuge in alcohol; this, seemingly, is how the alcoholic has learned to deal with feelings of anxiety. Certain individ-

[1] Reprinted by permission from the *Journal of Psychiatric Nursing and Mental Health Services*, Vol. 7, pp. 133–135, 1969. Copyright by Journal of Psychiatric Nursing and Mental Health Services, Thorofare, New Jersey 08086.

uals under tension, with the opportunity to consume alcohol, may drink. For some, the resultant reduction in tension increases the likelihood that they will increasingly resort to drinking in future situations wherein they experience anxiety. In this modern age of psychopharmacological enlightenment, with tranquilizers, energizers and esoteric psychedelic drugs so preponderant, let the fact not be overlooked that many millions of dollars are annually spent to purchase self-prescribed alcoholic beverages.

Alcohol is popularly believed to lift the spirits, to attenuate depression, to elevate the mood, even to be a source of energy. For some alcoholics (although this assertion may be denied), alcohol does somehow permit continued functioning, albeit with increasingly impaired efficiency in many cases. Some individuals appear to be able to keep their drinking under at least partial control, but many require increasing dosages of alcohol, taken at more frequent intervals. For the latter, the very commodity which they need, alcohol, produces new problems, problems of an economic, personal, vocational and interpersonal nature. Hence, their new conflict.

The alcoholic who loses control of his drinking may ultimately present himself—or be brought—to the hospital. On readmission to our hospital, one patient voiced his ambivalence over control of drinking: "I can't seem to control it to some extent; however, in a major way, I can control it." This man had been discharged 4 days earlier, and the admitting physician recorded that he had been drinking for the 4 days he had been out of the hospital. Another patient came to the admitting office following an episode wherein he "started to drink and couldn't stop." Then he was afraid he would lose everything he had; he was disgusted with himself. Thoughts came to him of hurting himself and the woman he lived with.

In terms of the present frame of reference, the reasons for the alcoholic's hospitalization may be subsumed under the concepts that his conflicts have largely remained unresolved; that alcohol has become less effective in attenuating his conflicts; and that an increasing resort to alcohol has engendered new and highly self-destructive conflicts. The latter category could include acute medical and psychiatric emergencies such as convulsions, avitaminosis, delirium tremens, etc. One veteran sought admission to our hospital saying, "I am an alcoholic and I need help. I started to drink again last Thursday and I didn't stop until now. I can't stop anymore." In one sense, entering the hospital may represent an act of surrender, akin perhaps to that characteristic of Alcoholics Anonymous members. This seems to occur when the liabilities associated with alcohol abuse outweigh its alleged assets from the patient's point of view. Stated otherwise, this happens when alcohol as a defense mechanism begins to cause more discomfort for its user than the original discomforts it was employed to alleviate.

Many alcoholics also seek a respite in a conflict-free environment so that they may perhaps later return to drinking at a lower level of intensity. Radó (3) suggested that alcohol might lose some of its euphoria-producing capacity with continued use, necessitating, for depressed alcoholics, abstinence from alcohol for a time in order to enable the drug to regain some of its euphoristic power. Alcoholics, then, may seek hospital-imposed abstinence so that alcohol can recover its ameliorative effects. For example, one patient who had lost control of his drinking said he "wanted to come back to the hospital and 'dry out.'"

Hospital treatment of alcoholism almost always involves enforced abstinence, and its ultimate aim is almost always total abstinence following discharge. Within the hospital milieu, abstinence is, relatively, an easily obtainable therapeutic goal. Why? Because it is likely that the psychogenic contingencies, the environmental, intrapersonal and interpersonal parameters producing alcohol abuse, are mitigated. Furthermore, the destructive cycle of conflicts (which results in drinking which, in turn, produces its own conflicts) is broken. The hospitalized alcoholic patient is controlled by the institutional regimen; he has supervision, routines to follow and external controls. He is occupied by a variety of rehabilitation activities. He is not confronted with his debilitating conflict over self-control.

Unfortunately, the entire experience may well be totally dissociated from that portion of the individual's life which has been associated with alcohol. Because of this, one may wonder about the wisdom of complete abstinence as either an inpatient or postdischarge goal. The subtle implication of such a treatment goal is that the patient who returns to alcohol in any measure is a failure. Such a self-definition by an alcoholic, already sensitized to feelings of low self-esteem, is often sufficient impetus for the resumption of full-scale drinking.

From a learning theory point of view, there is an interesting implication in the fact that inpatient treatment is accorded alcoholics only as long as they maintain abstinence. Storm and Smart (4) have pointed out that there is strong evidence of state-dependent or drug-dependent learning. In terms of alcoholism, this means that behavior learned in the nondrugged or sober state is often nontransferable to the drugged or intoxicated state, and vice versa. Hence, the fruits of psychotherapy in the hospital, of rehabilitation procedures, etc., may be of relatively little use to the discharged alcoholic who becomes inebriated. Conversely, the abstinent hospitalized alcoholic is in a conflict-free environment which is really dissociated from that of the community where he drinks. Such a patient often appears relatively comfortable in the hospital following detoxication. It is no wonder that hospital personnel react to him with some negative feeling (5). He does not look, nor does he act, as though he were ill, and in the light of his sobriety, it becomes easy for the staff to react to his previous drinking as really little more than an acting out of immorality.

One of the reasons that the hospitalized alcoholic may be relatively comfortable is that the hospital's insistence on abstinence resolves his conflict of "Should I drink or shouldn't I?" He has a long-standing intrinsic approach tendency to drink alcohol and, in the hospital, an extrinsically greatly strengthened avoidance tendency. The latter is probably sufficiently powerful to preclude his conflict about drinking from recurring.

It is important to examine exhaustively this question of why the hospitalized alcoholic can usually abstain from alcohol. His behavior cannot be attributed solely to the disapproval of the staff nor to their denigration of drinking. Prior to his hospitalization, the alcoholic had admonitions aplenty to be abstemious. Could the answer lie in the relative unavailability of alcohol for the inpatient? This undoubtedly is part of the picture. Although there have been numerous instances of alcoholics who drink on hospital grounds or who bring liquor to the hospital, it would appear that the majority of such patients maintained sobriety within the institution, even for prolonged periods. It is not unusual for patients to report no "urge" or desire to drink in the hospital. When drinking does occur, it is frequently during leaves from the hospital, for example, on weekend passes.

These facts support the contention that hospital life, relatively free of conflict, including the conflict over whether or not to drink, mitigates the need for alcohol. This is not inconsistent with the dissociation hypothesis: the hospital is not associated with drinking; it is linked to sobriety. Similarly, the hospital milieu is consonant with control. The alcoholic patient's confidence lies in the hospital as an effective enforcer of controls, not in himself. The implications of this for him when he is on his own, following discharge from the hospital to the community, are clear.

Alcoholism, then, seems to be a learned response. Sobriety in the hospital thus could be viewed as extinction. Is the alcoholic's return to drinking on discharge, therefore, a kind of spontaneous recovery of the earlier learning? Or does discharge represent a very threatening return to the conditions, internal and external, which fostered alcoholism?

Some clues to the answers to these questions can be garnered from cases in which our patients became intoxicated on the very day that they left the hospital. One man was on his way to his home in Philadelphia. He stopped off in Newark, went to a bar, and continued drinking until he became intoxicated. He finally went to the Regional Office and arrangements were made for his readmission to the Lyons Veterans Administration Hospital. One readmitted patient "started to drink as soon as he was discharged from the hospital." On a later readmission of this same man, when he was returned in an inebriated state by the local police, he explained that, as the routine developed in arranging for his discharge, he became more and more tense; when he left the hospital, he had to have a few drinks immediately. He then stated that he went to the police station and "doesn't know what happened afterwards." One readmitted patient acknowledged that he had been drinking "one or two quarts daily" since his discharge.

Another patient with innumerable hospitalizations stated that he started to drink just as soon as he left the hospital, and finally had to return. His ward psychiatrist said that he usually did not drink while in the hospital; it may have happened once. On readmission, 42 days later, the patient reported that he had left the hospital, registered at a hotel and started to drink immediately. In another 35 days, he was readmitted because, after leaving the hospital, he began to drink wine and continued until returned to the hospital by his friends. He again presented himself for admission, 49 days after this, with the report that he had gone to live with his mother, admitting that he "started to drink on the first day of discharge."

Discharge from the hospital was threatening to these men. They were threatened with reconfrontation with their primary conflicts, as well as with their conflicts over drinking per se. From the frame of reference of learning theory, we might speculate that they had learned to respond to conflict, threat or anxiety by resorting to alcohol. Further, they (or their friends and relatives) had learned to respond to their loss of control of drinking by returning to the hospital. The repetitive aspect emphasized the potency of the learning and also pointed up sharply the absence of a learned substitute response. One could take a page from the notebook of programs which have been successful in helping individuals stop smoking. One such study (6) indicated that, accompanying cigarette withdrawal, there was an increase in anxiety in subjects as well as augmented use of substitute activities.

If we may assume that some of the conditions which foster alcohol abuse include (1) living in a community setting with its attendant day-to-day stresses and anxieties; (2) internal personality conflicts; (3) the ready availability of alcohol; (4) the learned behavior of drinking alcohol to ease the tension and discomfort of internal and external problems; and (5) the resultant conflict over control of this learned response when the very agent, alcohol, employed to secure emotional homeostasis, begins to disrupt it, then it behooves us to reexamine the role of hospitalization in alcoholic rehabilitation.

Even without drug-dependent learning, there is undoubtedly milieu-dependent learning. Many alcoholics learn that the sole solution to their addictive cycle is hospitalization. It is no surprise, therefore, that they seek readmission after readmission. In terms of hospitalization, reanalysis of the five hypothesized parameters of alcoholism is in order: (1) the hospital environment makes few demands and is relatively stress-free; (2) internal conflicts are reduced and dependency is encouraged; (3) alcohol is unavailable; (4) alcohol is not consumed and this avoidance response is reinforced by the institution's insistence on abstinence; and (5) conflict over present controls, therefore, especially in light of hospital-supported external controls, is less of a problem.

Storm and Smart (4) suggested "incorporating direct learning under conditions of varying degrees of intoxication" in the clinic or hospital setting. This represented an attempt to counteract dissociative or nontransferable drug effects. It is now proposed that new techniques for minimizing dissociative environmental effects are, perhaps, also needed. Hopefully, such techniques could help reduce the incidence of discharged alcoholic patients who become intoxicated on the very day they leave the hospital, often en route to their homes.

REFERENCES

1. DOLLARD, J. and MILLER, N. E. Personality and psychotherapy. New York; McGraw-Hill; 1950.
2. FREED, E. X. The crucial factor in alcoholism. Am. J. Nurs. **68:** 2614–2616, 1968.

3. RADÓ, S. The psychoanalysis of pharmacothymia (drug addiction). Psychoanal. Q. 2: 1–23, 1933.
4. STORM, T. and SMART, R. G. Dissociation; a possible explanation of some features of alcoholism, and implication for its treatment. Q. J. Stud. Alcohol 26: 111–115, 1965.
5. FREED, E. X. Opinions of psychiatric hospital personnel and college students toward alcoholism, mental illness, and physical disability; an exploratory study. Psychol. Rep. 15: 615–618, 1964.
6. SCHWARTZ, J. L. and DUBITZKY, M. Changes in anxiety, mood, and self-esteem resulting from an attempt to stop smoking. Am. J. Psychiat. 124: 138–142, 1968.

24

Behavioral Approaches to the Treatment of Alcoholism[1]

Peter M. Miller, Ph.D. and David H. Barlow, Ph.D.

ALCOHOLISM constitutes a complex behavior pattern exhibited by approximately 9 million individuals in the United States alone (61). This "chronic behavioral disorder manifested by repeated drinking of alcoholic beverages in excess of the dietary and social uses of the community and to an extent that it interferes with the drinker's health or his social or economic functioning" has proven to be extremely resistant to change despite its growing incidence (30, *p. 2*). Traditional treatment approaches include individual and group psychodynamic therapy (12, 68), psychodrama (78), milieu therapy (31), medications such as tranquilizers, antidepressants, LSD (1, 31, 34), community abstinence groups (3) and disulfiram (Antabuse) (11, 25).

Treatment based on social-learning formulations (7, 20, 33) offers a promising alternative to traditional methods. Within this framework, alcohol abuse is viewed as a socially acquired, habitual behavior pattern maintained by reinforcement contingencies. Excessive drinking may enable an alcoholic to avoid or escape from unpleasant, anxiety-producing situations, exhibit more varied, spontaneous social behavior, gain increased social reinforcement (either positive or negative attention) from relatives and friends or avoid withdrawal symptoms associated with cessation of drinking. The apparent lack of influence of aversive consequences such as hangover, nausea, physical disorders, loss of family or employment, and arrests seems related to the long delay between actual drinking behavior and occurrence of these events. In addition, studies analyzing alcohol abuse as an approach–avoidance conflict (76)

[1] Reprinted by permission from the *Journal of Nervous and Mental Disease*, Vol. 157, pp. 10–20, 1973. Copyright 1973, The Williams and Wilkins Co., Baltimore, Maryland 21202.

illustrate that even low doses of alcohol reduce anxiety and concern regarding avoidance of punishment.

A comprehensive behavioral model requires a two-fold approach to treatment. First, techniques which decrease the immediate reinforcing properties of alcohol have been used (6, 9, 38). This has involved associating aversive or unpleasant stimuli with both the sequence of the drinking pattern (from urges to actual consumption) and the wide variety of environmental cues (e.g., sight or smell of liquor, liquor advertisements, drinking "buddies") which elicit the behavior. This approach also includes use of self-control techniques to control urges (13) and rearrangement of environmental stimuli associated with urges (49). Secondly, techniques designed to provide the alcoholic with behaviors which are incompatible with alcohol abuse have been reported. These include attempts to teach social drinking patterns as opposed to alcoholic ones (19, 55), with a goal of less than total abstinence. Alcoholics have also been taught alternative ways to deal with stressful social situations to obtain increased reinforcement from their environment (43, 57). In addition, significant persons in the environment are taught ways of reinforcing new, sober patterns of behavior and of punishing or extinguishing excessive drinking (17, 52, 72).

AVERSION THERAPY

According to Rachman and Teasdale (63), "aversion therapy is an attempt to associate an undesirable behaviour pattern with unpleasant stimulation or to make the unpleasant stimulation a consequence of the undesirable behaviour" (*p. xii*). Thus, both classical and instrumental paradigms are utilized. Research on learning suggests that the unpleasant stimulation must be intense and must occur in close temporal contiguity with the behavior in question. In the case of alcoholism, the whole chain of behaviors from urges to actual drinking behavior is involved. The most common aversive stimuli used with alcoholics are chemical, electrical and verbal.

Chemical Aversion

Perhaps the most extensive application of chemical aversion to alcoholism was performed by Voegtlin and his associates (74). In their procedure (39), the patient is asked to take 1 oz of whisky into his mouth just before nausea and vomiting (induced by emetine) occur. Two or three trials are held per session with each 45-min session being held on alternate days. The average number of treatments is four to six. A clinical observation made by these early investigators was the specificity of the conditioned reaction. When aversion to one type of alcoholic beverage, such as whisky, was successfully learned, the patient often drank beer, wine or rum while retaining his aversion to whisky. It is interesting to note that this phenomenon has been observed independently and more recently with both chemical (62) and verbal (14) aversion.

Lemere and Voegtlin (38) were able to obtain follow-up data on 4096 of their patients, some 10 to 13 years after treatment. The results 1 year after treatment yielded a rate of 60% total abstinence. Over the 13-year period, 51% of those treated were totally abstinent if one includes the patients who relapsed but were successfully retreated (39%). Voegtlin et al. (75) point out that patients receiving 2 or more booster sessions during the year following the initial treatment had a greatly improved chance of remaining abstinent for the full year (90% of 84 patients were abstinent). In addition to the conditioning process, certain patient motivational characteristics influenced long-term therapeutic success. For example, of 25 patients that wanted booster treatments but were prevented from accepting them because of distance from the hospital, 100% remained abstinent for a year.

In light of our present knowledge (2, 8), the instructions in this procedure may be very influential. The patient is told that he must never taste or experiment with liquor since the injections he has received serve to "sensitize" his nervous system so that the true aversive characteristics of liquor become more physiologically apparent. The instructions would lead patients to think that alcohol "intrinsically" produces nausea and vomiting even after treatment has been discontinued.

Although other investigations of chemical aversion have not been nearly as extensive, they yield comparable results. Using a procedure similar to that described above, Thimann (73) used emetine to condition 245 patients. A total of 51% of these alcoholics remained abstinent after a 4-year follow-up. Raymond (64) contends that nausea and not vomiting is sufficient for treatment and thus administers only a minimum dosage of apomorphine. He also uses a "choice situation" (in which patients choose either alcoholic or nonalcoholic beverages) to assess therapeutic progress and to reinforce nonalcoholic drinking behavior.

An interesting procedural innovation has been the application of chemical aversion to alcoholics in a group treatment setting (50, 80). It is possible that group procedures not only facilitate conditioning, but also provide mutual reinforcement for participation in therapy and maintenance of sobriety after treatment is complete. Also, since much drinking occurs in social settings, conditioning may generalize more easily to the natural environment.

A second aversive stimulus employed in chemical aversion therapy has been succinylcholine chloride dehydrate (Anectine). In association with the sight and smell of alcohol, the patient experiences total paralysis including inability to breathe as the result of Anectine injection. On the whole, the results of this procedure have been disappointing. Despite the powerful aversive stimulus and the improvement in the temporal relationship of the conditioned stimulus–unconditioned stimulus event, very few long-lasting abstentions have been noted (18, 23, 42, 66). The reasons for these poor results are not entirely clear. Perhaps the tendency in these studies to limit conditioning to visual and olfactory cues without including gustatory ones may have been a factor. Also, the absence of booster sessions may have limited long-term abstinence.

Electrical Aversion

In a treatment group containing 20 alcoholics, Kantorovich (29) repeatedly paired the sight, smell and taste of alcoholic beverages with electrical shock. After a follow-up ranging from 3 weeks to 20 months, 70% of the treatment group remained abstinent. On the other hand, 7 out of a control group of 10 patients receiving hypnotic suggestion or medication reverted to their drinking pattern in a few days after release from the hospital.

The most extensive series of cases treated by electrical aversion has been reported by Blake (9, 10). In his procedure, the patient chooses and mixes his alcoholic beverage and is instructed to sip, but not swallow the beverage. Concurrently, a shock previously described by the patient as unpleasant is delivered to the forearm. To terminate the shock the patient spits the alcohol into a bowl. Only 50% of the trials are actually shocked. In the aversion therapy group (at a 12-month follow-up), 23% were totally abstinent, 27% were improved, 27% had relapsed and 23% could not be followed. When relaxation training was combined with aversion, the figure rose to 46% abstinent, 13% improved, 30% relapsed and 11% could not be followed.

Hsu (28) used an avoidance learning situation in which he requested patients to drink a series of alcoholic and nonalcoholic beverages. Severe electrical shock (2 to 5 mA of 30-sec duration) to the head followed ingestion of alcoholic beverages, but shock could be avoided by choosing nonalcoholic drinks. Treatment was administered for 5 days with booster sessions at 1 and 6 months after hospital discharge. Preliminary results indicated that slightly less than 50% of the patients were abstinent at varying follow-up visits (from 2 to 6 months).

A well-controlled group study of electrical aversion was reported by Vogler et al. (77). Subjects were assigned randomly to treatments of pseudoconditioning (random shock delivery), sham conditioning (no shock), routine hospital care and aversion conditioning (contingent shock). Although relapse took significantly longer for aversion conditioning subjects (median of 21 days) than for any of the controls (median of 9 days), proportion of relapses for the conditioning group did not differ significantly from the other groups. Booster sessions helped subjects maintain sobriety in that relapse took significantly longer for booster subjects (median of 66 days) than for conditioning-only subjects (median of 19.5 days). These data must be interpreted carefully, however, since all subjects in the booster group voluntarily returned for follow-up visits while those in the conditioning-only group were subjects who failed to return for booster sessions.

Recently, more objective measures of actual drinking behavior have been used to evaluate effects of electrical aversion therapy. Morosko and Baer (56) and Chapman et al. (16) conducted aversion therapy in the context of a "choice situation" in which patients were instructed to choose from a number of beverages. Percentage of choice of alcoholic versus nonalcoholic beverages was used to evaluate success. Miller and Hersen (54) utilized a "taste test" measure in which alcoholics were asked to rate alcoholic and nonalcoholic beverages on various taste dimensions. After completion of the task, the experimenters calculated (without the subject's knowledge) the exact amount of alcohol consumed.

Despite the procedural advantages of electrical aversion such as precise timing and control of intensity and duration, this approach has not been demonstrated superior to chemical aversion. Evidence (26) indicates that the exact nature of the conditioning process may not be as essential to the outcome as other treatment variables.

Verbal Aversion

One of the newer developments in the treatment of alcoholism by aversion therapy is the use of noxious images as the aversive stimulus. This procedure has been labeled covert sensitization (14, 15). As described by Cautela, emphasis is placed on the use of the procedure in a self-control fashion. Scenes leading up to drinking are vividly described. These scenes include events or thoughts which initiate the chain of drinking behavior, the setting in which drinking occurs, drinking companions and types of alcohol usually consumed. After relaxation training, aversive scenes (typically, sensations and images of nausea and vomiting) are associated with all aspects of the sequence of behavior leading to drinking. Alternated randomly are scenes in which images of avoiding or refusing alcohol are associated with feelings of relief and relaxation. Patients are instructed to practice these associations on their own. Cautela (14) used this procedure to treat a 29-year-old female alcoholic. With only 8 to 9 weekly treatment sessions, the patient reported decreased urges and abstinence from drinking alcohol. At an 8-month follow-up the patient remained abstinent. Miller (51) used this approach with patients who were under hypnosis and indicated that 83% of 24 patients were completely abstinent at a 9-month follow-up. Strel'chuk (69) in Russia reported similar results with this procedure.

Anant (4) treated 26 patients using a group covert sensitization approach. After a minimum of 5 treatment sessions, 96% of these patients remained abstinent at follow-up contacts ranging from 8 to 15 months. However, in a later paper Anant (5) reported that only 3 of 15 patients remained abstinent at follow-up visits beyond the 8- to 15-month interval. These relapses may have been related to the absence of booster sessions. In the one controlled study evaluating verbal aversion with alcoholics, Ashem and Donner (6) administered 6 treatment sessions consisting of a total of 35 scenes. At a 6-month follow-up, 40% of 15 patients were abstinent. None of the 8 control subjects who received no treatment was abstinent. Verbal aversion may be applicable to more people than other aversion procedures since it is less unpleasant and has no medical contraindications. Also, the nature of the technique enhances generalization to the environment since the patient can use the aversive image to control urges in vivo.

RELAXATION TRAINING AND SYSTEMATIC DESENSITIZATION

Relaxation training and systematic densensitization (79) have been used to provide alcoholics with alternative ways of reducing anxiety in stressful situations. As discussed earlier, Blake (9) examined the therapeutic efficacy of combining electrical aversion therapy with relaxation training. Apparently, these patients were taught to use relaxation in a self-control manner to deal with stress in the environment. As noted earlier, this combined technique resulted in a higher abstinence rate (46%) than the use of electrical aversion therapy alone (23%).

Kraft (35) and Kraft and Al-Issa (36) reported a number of successful case studies in which alcoholics received systematic desensitization to lessen social anxiety about situations which typically induced excessive drinking. Hierarchies involved social settings with increasing numbers of people. Of eight young (all under 35 years) alcoholic patients treated, all were reported to have improved and to be able to drink socially in moderation.

Although more comprehensive hospital programs (43) have included systematic desensitization as part of their treatment regime, its individual contribution to outcome has not as yet been established. While it is unlikely that systematic desensitization alone is an effective treatment for alcoholism, it may be useful as one of a variety of procedures to help an alcoholic reduce his anxiety in specific stressful situations which set the occasion for drinking.

OPERANT APPROACHES

The view that addictive behaviors are operant and thus functionally related to their consequences has influenced treatment of obesity (24, 71), cigarette smoking (22) and drug abuse (53). Only recently have operant strategies been widely applied to the alteration of alcohol abuse. In his behavioral analysis of alcoholism, Bandura (7) stressed the role of stimulus cues and social reinforcement contingencies in the maintenance of excessive drinking behavior. Both inpatient and in vivo treatment programs have arranged positive and negative consequences in order to decrease alcohol consumption and increase more adaptive behaviors. In addition, operant systems have proven useful in the descriptive analysis of drinking patterns.

Inpatient Treatment Programs

A number of treatment programs have utilized operant conditioning procedures to modify alcoholics' vocational, social and actual drinking behaviors in a hospital setting. Mertens (49) described an operant learning approach aimed at increasing self-control and promoting behaviors which are incompatible with alcohol abuse. In order to develop self-control, patients were encouraged to rearrange alcohol cues in the environment by making them less prominent and to utilize thoughts of ultimate aversive consequences of drinking as a self-control device. Alternative ways of handling problem situations were taught and reinforced by staff members.

Narrol (57) reported the use of a token economy system to reinforce work behavior in hospitalized alcoholics. Patients were paid 100 points per hour for on- and off-ward work assignments. Out of these earnings, patients were required to pay for room and board, ground privileges, clothing maintenance, recreation, passes and therapy. Patients on this token economy unit averaged 8 hr of work per day compared with 4 hr a day for a group not on token economy. More recent programs of this nature $(65)^2$ reinforce a greater variety of behavioral categories such as personal–social (attending treatment sessions, engaging in more assertive social behavior), responsible (planning daily activities, keeping appointments on time) and vocational (working in the hospital, job hunting in the community) behaviors.

Cohen et al. (19) also utilized reinforcement contingencies to alter drinking behavior but in a much more direct manner. In a series of experiments with a hospitalized 39-year-old alcoholic, a free operant alcohol-drinking situation was utilized. During contingent weeks, if the subject drank 5 oz or less on a particular day, he was placed in an enriched (opportunity to work for money, private phone, recreation room, TV, etc.) ward environment. If he drank over 5 oz he was placed in an impoverished (loss of all privileges) environment for the rest of the day. Controlled drinking (under 5 oz per day) was maintained during contingent phases with reversal to excessive drinking during noncontingent phases. The authors suggest that such contingencies could be applied in an alcoholic's environment through his wife, friends, halfway house, etc.

In Vivo Treatment

Only a few case studies which apply operant conditioning outside of the hospital have been reported. As discussed earlier, social reinforcement contingencies in the environment may actually maintain alcohol abuse. Such consequences of drinking might include attention from "drinking buddies" or possibly negative attention from an otherwise nonattentive wife. Hersen et al. (27) report a descriptive analysis of nonverbal interactions between alcoholics and their

---

[2] Also, MILLER, P. M. A comprehensive social-learning approach to the treatment of alcoholism. [Unpublished ms., Veterans Administration Center, Jackson, Mississippi.]

wives which indicated that these wives attend more to alcohol-related as opposed to nonalcohol-related behaviors.

In attempting to rearrange social reinforcement in an alcoholic's environment, Sulzer (72) made peer companionship and spouse attention contingent on nonalcohol-drinking behavior. The patient's friends were instructed to meet him periodically for a "drink." At this meeting if he ordered an alcoholic beverage the friends were to leave immediately. If he ordered a nonalcoholic beverage they were to remain and provide social reinforcement. Sober behavior was socially reinforced by the wife and the therapist. Reportedly, the subject discontinued the use of alcohol and was functioning more efficiently in his life.

Cheek et al. (17) trained wives of alcoholics to use behavior modification techniques to change family interactions. They were to apply these techniques to their alcoholic husbands' behaviors (aggressiveness, social withdrawal and failure to accept a responsible adult role in the family) which were most disruptive to the family. Wives received instruction in relaxation training and systematic desensitization to help deal with marital tension and to apply contingencies more objectively. Most wives who completed the program reported at least moderate improvement in marital communication together with a lessening of family tension. Miller (52) applied behavioral contracting (70) to an alcoholic and his wife in order to alter reinforcement contingencies maintaining drinking behavior. Daily records of drinking behavior indicated a rapid decline in number of drinks consumed per day, with progress being maintained at a 6-month follow-up.

Descriptive Operant Analysis

Recently, operant systems have been used to investigate physiological and behavioral concomitants of prolonged experimental drinking (44–48, 58–60). Since a few of these studies have direct treatment implications they will be discussed briefly.

The work of Mello and Mendelson (44) represents an early attempt to analyze experimentally drinking patterns in alcoholics. In a hospital setting, two alcoholics could "work" for alcohol or money by pressing a translucent response key on which one of a series of colored lights was projected. The goal was to make the response key color change as often as possible since reinforcement occurred at that time. As the study progressed one subject tended to "work" in short, frequent sessions while the other responded during a few long sessions each day. In a later study (45), 15 hospitalized alcoholics could spend tokens to purchase 1 oz of alcohol dispensed from an apparatus on the wall similar to a vending machine. Immediate reinforcement (tokens earned could be spent immediately on alcohol) resulted in spaced, moderate drinking. Delayed reinforcement (tokens earned could not be spent until the next day) resulted in massed, binge drinking. These data would suggest that alcoholic drinking behavior can be altered through manipulation of schedules of reinforcement in the environment.

Nathan et al. (60) and Nathan and O'Brien (58) described a series of studies in which the social, affective and drinking behaviors of alcoholic versus nonalcoholic Skid Row volunteers were systematically evaluated on an operant task. Results indicated that alcoholics drank twice as much as nonalcoholics. Alcoholics began drinking heavily and then tapered off to a maintenance (in terms of blood alcohol concentrations) level. Nonalcoholics exhibited a more stable drinking pattern. Alcoholics tended to be social isolates before, during and after drinking episodes. Nonalcoholics engaged in more social behavior, especially during and after alcohol consumption. After drinking began, alcoholics actually were more depressed, less active and more pathological. Nonalcoholics also exhibited this pattern but to a lesser degree. Nathan and O'Brien (58) argue that social isolation may serve as a cue for excessive alcohol consumption. Thus, reduction in an alcoholic's social isolation may help reduce his alcohol consumption. Also, since an alcoholic usually experiences loss of memory during prolonged drinking, he is not affected by the aversive mood changes which occur as a consequence of drinking. Hence, if these "blackout" periods could be disrupted, drinking might be less pleasurable.

CONTROLLED DRINKING

The notion that alcoholics can learn to drink in moderation is a new and controversial one. Historically, the goal of alcoholism treatment has been total abstinence, with the assumption that even one alcoholic beverage would precipitate an uncontrolled drinking episode. Clinical evidence (21, 32) demonstrates that some alcoholics can return to and maintain social drinking patterns.

In order to establish a behavioral treatment regime with this goal in mind, Schaefer et al. (67) investigated baseline drinking behaviors in alcoholics and social drinkers. The authors converted a hospital dayroom into a cocktail lounge equipped with padded serving bar, dimmed lighting, music, bartender, etc. Alcoholics (16 state hospital patients) and social drinkers (15 community volunteers) were separately observed in this setting in groups and were allowed to order and consume drinks freely up to a total of 6 oz. Results indicated that alcoholics took significantly larger sips and drank more straight (nonmixed) drinks than did social drinkers.

Using this baseline information, Mills et al. (55) experimentally investigated the possibility of teaching alcoholics to drink like social drinkers. Alcoholic subjects in the bar setting described above were allowed to order alcoholic beverages ad libitum. Electric shock was made contingent on ordering a straight drink, gulping or ordering more than 3 drinks and sipping them. Six-week follow-up data revealed that 2 of 13 experimental subjects could be classified as social drinkers compared with none of 13 in the control groups. These follow-up results are very modest, and the authors discuss difficulties in generalization and maintenance of these new drinking patterns in the environment without the use of booster sessions and in vivo conditioning.

Lovibond and Caddy (40) recently developed an ingenious way to produce moderate drinking patterns. Through periodic feedback while drinking, outpatient alcoholics were initially trained to discriminate (on the basis of behavioral effects) their own blood alcohol concentrations. Each subject was then instructed to begin drinking pure alcohol in fruit juice until his blood alcohol level reached 0.065%. Electrical shock was made contingent on blood alcohol concentrations above this level. A control group receiving noncontingent shock was also included. Follow-up data (ranging from 16 to 60 weeks) from the experimental group indicated that 21 of 28 subjects were drinking in a controlled fashion and only rarely exceeding a 0.07% blood alcohol concentration. Control group subjects were drinking significantly more than the criterion level even during treatment sessions.

CONCLUSIONS

Despite the variety of behavioral treatments of alcoholism reported over the last several years, few of these have been systematically investigated under controlled conditions. Thus, in most reports it is difficult to rule out such factors as placebo effects, instructional sets or adjunctive advice and counseling in accounting for successful outcomes. It is apparent that an experimental analysis of individual treatment variables related to changes in alcohol consumption is warranted. Currently, such an analysis is seriously hampered by the paucity of valid, objective measures of drinking behavior that can be obtained conveniently with both outpatients and inpatients. At present, the most frequently used measure of therapeutic success is based on alcoholics' self-reports. Such information is often anecdotal in nature and prone to a variety of subjective distortions. Recent development of more quantitative measurement criteria in the form of "choice situations" (54, 56, 64) and operant systems (44, 58) will enable a more precise evaluation of treatment procedures. In order to utilize these measures fully in other than analogue studies, their validity in relation to drinking in the natural environment must eventually be assessed.

Even with a valid outcome measure, comparison of success rates between studies investigating the same treatment technique is complicated by differences in patient populations studied. Regardless of type of treatment, patient characteristics are highly related to outcome. In Lemere and Voegtlin's (38) extensive analysis of chemical aversion therapy, successful outcome was highly related to employment history and financial status. Lunde and Vogler (41) reviewed studies in which certain subject characteristics were more predictive of successful outcome than type of treatment administered. These characteristics included job stability, cooperation with treatment, living with a friend or relative, no criminal record, no history of delirium tremens, rural residence, "binge" as opposed to steady drinking and whisky or beer as opposed to wine drinking.

The importance of these social–environmental factors indicates that alcoholism treatment should be geared toward a comprehensive social learning approach. Thus, patients who have adequate vocational and interpersonal skills have sufficient alternative behaviors available to achieve gratification in the absence of alcohol. Other patients are in need of comprehensive treatment regimes (37, 43) which establish new social and vocational behavior patterns (via assertiveness training, systematic desensitization, vocational rehabilitation, etc.). These behaviors which are incompatible with excessive drinking behavior can be reinforced as excessive alcohol consumption is being suppressed.

As noted earlier, while aversion therapies may help to suppress urges in some patients temporarily, it is unlikely that they will provide a solution to the complex problem of alcoholism. In light of the descriptive findings of Nathan and O'Brien (58), Mendelson and La Dou (46) and others, viewing and treating excessive drinking as an operant response is more in line with present data. In vivo operant techniques aimed at changing reinforcement contingencies in the environment would seem to offer the most promise for future treatment. In this regard, treatment of another and perhaps similar addictive behavior, namely excessive eating (71), has been greatly enhanced by focusing away from isolated techniques such as desensitization and aversion and emphasizing an environmental approach in which cue sequence and reinforcement contingencies are altered.

REFERENCES

1. ABRAMSON, H. Use of LSD in psychotherapy. New York; Josiah Macy, Jr., Foundation; 1960.
2. AGRAS, W. S., LEITENBERG, H., BARLOW, D. H. and THOMPSON, L. E. Instructions and reinforcement in the modification of neurotic behavior. Am. J. Psychiat. 125: 1435–1439, 1969.
3. Alcoholics Anonymous. New York; Cornwall Press; 1955.
4. ANANT, S. S. A note on the treatment of alcoholics by a verbal aversion technique. Can. Psychol. 8: 19–22, 1967.
5. ANANT, S. S. Treatment of alcoholics and drug addicts by verbal aversion techniques. Int. J. Addict. 3: 381–388, 1968.
6. ASHEM, B. and DONNER, L. Covert sensitization with alcoholics; a controlled replication. Behav. Res. Ther. 6: 7–12, 1968.
7. BANDURA, A. Principles of behavior modification. New York; Holt, Rinehart & Winston; 1969.
8. BARLOW, D. H., LEITENBERG, H., AGRAS, W. S., CALLAHAN, E. J. and MOORE, R. C. The contribution of therapeutic instructions to covert sensitization. Behav. Res. Ther. 10: 411–415, 1972.
9. BLAKE, B. G. The application of behaviour therapy to the treatment of alcoholism. Behav. Res. Ther. 3: 75–85, 1965.
10. BLAKE, B. G. A follow-up of alcoholics treated by behaviour therapy. Behav. Res. Ther. 5: 89–94, 1967.
11. BROWN, C. T. and KNOBLOCK, E. C. Antabuse therapy in the army. U.S. Arm. Forces Med. J. 2: 191–202, 1951.
12. BRUNNER-ORNE, M. Group therapy of alcoholics; international conference. Q. J. Stud. Alcohol 19: 164–165, 1958.
13. CAUTELA, J. R. Treatment of compulsive behavior by covert sensitization. Psychol. Rec. 16: 33–41, 1966.
14. CAUTELA, J. R. Covert sensitization. Psychol. Rep. 20: 459–468, 1967.
15. CAUTELA, J. R. The treatment of alcoholism by covert sensitization. Psychotherapy, Chicago 7: 86–90, 1970.
16. CHAPMAN, R. F., BURT, D. W. and SMITH, J. W. Electrical aversion conditioning to alcohol; individual measurement. Presented at the annual meeting of the Western Psychological Association, Portland, Oregon, April 1972.
17. CHEEK, F. E., FRANKS, C. M., LAUCIUS, J. and BURTLE, V. Behavior-modification training for wives of alcoholics. Q. J. Stud. Alcohol 32: 456–461, 1971.
18. CLANCY, J., VANDERHOOF, E. and CAMPBELL, P. Evaluation of an aversive

technique as a treatment of alcoholism; controlled trial with succinylcholine-induced apnea. Q. J. Stud. Alcohol 28: 476–485, 1967.

19. COHEN, M., LIEBSON, I. and FAILLACE, L. A. The role of reinforcement contingencies in chronic alcoholism; an experimental analysis of one case. Behav. Res. Ther. 9: 375–379, 1971.

20. CONGER, J. J. Alcoholism; theory, problem and challenge. II. Reinforcement theory and the dynamics of alcoholism. Q. J. Stud. Alcohol 17: 296–305, 1956.

21. DAVIES, D. L. Normal drinking in recovered alcohol addicts. Q. J. Stud. Alcohol 23: 94–104, 1962.

22. ELLIOTT, R. and TIGHE, T. Breaking the cigarette habit; effects of a technique involving threatened loss of money. Psychol. Rec. 18: 503–513, 1968.

23. FARRAR, C. H., POWELL, B. J. and MARTIN, L. K. Punishment of alcohol consumption by apneic paralysis. Behav. Res. Ther. 6: 13–16, 1968.

24. FERSTER, C. B., NURNBERGER, J. I. and LEVITT, E. B. The control of eating. J. Mathetics 1: 87–109, 1962.

25. FOX, R. Disulfiram (Antabuse) as an adjunct in the treatment of alcoholism. Pp. 242–255. In: FOX, R., ed. Alcoholism; behavioral reseach, therapeutic approaches. New York; Springer; 1967.

26. HALLAM, R., RACHMAN, S. and FALKOWSKI, W. Subjective, attitudinal and physiological effects of electrical aversion therapy. Behav. Res. Ther. 10: 1–13, 1972.

27. HERSEN, M., MILLER, P. M. and EISLER, R. M. Interactions between alcoholics and their wives; a descriptive analysis of verbal and nonverbal behavior. Q. J. Stud. Alcohol 34: 516–520, 1973.

28. HSU, J. J. Electroconditioning therapy of alcoholics; a preliminary report. Q. J. Stud. Alcohol 26: 449–459, 1965.

29. KANTOROVICH, N. V. An attempt at associative-reflex therapy in alcoholism. [Russian text.] Nov. Refleksol. Fizl. Nerv. Sist. 3: 436–447, 1929.

30. KELLER, M. Alcoholism; nature and extent of the problem. Ann. Am. Acad. Pol. Soc. Sci. 315: 1–11, 1958.

31. KENDALL, L. The role of the nurse in the treatment of the alcoholic patient. Pp. 285–292. In: FOX, R. ed. Alcoholism; behavioral research, therapeutic approaches. New York; Springer; 1967.

32. KENDELL, R. E. Normal drinking by former alcohol addicts. Q. J. Stud. Alcohol 26: 247–257, 1965.

33. KEPNER, E. Application of learning theory to the etiology and treatment of alcoholism. Q. J. Stud. Alcohol 25: 279–291, 1964.

34. KISSIN, B. and CHARNOFF, S. M. Clinical evaluation of tranquilizers and antidepressant drugs in the long term treatment of alcoholism. Pp. 234–241. In: FOX, R. ed. Alcoholism; behavioral research, therapeutic approaches. New York; Springer; 1967.

35. KRAFT, T. Alcoholism treated by systematic desensitization; a follow-up of eight cases. R. Coll. Gen. Pract. 18: 336–340, 1969.

36. KRAFT, T. and AL-ISSA, I. Alcoholism treated by desensitization; a case report. Behav. Res. Ther. 5: 69–70, 1967.

37. LAZARUS, A. A. Towards the understanding and effective treatment of alcoholism. S. Afr. Med. J. 39: 736–741, 1965.

38. LEMERE, F. and VOEGTLIN, W. L. An evaluation of the aversion treatment of alcoholism. Q. J. Stud. Alcohol 11: 199–204, 1950.
39. LEMERE, F., VOEGTLIN, W. L., BROZ, W. R., O'HALLAREN, P. and TUPPER, W. E. Conditioned reflex treatment of chronic alcoholism. VII. Technic. Dis. Nerv. Syst. 3: 243–247, 1942.
40. LOVIBOND, S. H. and CADDY, G. Discriminated aversive control in the moderation of alcoholics' drinking behavior. Behav. Ther. 1: 437–444, 1970.
41. LUNDE, G. E. and VOGLER, R. E. Generalization of results in studies of aversion conditioning with alcoholics. Behav. Res. Ther. 8: 313–314, 1970.
42. MADILL, M. F., CAMPBELL, D., LAVERTY, S. G., SANDERSON, R. E. and VANDERWATER, S. L. Aversion treatment of alcoholics by succinylcholine-induced apneic paralysis; an analysis of early changes in drinking behavior. Q. J. Stud. Alcohol 27: 483–509, 1966.
43. MCBREARTY, J. F., DICHTER, M., GARFIELD, Z. and HEATH, G. A behaviorally oriented treatment program for alcoholism. Psychol. Rep. 22: 287–298, 1968.
44. MELLO, N. K. and MENDELSON, J. H. Operant analysis of drinking patterns of chronic alcoholics. Nature 206: 43–46, 1965.
45. MELLO, N. K. and MENDELSON, J. H. A quantitative analysis of drinking patterns in alcoholics. Archs Gen. Psychiat. 25: 527–539, 1971.
46. MENDELSON, J. H. and LA DOU, J. Experimentally induced chronic intoxication and withdrawal in alcoholics. II. Psychophysiological findings. Q. J. Stud. Alcohol, Suppl. No. 2, pp. 14–39, 1964.
47. MENDELSON, J. H. and MELLO, N. K. Experimental analysis of drinking behavior of chronic alcoholics. Ann. N.Y. Acad. Sci. 133: 828–845, 1966.
48. MENDELSON, J. H., LA DOU, J. and SOLOMON, P. Experimentally induced chronic intoxication and withdrawal in alcoholics. III. Psychiatric findings. Q. J. Stud. Alcohol, Suppl. No. 2, pp. 40–52, 1964.
49. MERTENS, G. C. An operant approach to self-control for alcoholics. Presented at the annual meeting of the American Psychological Association, Willmar, Minnesota, September 1964.
50. MILLER, E. C., DVORAK, B. A. and TURNER, D. W. A method of creating aversion to alcohol by reflex conditioning in a group setting. Q. J. Stud. Alcohol 21: 424–431, 1960.
51. MILLER, M. M. Treatment of chronic alcoholism by hypnotic aversion. J. Am. Med. Ass. 171: 1492–1495, 1959.
52. MILLER, P. M. The use of behavioral contracting in the treatment of alcoholism; a case report. Behav. Ther. 3: 593–596, 1972.
53. MILLER, P. M. Behavioral treatment of drug addiction; a review. Int. J. Addict. 8: 511–519, 1973.
54. MILLER, P. M. and HERSEN, M. Quantitative changes in alcohol consumption as a function of electrical aversion conditioning. J. Clin. Psychol. 28: 590–593, 1972.
55. MILLS, K. C., SOBELL, M. B. and SCHAEFER, H. H. Training social drinking as an alternative to abstinence for alcoholics. Behav. Ther. 2: 18–27, 1971.
56. MOROSKO, T. E. and BAER, P. E. Avoidance conditioning of alcoholics. Pp. 170–176. In: ULRICH, R., STACHNICH, T. and MABRY, J., eds. Control of human behavior. Vol. 2. Glenview, Ill.; Scott, Foresman; 1970.

57. NARROL, H. G. Experimental application of reinforcement principles to the analysis and treatment of hospitalized alcoholics. Q. J. Stud. Alcohol 28: 105–115, 1967.

58. NATHAN, P. E. and O'BRIEN, J. S. An experimental analysis of the behavior of alcoholics and nonalcoholics during prolonged experimental drinking; a necessary precursor of behavior therapy? Behav. Ther. 2: 455–476, 1971.

59. NATHAN, P. E., O'BRIEN, J. S. and NORTON, D. Comparative studies of the interpersonal and affective behavior of alcoholics and nonalcoholics during prolonged experimental drinking. Pp. 619–646. In: MELLO, N. K. and MENDELSON, J. H., eds. Recent advances in studies of alcoholism; an interdisciplinary symposium. Rockville, Md.; U.S. National Institute on Alcohol Abuse and Alcoholism; 1971.

60. NATHAN, P. E., TITLER, N. A., LOWENSTEIN, L. M., SOLOMON, P. and ROSSI, A. M. Behavioral analysis of chronic alcoholism; interaction of alcohol and human contact. Archs Gen. Psychiat. 22: 419–430, 1970.

61. NATIONAL INSTITUTE ON ALCOHOL ABUSE AND ALCOHOLISM. National Institute on Alcohol Abuse and Alcoholism. (DHEW Publ. No. HSM-72-9019.) Washington, D.C.; U.S. Govt Print. Off.; 1972.

62. QUINN, J. T. and HENBEST, R. Partial failure of generalization in alcoholics following aversion therapy. Q. J. Stud. Alcohol 28: 70–75, 1967.

63. RACHMAN, S. and TEASDALE, J. Aversion therapy and behavior disorders. Coral Gables, Fla.; University of Miami Press; 1969.

64. RAYMOND, M. J. The treatment of addiction by aversion conditioning with apomorphine. Behav. Res. Ther. 1: 287–291; 1964.

65. ROZYNKO, V. V., FLINT, G. A., HAMMER, C. E., JR., SWIFT, K. D., KLINE, J. A. and KING, R. M. An operant behavior modification program for alcoholics. Presented at the annual meeting of the Western Psychological Association, Mendocino, California, April 1971.

66. SANDERSON, R. E., CAMPBELL, D. and LAVERTY, S. G. An investigation of a new aversive conditioning treatment for alcoholism. Q. J. Stud. Alcohol 24: 261–275, 1963.

67. SCHAEFER, H. H., SOBELL, M. B. and MILLS, K. C. Baseline drinking behaviors in alcoholics and social drinkers; kinds of drinks and sip magnitude. Behav. Res. Ther. 9: 23–27, 1971.

68. SILBER, A. Psychotherapy with alcoholics. J. Nerv. Ment. Dis. 129: 477–485, 1959.

69. STREL'CHUK, I. V. O novykh sovremyennykh metodakh lecheniya bol'nykh alkogolizmom. (New contemporary methods of treating patients with alcoholism.) Sov. Med. 21: 26–33, 1957.

70. STUART, R. B. Behavioral contracting within the families of delinquents. J. Behav. Ther. & Exp. Psychiat. 2: 1–11, 1971.

71. STUART, R. B. and DAVIS, B. Slim chance in a fat world; behavioral control of obesity. Champaign, Ill.; Research Press; 1972.

72. SULZER, E. S. Behavior modification in adult psychiatric patients. Pp. 196–199. In: ULLMAN, L. P. and KRASNER, L., eds. Case studies in behavior modification. New York; Holt, Rinehart & Winston; 1965.

73. THIMANN, J. Conditioned reflex treatment of alcoholism. II. The risks of its application, its indications, contraindications and psychotherapeutic aspects. N. Engl. J. Med. 241: 406–410, 1949.

74. VOEGTLIN, W. L. The treatment of alcoholism by establishing a conditioned reflex. Am. J. Med. Sci. **199**: 802–809, 1940.
75. VOEGTLIN, W. L., LEMERE, F., BROZ, W. R. and O'HOLLAREN, P. Conditioned reflex therapy of chronic alcoholism. IV. A preliminary report on the value of reinforcement. Q. J. Stud. Alcohol 2: 505–511, 1941.
76. VOGEL-SPROTT, M. D. and BANKS, R. K. The effect of delayed punishment on an immediately rewarded response in alcoholics and nonalcoholics. Behav. Res. Ther. 3: 69–73, 1965.
77. VOGLER, R. E., LUNDE, S. E., JOHNSON, G. R. and MARTIN, P. L. Electrical aversion conditioning with chronic alcoholics. J. Consult. Clin. Psychol. 34: 302–307, 1970.
78. WEINER, H. B. Psychodramatic treatment for the alcoholic. Pp. 218–233. In: FOX, R., ed. Alcoholism; behavioral research, therapeutic approaches. New York; Springer; 1967.
79. WOLPE, J. and LAZARUS, A. A. Behavior therapy techniques. New York; Pergamon Press; 1966.
80. ZVONIKOV, M. Z. Modifikatsiya tekhniki provedeniya uslovnoreflektornoi apomorfinovoi i suggestivnoi terapii alkogolizma. (A modification of the technique of conditioned-reflex treatment of alcoholism with apomorphine and suggestion.) Zh. Nevropat. Psikhiat. **68**: 596–599, 1968.

Concluding Remarks

An overview of mental health interfaces with alcoholism seems to indicate that, by and large, the significant relationships with the mental health disciplines occur after the development of alcoholism. Pathognomic psychodynamic precursors of alcoholism have not been isolated nor identified. Although alcoholism does not seem to have significant specific connections to other forms of psychopathology, mental health treatment modalities are called upon in dealing with the mental health adjustment difficulties of alcoholics. Of course, the same could be said of orthopedic and other medical patients. The difference is that in the case of alcoholism it seems so logical a priori that alcoholics should seek conflict resolution, tension reduction and need gratification via alcohol (and it may, in fact, hold for some). This is an instance where there is a hypothesis and, oddly, it is strongly held despite the lack of scientific data.

There is the convincing suggestion that a mental health and sociological coalition would augment and enhance the multidisciplinary approach. But it has to be truly multidisciplinary—the product of individual contributions will far exceed their sum. There have been some starts in this direction but they are not as all-inclusive of a variety of orientations as might be the ideal. For example, Whitehead and Harvey (1), seeking an explanatory context for alcoholism, wrote, "what appears indicated is a framework that is based on both an appreciation of the sociocultural climate in which alcoholic beverages of various types are consumed as well as the physical complications associated with consumption on both a societal and individual level." The mental health approach would, presumably, probe the "individual level" in depth.

Addressing the issue of health research in general, not just mental health, an American Psychological Association (2) task force concluded that "the emergence of health as a social issue has been accompanied by a slow but evident shift in responsibility for coping with the problem. Health care delivery is no longer solely within the purview of medicine." Consumers, economists, sociologists and psychologists are cited as adopting—and needing to adopt—participant roles.

We assume that there is an entity, alcohol addiction, and because it appears to be so dramatic in terms of its consequences, we tend to overlook less striking, prescriptive, normative or nonproblem drinking, but this too is surely an important mental health–sociological interface. Kiev (3) has discussed whether psychiatry is a White, middle-class invention and whether its practitioners can understand—and be understood by—poor minority group members. The latter constitute a not insignificant proportion of the total of problem drinkers, and, if the above statement is valid, where are they to seek and receive help?

While psychiatric or mental health disorders are distinguished and discriminable by pathognomic signs, they also sometimes bear significant relationships to one another. At least, knowledge of one helps to cast some light on another or provides a frame of reference for comparison. Dunham (4), however, has questioned the differentiation of mental syndromes, pointing out that they may form "a unity of a more generic nature." Would alcoholism be part of this unity? I have attempted (Chapters 11 and 15) to ascertain details about the relationships between alcoholism on the one hand and schizophrenia, mood and conflict on the other. Various investigators have done the same with different aspects of psychopathology. The results have not been particularly gratifying nor illuminating. Although important psychological links to alcoholism have not been demonstrated, alcoholism is increasingly incorporated into the psychological domain. This is enigmatic in the light of the increasing evidence of—and the spate of books documenting—the biological aspects of alcoholism. It becomes particularly puzzling considering that hypothesized biological parameters are regarded as significant in the etiology of alcoholism, as well as in the maintenance of a pattern of alcohol misuse, but that psychological techniques are then invoked for its treatment. It is unclear whether the "psycho"-therapies are intended only to help to alter the specific behavior of drinking (as one might seek to mitigate nail biting or gambling), to attenuate the postulated underlying need for same, to reduce the anxiety and uncertainty aroused by any change in behavior, to help sustain the motivation for change, to be a source of support, to accomplish all the foregoing, or to serve a host of other ends.

Depending on what mental health treatments are intended to achieve, the next question is whether alcoholics belong in mental hospitals, and, if not, what sorts of health care facilities and resources are more appropriate. An article about a New Jersey psychiatric hospital in the 31 March 1976 *New York Times* quoted the chairman of the board of trustees as saying, "We have to accept alcoholics and drug addicts who don't belong here, because there is no other place to put them."

Many have noted that the course of an alcoholic's hospitalization generally tends to differ from that of other psychiatric patients. Following a relatively brief period of detoxication, a hospitalized alcoholic is usually in excellent contact, he is alert and he perceives himself as totally different from psychotic, depressed, even neurotic patients because he is not anxiously agitated, is neither delusional nor hallucinating, and he shows little overt affective disturbance. Of course, this may represent massive denial. Even so, in the hospital, sober, in the throes of new resolve, without alcohol at hand, removed from conflict and decision making and receiving support, he does not see himself as emotionally disturbed. Hospitals with special alcoholism rehabilitation units reinforce this kind of exclusiveness as do those institutions which use a "buddy system" to pair alcoholics as in Alcoholics Anonymous. A valid question, then, is whether psychiatric hospital treatment for alcoholism should go beyond the detoxication stage and, if so, what the treatment focus should be. If the goal is removal of the alcoholic from a life-style and a milieu whose contingencies reinforce a pattern of drinking, then should this segregation be to a mental health facility? Such removal or dramatic change in environment tends to lead to dissociated learning. The alcoholic thus might learn to abstain in the hospital because of the strictures against drinking and because of associated aversive contingencies but may not be able to maintain this behavior outside of the hospital.

For an alcoholic sufficiently debilitated to go or to be sent to a psychiatric facility, detoxication is surely an initial necessity. There is the suggestion, however, that following this, a real selection process or triage should take place so that different treatment tracks are made available. What these would be depends on the success of mental health professionals in devising criteria and methodologies for classification. Pattison (5) made a good start in this direction with his multivariate model for treatment, spelling out the major factors of population, treatment facility and outcome. Similarly, Ewing (6) argued for "a holistic approach to the alcoholic, utilizing all or any methods of therapy that seem appropriate." The following are some of the many possible treatment alternatives:

(*a*) A long-term psychodynamic and psychotherapeutic approach is indicated for alcoholics or problem drinkers who are in need of and able to effect personality change and integration, who have a defensive structure able to sustain the kind of uncovering process involved, and who are not diagnosed as suffering an underlying psychotic disorder masked by their drinking behavior. Such treatment obviously does not have to take place in a hospital; it doesn't for nonalcoholic patients. These patients would not be too likely to act out and would probably have evidenced some stability in their vocational and interpersonal adjustments. Nevertheless, Lynn (7) has observed that "the needs of alcoholics are multiple with medical, social, legal, and economic ramifications. When these needs are not satisfied, the best psychotherapy is doomed to failure."

(b) Discharge following detoxication—the revolving door—is sometimes appropriate because even the idealized sort of multidisciplinary mental health approach has little to offer to the long-term, recidivistic alcoholic who awakens to find himself in the hospital, is unmotivated to seek and to accept help and lacks the personal resources to assimilate the content of treatment offered him. While for such individuals it may be pro forma and to little avail, supportive community resources such as A.A., the Salvation Army and other social service, welfare and health agencies should be suggested. The sad but inescapable fact is that the life course of such determined (albeit not consciously) alcoholics is a progressively deteriorating one and often results in brain damage, which itself may require psychiatric hospitalization. It is ironic that such a pattern of 20 or 30 years of unhappiness, self-destruction, social and personal alienation, of existing rather than living, essentially falls outside of the purview of the mental health professions because in terms of actual need, not necessarily felt need or want, such alcoholics truly require help.

(c) A behavior modification approach seems indicated for alcoholics who are able to make appropriate follow-up "booster" visits to effect reinforcement. Whether abstinence or controlled drinking were the desired outcome, therapy would be aimed at interrupting the repetitive behavior of alcohol misuse. For example, attempts could be made, as they have been (e.g., 8), to train alcoholics to recognize critical blood alcohol concentrations. If abstinence were the target, A.A. affiliation would be efficacious. The keynote here would be contingency management and the teaching of limits.

(d) Alcoholics who appear fairly well integrated, who have jobs and families to return to, but who are not regarded as candidates for the more probing psychotherapies, might profit from a rehabilitation-oriented approach. Such a treatment program, again not a prolonged inpatient one, would emphasize group therapy, structured learning and didactic experiences. Family therapy and marriage counseling would be valuable treatment components.

(e) For some alcoholics who are motivated and who seem to require a reduction in the number of drinking decisions they have to make daily, disulfiram therapy has had positive results.

(f) Lynn (7) wrote that "those of us who need immediate gratification need not apply" as psychotherapists for alcoholics. However, one can help without necessarily "curing." Sometimes the best treatment a therapist can render is to make the most appropriate referral, and this mental health role needs to be reemphasized. Many alcoholics can profit from specific vocational, rehabilitation, social work, psychiatric, chaplaincy, nursing and other services, both as in- and outpatients. Furthermore, their families and employers often can benefit from similar services. The use of multidisciplinary treatment personnel and facilities for custodial care of alcoholics seems to be uneconomical, and every effort should be pressed to make these treatment resources available to those who can benefit from them.

(g) The value of nonhospital, residential treatment settings has not been tested exhaustively, but facilities such as halfway houses, hostels, day treatment centers, night hospitals and mental hygiene clinics may be useful for alcoholics unable to handle an abrupt transition from hospital to community.

Underlying all of the above suggestions is the need for patient identification, classification or selection. An attempt at dividing patients into groups amenable to different treatment strategies was reported by Lundquist (9), and one based on multivariable diagnosis has been suggested by Strauss (10). The alcoholisms are multiple and pluralistic. One is reminded of the heterogeneity of the schizophrenias. Clearly, a multifaceted therapeutic armamentarium is called for, and appropriate mental health contributions, depending on the alcoholic's needs, seem valid and worthwhile. The same pertains to other substance misusers—those who misuse nicotine, drugs, cholesterol and calories. But mention of these substances highlights the key variable of attitude toward—or perception of—alcoholics. I mean much more than the need for abandonment of the stereotype of the Skid Row alcoholic. Here, sociologists and social philosophers have much to teach us about the relationships between society and the alcoholic. Their literature (e.g., 11) now has numerous references to the implications of the labeling of deviance. Still, a recent newspaper article described debate about the

Health and Social Service Budget in the Bermuda Legislative Council. One item in the budget concerned a hostel for alcoholics instituted by the government in cooperation with the Salvation Army. The hostel was described as one for "wayward men" and, while it may be a sort of legalese, there was reference to "the drunk and incapable." Like it or not, in a discipline which has flourished, in the opinion of many, as a result of the Freudian concept of the unconscious, alcoholism still is often stigmatized as a willful, consciously determined excess. This attitude is one which Beauchamp (12) has called "alcoholism as blaming the alcoholic."

Because of the personally devastating effects of alcoholism, its multiplication and its social consequences, it would seem that outreach and prevention should be given the highest priorities. However, we seem to be stumped in this area other than in the initiation of educational programs. One does not become a deviant drinker overnight. The course of alcoholism is not a two-stage process, sobriety to addiciton. The question is what can be done to prevent drinkers from becoming alcoholics. It would seem that intensive longitudinal or life-history studies might yield fruitful clues. Recognition is the necessary precursor to prevention.

I am loath to close with a section on "suggestions for further research." Rather, a section on "suggestions for further thought" is indicated. While I would never say that we have all the information on alcoholism we need, we certainly have a body of knowledge. I think that we lack creative interpretations of that knowledge. I recall an undergraduate exercise in which the students were given a description of an experiment complete with results and were required to interpret the results and to write conclusions from the theoretical orientations of Hull, Guthrie and Tolman. While these were not the only learning theorists then extant, they were the only ones respected by the professor. My point is that well-organized, theoretical mental health frameworks for alcoholism do not have such prominent representation and thus studies are done without the kinds of preexperimental theorizing and post-publication integration which would enhance understanding. In this respect, we have knowledge, a compendium of facts, but we lack understanding.

The mental health field's need for a point of view, an organized stance, a raison d'être vis-à-vis alcoholism brings to mind an anecdote. A number of graduate students were discussing research ideas. A classmate described a "far out" study and another fellow said, "But your hypothesis is all wrong." The designer of the experiment replied, "That's where I've got you—I don't have a hypothesis!" Such a shotgun approach will not avail. Investigations require organized and directed expectations. If fringe benefits accrue also, they are bonuses in knowledge.

The issue of, essentially, self-evaluation by the mental health disciplines in terms of their relationships to alcoholism is a vexing one. Elsewhere, with regard to orthomolecular psychiatry, I (13) wrote about a similar problem in discussing the need for evaluative work by independent researchers: "The problem. . . . is that a clinical researcher needs to have strong positive or negative affect or conviction vis-à-vis the theory, and perhaps such a biased person shouldn't conduct the study. And one whose interests and expertise lie elsewhere cannot really be commissioned to undertake it." It is hoped that the contents of this book will contribute to the exploration of the interfaces between alcoholism and mental health.

REFERENCES

1. WHITEHEAD, P. C. and HARVEY, C. Explaining alcoholism; an empirical test and reformulation. J. Health Soc. Behav. **15**: 57–65, 1974.
2. AMERICAN PSYCHOLOGICAL ASSOCIATION. TASK FORCE ON HEALTH RESEARCH. Contributions of psychology to health research; patterns, problems, and potentials. Am. Psychol. **31**: 263–274, 1976.
3. KIEV, A. Is psychiatry a white-middle-class invention? Sat. Rev. **3** (No. 10): 18–19, 1976.
4. DUNHAM, H. W. Society, culture and mental disorder. Archs Gen. Psychiat. **33**: 147–156, 1976.
5. PATTISON, E. M. Drinking outcomes of alcoholism treatment; abstinence, social, modified, controlled, and normal drinking. Proc. 1st Int. Med. Conf. Alcsm (London, 10–14 September 1973), pp. 57–74, 1974.
6. EWING, J. A. Behavioral approaches for problems with alcohol. Int. J. Addict. **9**: 389–399, 1974.
7. LYNN, E. J. Treatment for alcoholism; psychotherapy is still alive and well. Hosp. Community Psychiat. **27**: 282–283, 1976.
8. SILVERSTEIN, S. J., NATHAN, P. E. and TAYLOR, H. A. Blood alcohol level estimation and controlled drinking by chronic alcoholics. Behav. Ther. **5**: 1–15, 1974.
9. LUNDQUIST, G. A. R. Strategies and goals in the treatment and control of alcoholism. Proc. 1st Int. Med. Conf. Alcsm (London, 10–14 September 1973), pp. 168–172, 1974.
10. STRAUSS, J. S. A comprehensive approach to psychiatric diagnosis. Am. J. Psychiat. **132**: 1193–1197, 1975.

11. GOVE, W. R., ed. The labelling of deviance. New York; Wiley; 1975.
12. BEAUCHAMP, D. E. Alcoholism as blaming the alcoholic. Int. J. Addict. 11:
     41–52, 1976.
13. FREED, E. X. Review of HAWKINS, D. and PAULING, L., eds. Orthomolecular
     psychiatry; treatment of schizophrenia. Q. J. Stud. Alcohol 35: 784–785,
     1974.

Index of Names

Vogler, R. E., 356, 363
Vorontsova, G. A., 167

Wahl, C. W., 218
Wahl, O., 175
Wallerstein, R. S., 29, 180
Walton, D., 226
Walton, H., 68
Walton, H. J., 140
Wanberg, K. W., 250, 289, 291
Warren, G. H., 254
Washburn, S. L., 303
Weidman, H. H., 235
Weijl, S., 310
Wessman, A. E., 239
West, L., 30, 31
Whitehead, A. N., 326
Whitehead, P. C., 369
Wikler, A., 83
Wilkinson, A. E., 190
Williams, A., 4

Williams, A. F., 253
Williams, E. L., 68, 150, 159
Williams, R. J., 207, 233
Williams, T. K., 82
Winokur, G., 141, 189, 190, 245
Winship, G. M., 168
Wishner, J., 175
Witkin, H. A., 225
Wolf, I., 5
Wolfensberger, M., 167
Woodruff, R. A., Jr., 3, 4, 245, 302
World Health Organization, Expert Committee on Mental Health, 202, 203, 204, 208, 209, 225

Zealley, A. K., 4
Zehner, L., 171
Zuckerman, M., 242
Zung, W. W., 240, 242
Zwerling, I., 209, 213, 303, 318

Index of Subjects